common core

8 Performance Coach™

Mathematics

Performance Coach™, Mathematics, Grade 8 315NASE ISBN-13: 978-1-62362-810-9
Cover Illustration: © Thinkstock

Triumph Learning® 136 Madison Avenue, 7th Floor, New York, NY 10016

CONTENTS

Standards

DEAR STUDENT

Welcome to *Performance Coach*!

We made this book to help you strengthen your mathematics skills. These skills are important to have for every subject you study this year, not just Mathematics.

Each lesson in this book has three parts:

GETTING THE IDEA ➊

Review some of the basic concepts and skills you've already learned.

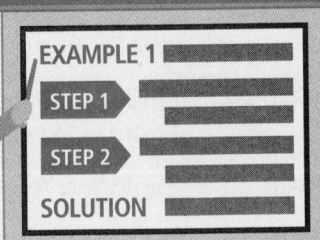

➋ COACHED EXAMPLE

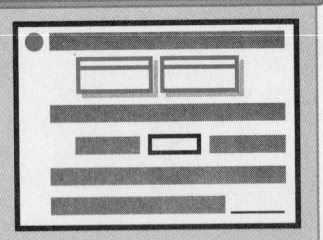

Solve a problem. There are several questions that will help you along the way!

LESSON PRACTICE ➌

Now you're on your own! This part contains more problems to solve.

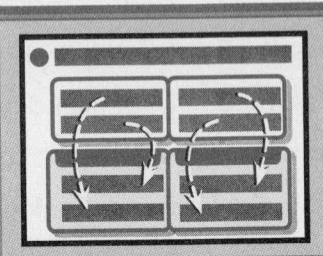

There are many different types of test items in *Performance Coach*. For some, you will have to choose more than one answer. For others, you will write out your answer. You will also see items that ask you to complete a graph, table, or sentence. Many items have more than one part. Be sure to read the directions carefully so you know how to answer each item.

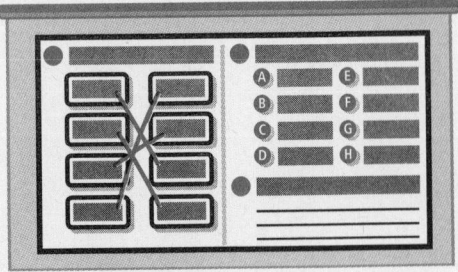

HAVE A GREAT YEAR! Sincerely,
TRIUMPH LEARNING

DOMAIN 1

The Number System

8.NS.1

Understanding Rational and Irrational Numbers

A **rational number** is a number that can be expressed as a ratio $\frac{a}{b}$, where a and b are integers and $b \neq 0$. A **terminating decimal** is a decimal that has a finite number of digits. A **repeating decimal** has a repeating pattern of digits. Terminating decimals, repeating decimals, integers, and counting numbers are all rational numbers.

Any real number that cannot be expressed in the form $\frac{a}{b}$ is an **irrational number**. A decimal that neither repeats nor terminates is an irrational number. The square root of an integer is irrational if the integer is not a perfect square.

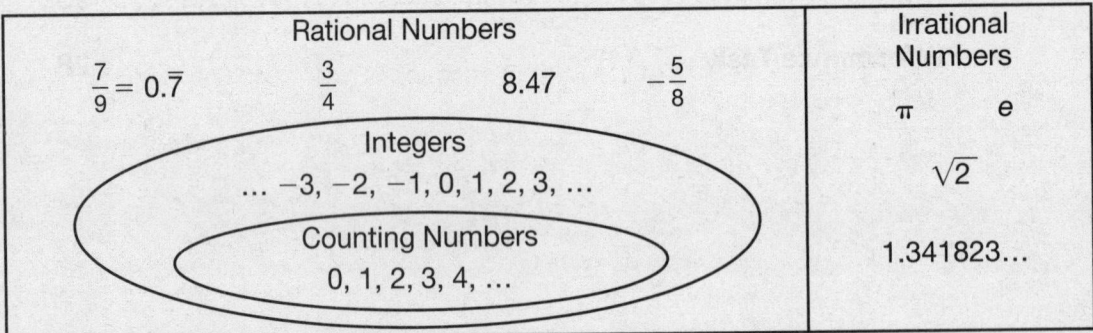

Real Numbers

Rational Numbers

$\frac{7}{9} = 0.\overline{7}$ $\frac{3}{4}$ 8.47 $-\frac{5}{8}$

Integers

... −3, −2, −1, 0, 1, 2, 3, ...

Counting Numbers

0, 1, 2, 3, 4, ...

Irrational Numbers

π e

$\sqrt{2}$

1.341823...

Example 1

Is 6.434 a rational number or an irrational number?

Strategy   Apply the definitions of rational and irrational numbers.

Step 1   Identify the digits to the right of the decimal point.

6.$\boxed{434}$

Step 2   Determine if the decimal terminates, repeats, or neither.

There is a finite number of digits after the decimal point. Therefore, 6.434 is a terminating decimal.

All terminating decimals are rational numbers.

Solution   The number 6.434 is a rational number.

Example 2

Is $4.\overline{3}$ a rational number or an irrational number?

Strategy   Apply the definitions of rational and irrational numbers.

The bar over the 3 shows that number can be written as 4.33333 ... The digit 3 repeats. A decimal that repeats is a rational number.

Solution   The number $4.\overline{3}$ is a rational number.

Example 3

Is 6.183782946 ... a rational number or an irrational number?

Strategy   Apply the definitions of rational and irrational numbers.

The digits to the right of the decimal point do not repeat and do not terminate. A decimal that does not repeat or terminate is an irrational number.

Solution   6.183782946 ... is an irrational number.

Example 4

Is $\sqrt{11}$ a rational number or an irrational number?

Strategy   **If the number under the square root is an integer, then determine whether this integer is a perfect square. Then apply the definitions of rational and irrational numbers.**

The number 11 cannot be written as the square of an integer. Therefore, 11 is not a perfect square.
A square root is irrational if the integer under the square root symbol is not a perfect square.

Solution   The number $\sqrt{11}$ is an irrational number.

Example 5

Convert $0.2\overline{7}$ to a fraction.

Strategy   **Use algebra to write the repeating decimal as a fraction.**

Step 1   Write an equation. Let the variable n equal the decimal.
$$n = 0.2\overline{7}$$

Step 2   Write a new equation by multiplying both sides by 10^p, where p is the number of digits that repeat.

Only one digit repeats, 7, so $p = 1$.
Multiply both sides of $n = 0.2.7\overline{7}$ by 10^1.
$$10n = 2.7\overline{7}$$

Step 3 Subtract the original equation from the new equation.

$$10n = 2.7\overline{7}$$
$$- \quad n = 0.2\overline{7}$$
$$\overline{9n = 2.5}$$

Step 4 Solve for n. Write n as a fraction in simplest form.

$$9n = 2.5$$
$$n = \frac{2.5}{9} = \frac{25}{90} = \frac{5}{18}$$

Solution The decimal $0.2\overline{7}$ is equivalent to the fraction $\frac{5}{18}$.

Example 6

Convert $4.\overline{15}$ to a fraction.

Strategy **Use algebra to write the repeating decimal as a fraction.**

Step 1 Write an equation. Let the variable n equal the decimal.

$$n = 4.\overline{15}$$

Step 2 Write a new equation by multiplying both sides by 10^p, where p is the number of digits that repeat.

Only two digits repeat, 15, so $p = 2$.

Multiply both sides of $n = 4.\overline{15}$ by 10^2.

$$100n = 415.\overline{15}$$

Step 3 Subtract the original equation from the new equation and solve for n. Write n as a fraction in simplest form.

$$100n = 415.\overline{15}$$
$$- \quad n = \quad 4.\overline{15}$$
$$\overline{99n = 411}$$
$$n = \frac{411}{99} = \frac{137}{33}$$

Solution The decimal $4.\overline{15}$ is equivalent to the fraction $\frac{137}{33}$.

Example 7

Convert $8.\overline{139}$ to a fraction.

Strategy **Use algebra to write the repeating decimal as a fraction.**

Step 1 Write an equation. Let the variable n equal the decimal.

$$n = 8.\overline{139}$$

Step 2 Write a new equation by multiplying both sides by 10^3.

$$1,000n = 8,139.\overline{139}$$

Step 3 Subtract the original equation from the new equation and solve for n. Write n as a fraction in simplest form.

$$\begin{array}{r} 1{,}000n = 8{,}139.\overline{139} \\ -\quad n = \quad\ \ 8.\overline{139} \\ \hline 999n = 8{,}131 \end{array}$$

$$n = \frac{8{,}131}{999}$$

Solution The decimal $8.\overline{139}$ is equivalent to the fraction $\frac{8{,}131}{999}$.

Example 8

Identify $\sqrt{67}$ as a rational or irrational number by writing it as a decimal.

Strategy Use a calculator to write the number as a decimal. Then determine if the decimal repeats or terminates.

Step 1 Use a calculator to write $\sqrt{67}$ as a decimal.

$$\sqrt{67} = 8.185352771\ldots$$

Step 2 Determine if the decimal repeats or terminates.

The decimal neither repeats nor terminates.

Solution The number $\sqrt{67}$ is an irrational number.

---

② COACHED EXAMPLE

Write $9.2\overline{68}$ as a fraction.

Write an equation by setting the variable n equal to the given decimal.

$n = $ _____

The decimal has _____ repeating digits.

Write a new equation by multiplying both sides of the equation by _____.

_____ $n = $ _____

Subtract the original equation from the new equation.

$$\begin{array}{r} 100n = 926.8\overline{68} \\ -\quad n = \quad\ 9.2\overline{68} \\ \hline n = \text{_____} \end{array}$$

Solve for n. Write n as a fraction in simplest form.

$n = $ _____ $=$ _____

The decimal $9.2\overline{68}$ is equivalent to the fraction _____.

1 Nolan wrote $1.\overline{63}$ and $0.\overline{2}$ as fractions in simplest form. Use numbers from the box to write the fraction.

$1.\overline{63} =$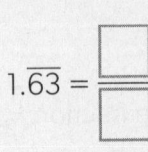

$0.\overline{2} =$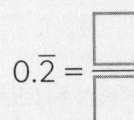

| 2 |
| 7 |
| 9 |
| 10 |
| 11 |
| 18 |

2 Which of the following is a rational number? Circle all that apply.

A. π

B. $21.08\overline{2}$

C. $\sqrt{9}$

D. $1.4382768\ldots$

E. $\frac{2}{7}$

3 Write the number $12.\overline{1}$ as a fraction in simplest form. Show your work.

4 Select True or False for each statement.

A. $\sqrt{19}$ is equal to 4.358.   ○ True ○ False

B. $3.\overline{6}$ is equal to $\frac{11}{3}$.   ○ True ○ False

C. $\sqrt{44}$ is a rational number.   ○ True ○ False

D. $\frac{9}{12}$ is a rational number.   ○ True ○ False

E. $0.529639\ldots$ is an irrational number.   ○ True ○ False

5 Which fractions are equivalent to $1.\overline{27}$? Circle all that apply.

A. $\dfrac{9}{7}$ D. $\dfrac{28}{19}$

B. $\dfrac{12}{5}$ E. $\dfrac{42}{33}$

C. $\dfrac{14}{11}$ F. $\dfrac{60}{27}$

6 Determine whether each number is rational or irrational. Write the number in the correct box.

$\sqrt{6}$ 2.22 $\dfrac{19}{3}$ 14.3729... $\dfrac{21}{5}$ $7.09\overline{24}$

Rational Number	Irrational Number

7 Is the fraction equivalent to a repeating decimal? Select Yes or No.

A. $\dfrac{6}{7}$ ○ Yes ○ No

B. $\dfrac{17}{8}$ ○ Yes ○ No

C. $\dfrac{2}{13}$ ○ Yes ○ No

D. $\dfrac{34}{16}$ ○ Yes ○ No

E. $\dfrac{5}{24}$ ○ Yes ○ No

F. $\dfrac{17}{24}$ ○ Yes ○ No

8 Use fractions from the box to complete the table.

Decimal	Equivalent Fraction
$6.\overline{75}$	
$0.\overline{375}$	
$0.4\overline{2}$	
$1.\overline{027}$	

$\dfrac{14}{33}$

$\dfrac{23}{111}$

$\dfrac{114}{111}$

$\dfrac{223}{33}$

$\dfrac{47}{999}$

$\dfrac{125}{333}$

9 Look at each square root. Is it a rational or irrational number? Select Rational or Irrational.

A. $\sqrt{10}$ ○ Rational ○ Irrational

B. $\sqrt{12}$ ○ Rational ○ Irrational

C. $\sqrt{16}$ ○ Rational ○ Irrational

D. $\sqrt{36}$ ○ Rational ○ Irrational

E. $\sqrt{48}$ ○ Rational ○ Irrational

10 Draw a line from each fraction to its decimal equivalent.

A. $\dfrac{74}{9}$ • • $8.\overline{5}$

B. $\dfrac{42}{9}$ • • $8.\overline{2}$

C. $\dfrac{77}{9}$ • • $4.\overline{6}$

D. $\dfrac{37}{9}$ • • $4.\overline{1}$

11 Omar wrote the distance in miles from his house to the library as the decimal $3.\overline{48}$. He wrote the distance from his house to school as the decimal $1.\overline{07}$. He then changed the decimals to fractions. Use numbers from the box to write each equivalent fraction.

distance to the library: $\dfrac{}{}$

distance to the school: $\dfrac{}{}$

99
348
106
33
107
115
999

12 Diya and Leo both write the decimal $2.1\overline{5}$ as a fraction.

Diya's fraction: $\dfrac{97}{45}$ Leo's fraction: $\dfrac{97}{5}$

Part A

Which student wrote the correct fraction? Show calculations to support your response.

Part B

Describe a mistake that could have been made by the student who wrote the incorrect fraction.

Estimating the Value of Irrational Expressions

1 GETTING THE IDEA

You can approximate the values of **irrational numbers** by identifying nearby rational numbers on a number line.

For example, the irrational number 1.28437... is between 1 and 2 on a number line. Since it is closer to 1, a close approximation for 1.28437... is 1. If you look at the tenths place, you can get an even closer approximation. The number 1.28437... is also between 1.2 and 1.3. Since it is closer to 1.3, a closer approximation for 1.28437... is the rational number 1.3.

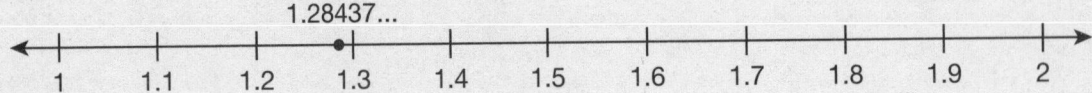

Example 1

Locate 3.9, $-2\frac{3}{8}$, $1.\overline{69}$, and $-\sqrt{16}$ on a number line.

Strategy   Convert each number to a decimal. Then plot the decimals on a number line.

> **Step 1**   Write each number as a decimal.
>
> 3.9 is a decimal. $-2\frac{3}{8} = -\frac{19}{8}$ $1.\overline{69}$ rounds to 1.7 $-\sqrt{16} = -4$
>
> $$= -19 \div 8$$
> $$= -2.375$$

> **Step 2**   Make a list of the decimals.
>
> 3.9 -2.375 1.7 -4

> **Step 3**   Draw a number line. Plot a point corresponding to each decimal. Label the points with the original numbers.

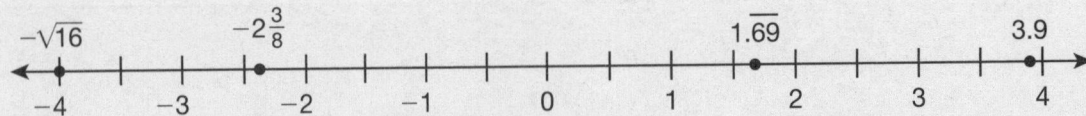

Solution   On a number line, $-\sqrt{16}$ is located at -4, $-2\frac{3}{8}$ is located slightly to the left of -2, $1.\overline{69}$ is located between 1.5 and 2, and 3.9 is located almost at 4.

You can use rational approximations to locate an irrational number on a number line.

Example 2

Locate $-\pi$, $\sqrt{5}$, and 0.582083... on a number line.

Strategy Estimate a rational approximation for each irrational number, and plot the rational numbers on a number line.

Step 1 Approximate the value of $-\pi$ to the nearest tenth.

Since $\pi = 3.14159...$, it is between 3.1 and 3.2. It is closer to 3.1, so a close approximation for π to the nearest tenth is 3.1.

Therefore, a rational approximation for $-\pi$ is -3.1.

Step 2 Approximate the value of $\sqrt{5}$ to the nearest tenth.

Since 5 is not a perfect square, first determine the perfect square closest to 5.

The first five perfect squares are 1, 4, 9, 16, and 25.

The perfect square closest to 5 is 4.

So, a close approximation for $\sqrt{5}$ is $\sqrt{4} = 2$.

For a closer approximation, square decimals to the tenths place that are close to 2, and compare the squares to 5.

$2.1^2 = 4.41$, so $\sqrt{4.41} = 2.1$

$2.2^2 = 4.84$, so $\sqrt{4.84} = 2.2$

$2.3^2 = 5.29$, so $\sqrt{5.29} = 2.3$

Since 5 is closest to 4.84, an approximation of $\sqrt{5}$ to the tenths place is 2.2.

Step 3 Approximate the value of 0.582083... to the nearest tenth.

0.582083... rounds to 0.6.

Step 4 Make a list of all of the decimal approximations.

$-\pi \approx -3.1$ $\sqrt{5} \approx 2.2$ $0.582083... \approx 0.6$

Step 5 Draw a number line. Plot a point corresponding to each decimal. Label the points with the original numbers.

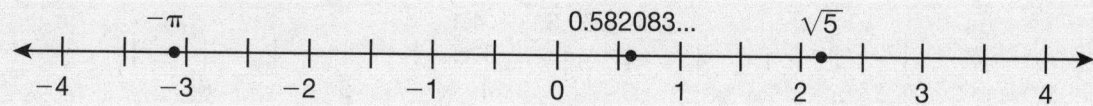

Solution On a number line, $-\pi$ is located slightly to the left of -3, $\sqrt{5}$ is located slightly to the right of 2, and 0.582083... is located slightly to the right of 0.5.

You can use rational approximations to help compare and order irrational numbers or expressions that contain irrational numbers.

Example 3

Order from least to greatest: 2π, $\frac{8}{15}$, $2\sqrt{3}$, and 4.1.

Strategy   Write each as a decimal, using a decimal approximation for irrational numbers. Then plot the decimals on a number line.

Step 1   Write 2π as a decimal rounded to the nearest tenth.

π = 3.14159..., so π is about 3.1.

Therefore, rounded to the nearest tenth, 2π is approximately 2(3.1), or 6.2.

Step 2   Write $\frac{8}{15}$ as a decimal rounded to the nearest tenth.

$\frac{8}{15} = 8 \div 15 = 0.5\overline{3}$

Rounded to the nearest tenth, $\frac{8}{15}$ is 0.5.

Step 3   Write $2\sqrt{3}$ as a decimal rounded to the nearest tenth.

Since 3 is not a perfect square, first determine the nearest perfect squares.

$1^2 = 1$, so $\sqrt{1} = 1$

$2^2 = 4$, so $\sqrt{4} = 2$

Since 3 is closer to 4 than to 1, a close approximation for $\sqrt{3}$ is 2. For a closer approximation, square decimals to the tenths place, and compare them to 3.

$1.7^2 = 2.89$, so $\sqrt{2.89} = 1.7$

$1.8^2 = 3.24$, so $\sqrt{3.24} = 1.8$

Since 3 is closer to 2.89, a closer approximation of $\sqrt{3}$ is 1.7. A close approximation of $2\sqrt{3}$ is therefore approximately 2(1.7), or 3.4.

Step 4   Make a list of all of the decimal approximations.

$2\pi \approx 6.2$ $\frac{8}{15} \approx 0.5$ $2\sqrt{3} \approx 3.4$ 4.1

Step 5   Locate each decimal on a number line to compare them.

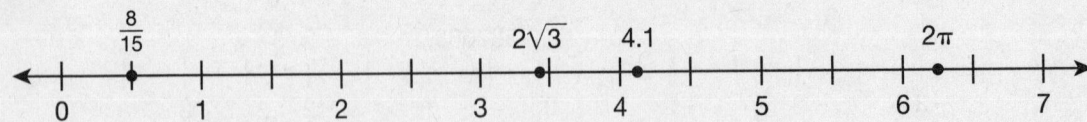

Solution   From least to greatest, the numbers are $\frac{8}{15}$, $2\sqrt{3}$, 4.1, and 2π.

Example 4

Approximate the value of $\sqrt{85}$ to the nearest thousandth.

Strategy   Use perfect squares to estimate the closest integer, the closest tenth, the closest hundredth, and then the closest thousandth to $\sqrt{85}$.

Step 1   Approximate the value of $\sqrt{85}$ to the nearest integer.

Find the perfect squares closest to 85.

$9^2 = 81$, so $\sqrt{81} = 9$ $\sqrt{81} < \sqrt{85} < \sqrt{100}$

$10^2 = 100$, so $\sqrt{100} = 10$ $9 < \sqrt{85} < 10$

Since 85 is closer to 81 than to 100, the approximation of $\sqrt{85}$ to the nearest integer is 9.

Step 2   Approximate the value of $\sqrt{85}$ to the nearest tenth.

Find decimals to the tenths place with squares closest to 85.

$9.1^2 = 82.81$, so $\sqrt{82.81} = 9.1$ $\sqrt{84.64} < \sqrt{85} < \sqrt{86.49}$

$9.2^2 = 84.64$, so $\sqrt{84.64} = 9.2$ $9.2 < \sqrt{85} < 9.3$

$9.3^2 = 86.49$, so $\sqrt{86.49} = 9.3$

Since 85 is closer to 84.64 than to 86.49, the approximation of $\sqrt{85}$ to the nearest tenth is 9.2.

Step 3   Approximate the value of $\sqrt{85}$ to the nearest hundredth.

Find decimals to the hundredths place with squares closest to 85.

$9.21^2 = 84.8241$, so $\sqrt{84.8241} = 9.21$ $\sqrt{84.8241} < \sqrt{85} < \sqrt{85.0084}$

$9.22^2 = 85.0084$, so $\sqrt{85.0084} = 9.22$ $9.21 < \sqrt{85} < 9.22$

Since 85 is closer to 85.0084 than to 84.8241, the approximation of $\sqrt{85}$ to the nearest hundredth is 9.22.

Step 4   Approximate the value of $\sqrt{85}$ to the nearest thousandth.

Find decimals to the thousandths place with squares closest to 85.

$9.218^2 = 84.971524$, so $\sqrt{84.971524} = 9.218$ $\sqrt{84.989961} < \sqrt{85} < \sqrt{85.0084}$

$9.219^2 = 84.989961$, so $\sqrt{84.989961} = 9.219$ $9.219 < \sqrt{85} < 9.22$

$9.220^2 = 85.0084$, so $\sqrt{85.0084} = 9.220$

Since 85 is closer to 85.0084 than to 84.989961, the approximation of $\sqrt{85}$ to the nearest thousandth is 9.220.

Solution   To the nearest thousandth, $\sqrt{85}$ is approximately equal to 9.220.

Approximate the value of $\sqrt{\pi}$ to the nearest hundredth.

An approximate value of π to the nearest hundredth is _____.

This approximate value of π is between the two perfect squares _____ and _____.

Which of these two perfect squares is closer to the approximate value of π? _____

The positive square root of this perfect square is _____.

Find decimals to the tenths place with squares closest to the approximate value of π.

Which of the squares is closest to your approximation of π?

The positive square root of this number is _____.

Find decimals to the hundredths place with squares closest to the approximate value of π.

Which of the squares is closest to your approximation of π?

The positive square root of this number is _____.

The approximate value of $\sqrt{\pi}$ to the nearest hundredth is _____.

1   Ian plotted four points on a number line. Use numbers from the box to identify the approximate location of each point.

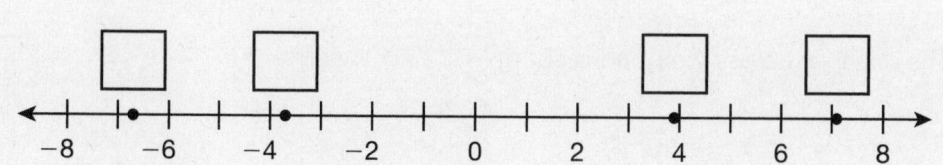

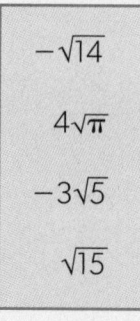

$-\sqrt{14}$

$4\sqrt{\pi}$

$-3\sqrt{5}$

$\sqrt{15}$

2   Select True or False for each statement.

A. $\sqrt{65}$ is between 6 and 7.   ○ True   ○ False

B. $2\sqrt{8}$ is between 5 and 6.   ○ True   ○ False

C. $5\sqrt{3}$ is between 8 and 9.   ○ True   ○ False

D. $\sqrt{3}$ is between 1 and 2.   ○ True   ○ False

E. $3\sqrt{15}$ is between 12 and 13.   ○ True   ○ False

3   Terri makes a quilt using three sizes of fabric squares. The side length of each fabric square is the square root of the area. The areas of the fabric squares are 29, 40, and 62 square inches. Which could be the approximate side length of a square on the quilt? Circle all that apply.

A. 2.9 in.

B. 6.3 in.

C. 9.4 in.

D. 5.4 in.

E. 7.9 in.

4   Is the number between 4 and 5? Select Yes or No.

A. $3\sqrt{2}$ ○ Yes   ○ No

B. $2\sqrt{\pi}$ ○ Yes   ○ No

C. $\frac{1}{2}\sqrt{68}$ ○ Yes   ○ No

D. $\sqrt{17}$ ○ Yes   ○ No

E. $2\sqrt{7}$ ○ Yes   ○ No

5 Alonso estimated the distance across a pond as $\sqrt{232}$ meters. Circle the number that represents the approximate distance to the nearest thousandth.

15.032

The distance across the pond is about   15.232   meters.

15.632

6 Compare the value of each expression to 7. Write the expression in the correct box.

$\sqrt{42}$ $6\sqrt{2}$ $4\sqrt{3}$ $\sqrt{\pi}$ $3\sqrt{8}$ $3\sqrt{5}$

Less Than 7	Greater Than 7

7 Draw a line from each expression to the point that represents its approximate location on the number line.

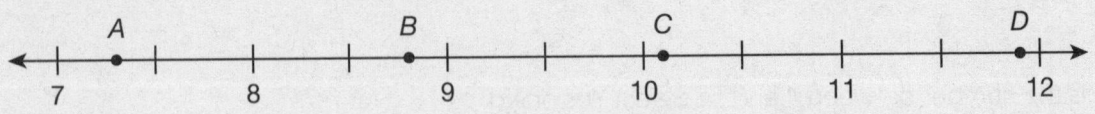

A. $\sqrt{102}$ •   • point A

B. $\sqrt{143}$ •   • point B

C. $3\sqrt{6}$ •   • point C

D. $5\sqrt{\pi}$ •   • point D

8 Use decimals from the box to approximate the value of each square root to the nearest tenth.

Square Root	Decimal Approximation
$\sqrt{57}$	
$\sqrt{86}$	
$\sqrt{94}$	
$\sqrt{62}$	

7.1

8.4

7.9

9.7

9.3

7.5

6.8

8.8

9 Which expression is less than 4.47? Circle all that apply.

A. $\sqrt{14}$

B. 4π

C. $\sqrt{19}$

D. $3\sqrt{2}$

E. $\sqrt{24}$

10 Three students write the widths, in meters, of their backyards as expressions with square roots.

Student	Backyard Width
Kyle	$\sqrt{229} + 14$
Nadira	$\sqrt{608} + 2$
Sam	$\sqrt{705} - 7$

Approximate the width of each student's yard to the nearest hundredth of a meter.

11 David wrote on a test that an approximate value of $\sqrt{140}$ is 10.7.

Part A

Explain how you can determine that David's answer is incorrect without using a calculator.

Part B

Find an approximate value of $\sqrt{140}$ to the tenths place. Show your calculations.

1 Which of the following are irrational numbers? Circle all that apply.

A. $\sqrt{49}$

B. 7.508508507…

C. $\frac{8}{9}$

D. $\sqrt{10}$

E. $6.\overline{25}$

2 The maximum speed an animal can walk in feet per second is $s = 5.7\sqrt{l}$, where l is the animal's leg length in feet. What is the maximum walking speed for a camel with a leg length of 5.7 feet? Circle the number that represents the approximate speed.

The maximum walking speed for a camel is about

| 5.7 |
| 11.4 |
| 13.6 |

feet per second.

3 Look at each number. Is it a rational or irrational number? Select Rational or Irrational.

A. 128.5   ○ Rational   ○ Irrational

B. $\sqrt{15}$ ○ Rational   ○ Irrational

C. 6.415418 …   ○ Rational   ○ Irrational

D. $\sqrt{81}$ ○ Rational   ○ Irrational

E. $\frac{13}{5}$ ○ Rational   ○ Irrational

4 Select True or False for each statement.

A. $\sqrt{74}$ is between 7 and 8.   ○ True   ○ False

B. $3\sqrt{10}$ is between 9 and 10.   ○ True   ○ False

C. $4\sqrt{2}$ is between 4 and 5.   ○ True   ○ False

D. $\sqrt{29}$ is between 5 and 6.   ○ True   ○ False

E. $2\sqrt{50}$ is between 15 and 16.   ○ True   ○ False

5 Yvette is making a blanket. She is going to the craft store for supplies. She wrote her measurements as decimals. Yvette needs $4.\overline{6}$ yards of fabric. She also needs $1.8\overline{3}$ feet of cording for the border. Use numbers from the box to write each measurement as a fraction.

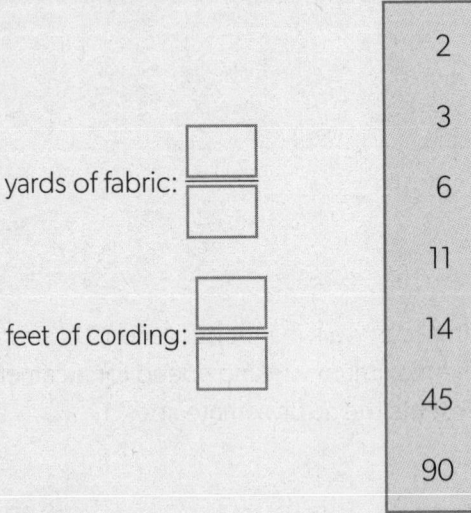

yards of fabric: ☐/☐

feet of cording: ☐/☐

2
3
6
11
14
45
90

6 Which expressions are greater than 12.5? Circle all that apply.

A. $\sqrt{130}$ D. $8\sqrt{\pi}$

B. 4π E. $\sqrt{142}$

C. $2\sqrt{95}$

7 Determine whether each fraction is equivalent to a terminating or repeating decimal. Write the fraction in the correct box.

$\frac{12}{5}$	$\frac{4}{11}$	$\frac{25}{6}$	$\frac{3}{20}$	$\frac{32}{9}$	$\frac{4}{21}$

Fractions Equivalent to Terminating Decimals	Fractions Equivalent to Repeating Decimals

Duplicating any part of this book is prohibited by law. © 2015 Triumph Learning, LLC

8 The rational number $\frac{22}{7}$ is sometimes used as an approximation for the irrational number π. Divide 22 by 7 to find the repeating decimal that is equivalent to $\frac{22}{7}$.

The repeating decimal _____ is equivalent to $\frac{22}{7}$.

9 Use decimals from the box to approximate the value of each square root to the nearest tenth.

Square Root	Decimal Approximation
$\sqrt{75}$	
$\sqrt{58}$	
$\sqrt{40}$	
$\sqrt{92}$	

7.6
6.4
9.5
8.6
7.7
9.6
6.3
8.7

10 Matt claims that the decimal $6.\overline{25}$ is equivalent to the fraction $\frac{25}{4}$.

Part A

How would you show Matt that his claim is incorrect? Explain your reasoning.

Part B

Show how to correctly write the decimal $6.\overline{25}$ as a fraction.

11 Ben is planning to make a square patio. He has enough bricks to make a patio with an area of 150 square feet. The side length of the patio is the square root of the area.

Part A

Find the side length of Ben's patio to the nearest tenth of a foot. Show your work.

Part B

Ben wonders if doubling the area of the patio will double the patio's side length. Find the side length of the patio if Ben doubles the area. Will doubling the area double the side length? Explain.

12 Look at each number. Can the number be written as a ratio of two integers? Select Yes or No.

A. -38 ◯ Yes ◯ No

B. $\sqrt{49}$ ◯ Yes ◯ No

C. $4.1\overline{568}$ ◯ Yes ◯ No

D. $\sqrt{18}$ ◯ Yes ◯ No

E. π ◯ Yes ◯ No

13 Frank uses an online calculator to convert a temperature from degrees Fahrenheit to degrees Celsius. The online calculator shows the temperature as $23.\overline{8}$ degrees Celsius. Write $23.\overline{8}$ as a fraction in simplest form. Show your calculations.

14 Draw a line from each expression to the point that represents its approximate location on the number line.

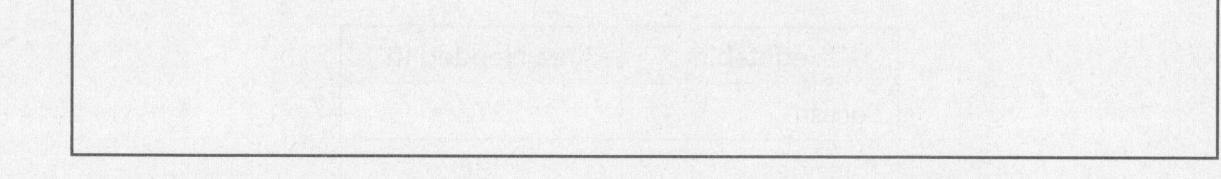

A. $\sqrt{85}$ •   • point A

B. 2π •   • point B

C. $\sqrt{56}$ •   • point C

D. $3\sqrt{15}$ •   • point D

15 Li and two friends are at the ocean studying the wildlife. They are all looking at the horizon from different points along the coastline. The table shows the distance each friend can see to the horizon based on their location.

Friend	Distance (in miles)
Li	$\sqrt{12}$
John	$\sqrt{27}$
Maya	$\sqrt{24}$

Approximate the distance each friend can see to the horizon to the nearest tenth of a mile. Plot a point on the number line below to show each distance. Label each point with the friend's name.

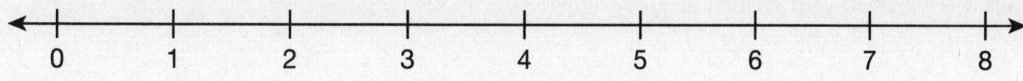

Melia's Vegetable Garden

Melia is making plans for a square vegetable garden. The table shows the amount of space that Melia needs for each type of vegetable she will plant.

Vegetable	Area Needed (ft^2)
Squash	272
Tomatoes	136
Beans	68
Peppers	68
Kale	68

Part A Melia has divided her square garden into five sections: four squares and a rectangle, shown in the diagram. Label the diagram to show a plan for planting Melia's vegetables. In each section, write the name of the vegetable and the area needed for it.

Part B To build a small fence around each vegetable's section, Melia needs the dimensions of each section of her garden. Find the approximate side length of each section to the nearest tenth of a foot. Record these measurements on the diagram.

Part C Are the actual measurements of the side lengths for each section of the garden rational or irrational? Explain your answer.

Part D What is the side length of the bottom edge of the entire garden? Show two different ways for finding this length.

Part E Which method will provide a more accurate approximation of the side length of the garden? Explain your reasoning.

Part F Could you improve your approximations so that they are closer to the actual measurements? If so, explain the method you would use.

DOMAIN 2

Expressions and Equations

Writing Equivalent Numerical Expressions

1 GETTING THE IDEA

You can use properties of exponents to help simplify expressions containing powers. Remember, an **exponent** tells how many times to use a number, called the **base**, as a **factor**. In an exponential term, the exponent is sometimes referred to as **power**.

$$\text{base} \qquad \text{exponent or power}$$

$$\underbrace{3^4}_{\text{term}} = \underbrace{3 \times 3 \times 3 \times 3}_{\text{4 factors of 3}} = 81$$

Product of Powers Property

To multiply exponential terms with the same base, add the exponents.
$x^a \cdot x^b = x^{(a + b)}$, where x is a real number and a and b are integers.

For example, $4^2 \cdot 4^3 = 4^{(2 + 3)} = 4^5$

because $4^2 \cdot 4^3 = (4 \cdot 4) \cdot (4 \cdot 4 \cdot 4)$

$$= 16 \cdot 64 = 1{,}024$$

Quotient of Powers Property

To divide exponential terms with the same base, subtract the exponents.
$\frac{x^b}{x^a} = x^{(b - a)}$, where x is a real number and a and b are integers.

For example, $\frac{5^5}{5^2} = 5^{5 - 2} = 5^3$

because $\frac{5^5}{5^2} = \frac{5 \cdot 5 \cdot 5 \cdot 5 \cdot 5}{5 \cdot 5}$

$$= \frac{3{,}125}{25} = 125$$

Example 1

Write $7^3 \cdot 7^5$ using a single exponent.

Strategy   Use the properties of exponents to multiply.

Step 1   Use the product of powers property.

The terms have the same base, so add the exponents.

$$7^3 \cdot 7^5 = 7^{(3+5)}$$

Step 2   Simplify.

$$= 7^{(3+5)}$$
$$= 7^8$$

Solution $7^3 \cdot 7^5 = 7^8$

Example 2

Write $\dfrac{9^6}{9^4}$ using a single exponent.

Strategy   Use the properties of exponents to divide.

Step 1   Use the quotient of powers property.

The terms have the same base, so subtract the exponents.

$$\frac{9^6}{9^4} = 9^{(6-4)}$$

Step 2   Simplify.

$$= 9^{(6-4)}$$
$$= 9^2$$

Solution $\dfrac{9^6}{9^4} = 9^2$

Power of a Power Property

To raise an exponential term to a power, multiply the exponents.

$(x^a)^b = x^{ab}$, where x is a real number and a and b are integers.

For example, $(7^3)^2 = 7^{3 \cdot 2} = 7^6$

because $(7^3)^2 = (7 \cdot 7 \cdot 7) \cdot (7 \cdot 7 \cdot 7)$

$$= 343 \cdot 343 = 117{,}649$$

Power of a Product Property

To raise a product to a power, raise each factor to the same power.

$(xy)^a = x^a y^a$, where x and y are real numbers and a is an integer.

For example, $(3 \cdot 2)^4 = 3^4 \cdot 2^4$

because $(3 \cdot 2)^4 = (3 \cdot 2) \cdot (3 \cdot 2) \cdot (3 \cdot 2) \cdot (3 \cdot 2)$

$$= (3 \cdot 3 \cdot 3 \cdot 3) \cdot (2 \cdot 2 \cdot 2 \cdot 2)$$

$$= 81 \cdot 16 = 1{,}296$$

Power of a Quotient Property

To raise a quotient to a power, raise the numerator (dividend) and the denominator (divisor) to the same power.

$\left(\frac{x}{y}\right)^a$, where x and y are real numbers and a is an integer.

For example, $\left(\frac{2}{3}\right)^3 = \frac{2^3}{3^3}$

because $\left(\frac{2}{3}\right)^3 = \left(\frac{2}{3}\right) \cdot \left(\frac{2}{3}\right) \cdot \left(\frac{2}{3}\right)$

$$= \frac{2 \cdot 2 \cdot 2}{3 \cdot 3 \cdot 3}$$

$$= \frac{8}{27}$$

Example 3

Write $(8^3)^5$ using a single exponent.

Strategy Use the properties of exponents to raise an exponential term to a power.

Step 1 Use the power of a power property.

Multiply the exponents.

$(8^3)^5 = 8^{3 \cdot 5}$

Step 2 Simplify.

$= 8^{3 \cdot 5}$

$= 8^{15}$

Solution $(8^3)^5 = 8^{15}$

Example 4

Evaluate: $(4 \cdot 2)^2$.

Strategy Use the properties of exponents.

Step 1 Use the power of a product property.

Raise each factor to the power of 2.

$(4 \cdot 2)^2 = 4^2 \cdot 2^2$

Step 2 Evaluate each exponential term.

$= 4^2 \cdot 2^2$

$= (4 \cdot 4) \cdot (2 \cdot 2)$

$= 16 \cdot 4$

Step 3 Multiply.

$= 16 \cdot 4$

$= 64$

Solution $(4 \cdot 2)^2 = 64$

Example 5

Evaluate: $\left(\frac{3}{8}\right)^4$.

Strategy   Use the properties of exponents.

Step 1   Use the power of a quotient property.

Raise the numerator and the denominator to the power of 4.

$$\left(\frac{3}{8}\right)^4 = \frac{3^4}{8^4}$$

Step 2   Evaluate the exponential terms in the numerator and the denominator.

$$= \frac{3^4}{8^4}$$

$$= \frac{3 \cdot 3 \cdot 3 \cdot 3}{8 \cdot 8 \cdot 8 \cdot 8}$$

$$= \frac{81}{4{,}096}$$

Solution $\left(\frac{3}{8}\right)^4 = \frac{81}{4{,}096}$

An exponential term may include an exponent of 0 or a negative exponent.

Zero Exponent Property

Any nonzero number raised to the power of 0 is 1.

$x^0 = 1$, where $x \neq 0$.

For example: $125^0 = 1$

Negative Exponent Property

For any nonzero number x and integer a,

$x^{-a} = \frac{1}{x^a}$.

For example, $5^{-4} = \frac{1}{5^4}$

because $5^{-4} = \frac{1}{5^4} = \frac{1}{5 \cdot 5 \cdot 5 \cdot 5} = \frac{1}{625}$

Example 6

Evaluate: $(-4)^0$.

Strategy   Use the properties of exponents.

Use the zero exponent property to simplify the expression.

Any nonzero number raised to the power of 0 is equal to 1.

$$(-4)^0 = 1$$

Solution $(-4)^0 = 1$

Example 7

Evaluate: 4^{-3}.

Strategy   Use the properties of exponents.

Step 1   Use the negative exponent property.

Take the reciprocal of the base and change the sign of the exponent.

$$4^{-3} = \frac{1}{4^3}$$

Step 2   Evaluate the exponential term in the denominator.

$$= \frac{1}{4^3}$$

$$= \frac{1}{4 \cdot 4 \cdot 4}$$

$$= \frac{1}{64}$$

Solution $4^{-3} = \frac{1}{64}$

Example 8

Simplify: $(3^2)^3 \cdot (5^0 \cdot 3^{-1})$

Strategy   Use the properties of exponents to simplify the expression.

Step 1   Use the power of a power property to simplify $(3^2)^3$.

$$(3^2)^3 \cdot (5^0 \cdot 3^{-1}) = 3^6 \cdot (5^0 \cdot 3^{-1})$$

Step 2   Use the zero exponent property to simplify 5^0.

$$= 3^6 \cdot (5^0 \cdot 3^{-1})$$
$$= 3^6 \cdot (1 \cdot 3^{-1})$$

Step 3   Use the identity property of multiplication to simplify $1 \cdot 3^{-1}$.

$$= 3^6 \cdot (1 \cdot 3^{-1})$$
$$= 3^6 \cdot 3^{-1}$$

Step 4   Use the product of powers property to simplify $3^6 \cdot 3^{-1}$.

$$= 3^6 \cdot 3^{-1}$$
$$= 3^{6 + (-1)}$$
$$= 3^5$$

Solution $(3^2)^3 \cdot (5^0 \cdot 3^{-1}) = 3^5$

Simplify: $(4^3)^4 \cdot (4^{-2} \cdot 3^0)$

First, simplify $(4^3)^4$.

    Use the power of a _____ property.

    To raise an exponential term to a power, _____ the exponents.

    $(4^3)^4 \cdot (4^{-2} \cdot 3^0) = 4^{\text{——}} \cdot (4^{-2} \cdot 3^0)$

Next, simplify 3^0.

    Use the _____ exponent property.

    $= 4^{12} \cdot (4^{-2} \cdot 3^0)$

    $= 4^{12} \cdot (4^{-2} \cdot \text{——})$

Then, simplify $4^{-2} \cdot 1$.

    $= 4^{12} \cdot (4^{-2} \cdot 1)$

    $= 4^{12} \cdot \text{——}$

Last, simplify $4^{12} \cdot 4^{-2}$.

    Use the product of _____ property.

    $= 4^{12} \cdot 4^{-2}$

    $= 4^{\text{——} + \text{——}}$

    $= 4^{\text{——}}$

$(4^3)^4 \cdot (4^{-2} \cdot 3^0) = $ _____

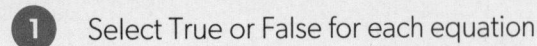
1 Select True or False for each equation.

A. $9^3 \cdot 9^4 = 9^{12}$ ○ True ○ False

B. $(5^2)^5 = 5^{10}$ ○ True ○ False

C. $(2 \cdot 4)^6 = 2^6 \cdot 4^6$ ○ True ○ False

D. $8^0 = 0$ ○ True ○ False

E. $\dfrac{7^8}{7^4} = 7^2$ ○ True ○ False

F. $3^{-2} = \dfrac{1}{9}$ ○ True ○ False

2 Is each expression equivalent to 16? Select Yes or No.

A. $\dfrac{4^8}{4^6}$ ○ Yes ○ No

B. 16^0 ○ Yes ○ No

C. $2^1 \cdot 2^3$ ○ Yes ○ No

D. $(2 \cdot 2)^2$ ○ Yes ○ No

E. 8^2 ○ Yes ○ No

F. 4^{-2} ○ Yes ○ No

3 Circle the exponential expression or value that makes each equation true.

$$5^2 \cdot \begin{array}{|c|} \hline 5^3 \\ \hline 5^4 \\ \hline 5^{12} \\ \hline \end{array} = 5^6 \qquad 2^0 = \begin{array}{|c|} \hline 0 \\ \hline 1 \\ \hline 2 \\ \hline \end{array}$$

4 Kate ate $\frac{1}{8}$ of a veggie pizza. Which expressions are equivalent to $\frac{1}{8}$? Circle all that apply.

A. 2^{-3}

B. $(-8)^1$

C. $\left(\frac{32}{4}\right)^{-1}$

D. $8^8 - 8^9$

E. $\frac{8^8}{8^9}$

F. $\left(\frac{1}{8}\right)^0$

G. $(2^3)^{-1}$

5 Compare the value of each expression to 64. Write the expression in the correct box.

$2^3 \cdot 2^2$	$\frac{4^7}{4^3}$	$(8^2)^2$	64^0	$(2 \cdot 4)^3$

Less Than 64	Greater Than 64

6 Draw a line from each expression to its equivalent expression.

A. $(9^3)^6$ •   • 9^3

B. $(9 \cdot 3)^6$ •   • $\frac{9^6}{3^6}$

C. $\left(\frac{9}{3}\right)^6$ •   • $9^6 \cdot 3^6$

D. $\frac{9^6}{9^3}$ •   • 9^{18}

7 Luis used the properties of exponents to write two equations equal to 81. Use exponential terms from the box to complete the equations.

$$81 = \underline{\hspace{1cm}} \cdot \underline{\hspace{1cm}}$$

$$81 = \underline{\hspace{1cm}} \div \underline{\hspace{1cm}}$$

3^1
3^3
3^4
9^4
9^6
9^8
$(3^2)^3$

8 For each expression in the table, indicate with an "X" whether the value of the expression is less than 1, equal to 1, or greater than 1.

Expression	Less Than 1	Equal to 1	Greater Than 1
$(4 \cdot 7)^{-2}$			
$\left(\dfrac{18}{6}\right)^3$			
$(12^0)^1$			

9 **Part A**

Write 5^8 as a quotient of two exponential terms with the same base in four different ways. Use only positive nonzero exponents.

Part B

Write 5^8 as a quotient of two exponential terms with the same base in four different ways. Use negative and/or zero exponents.

Part C

How many ways can you write 5^8 as a quotient of two exponential terms? Explain your reasoning.

Evaluating Square Roots and Cube Roots

1 GETTING THE IDEA

A number that is the square of an integer is called a **perfect square**. For example, 16 is a perfect square because $16 = 4^2$.

A **square root** of a number is a number that, when multiplied by itself, is equal to the given number. Every positive real number has a positive square root and a negative square root.

5 and -5 are the square roots of 25.

$$5 \cdot 5 = 5^2 = 25$$

$$-5 \cdot -5 = (-5)^2 = 25$$

You can use the symbol $\pm$ to indicate both square roots of 25: ± 5.

The radical symbol $\sqrt{}$ indicates the square root of a number. When you simplify a square-root expression, like the ones below, you give only the nonnegative square root, or the **principal square root**.

$$\sqrt{1} = 1 \qquad \sqrt{9} = 3 \qquad \sqrt{49} = 7 \qquad \sqrt{x^2} = x$$

You can solve equations of the form $x^2 = p$ by taking the square root of each side of the equation. When you solve a square-root equation with a variable, you must include both the positive and the negative square roots unless indicated otherwise.

Example 1

What are the solutions of $x^2 = 169$?

Strategy   Find the square roots of each side of the equation, and simplify.

Step 1   Find the square root of each side of the equation.

$$x^2 = 169$$

$$\sqrt{x^2} = \pm\sqrt{169}$$

$$\sqrt{x \cdot x} = \pm\sqrt{13 \cdot 13}$$

| Step 2 | Simplify the radicals. |

$$\sqrt{x \cdot x} = \pm\sqrt{13 \cdot 13}$$
$$x = \pm13$$

Solution   The solutions of $x^2 = 169$ are ±13.

If a positive real number is not a perfect square, then its square root is irrational. For example, 2 is not a perfect square, so $\sqrt{2}$ is irrational. When a number is not a perfect square, you can estimate its square root by using the square root of the nearest perfect square. You could also use a calculator to find the square root.

Example 2

Find the solutions of $x^2 = 30$. Then estimate the values of the solutions.

Strategy   **Find the square roots of each side of the equation. Then estimate the values of the square roots.**

| Step 1 | Find the square root of each side of the equation. |

$$x^2 = 30$$
$$\sqrt{x^2} = \pm\sqrt{30}$$
$$x = \pm\sqrt{30}$$

| Step 2 | Estimate the value of $\pm\sqrt{30}$ to the nearest integer by finding the closest perfect squares. |

The closest perfect square less than 30 is 25. The closest perfect square greater than 30 is 36.

Since 30 is closer to 25 than to 36, $\sqrt{30}$ is closer to 5 than to 6.

$$x \approx \pm5$$

| Step 3 | To get a closer estimate of $\pm\sqrt{30}$, square decimals to the tenths place and compare them to 30. |

$$5.4^2 = 29.16$$
$$5.5^2 = 30.25$$

30 is closer to 30.25, so $\pm\sqrt{30} \approx \pm5.5$.

Solution   **The solutions of $x^2 = 30$ are $\pm\sqrt{30}$ or approximately ±5.5.**

To find the square root of a rational number in the form $\frac{a}{b}$, where $a \geq 0$ and $b > 0$, find the square root of the numerator, a, and the square root of the denominator, b. Then simplify.

$$\sqrt{\frac{4}{9}} = \frac{\sqrt{4}}{\sqrt{9}}, \text{ or } \frac{2}{3}$$

Example 3

Alana drew a diagram of a local park. The park has a square shape. What is the length of each side of the park?

$$A = \frac{49}{100} \text{mi}^2$$

Strategy   Find the square root of each side of an equation, and then simplify.

Step 1   Write an equation. Use the formula for the area of a square.

$$A = s^2$$

Substitute $\frac{49}{100}$ for A.

$$\frac{49}{100} = s^2$$

Step 2   Find the square root of each side of the equation.

$$\frac{49}{100} = s^2$$

$$\pm\sqrt{\frac{49}{100}} = \pm\sqrt{s^2}$$

$$\pm\sqrt{\frac{49}{100}} = s$$

Step 3   To find $\pm\sqrt{\frac{49}{100}}$, take the square root of the numerator and the square root of the denominator.

$$\pm\sqrt{\frac{49}{100}} = s$$

$$\pm\frac{\sqrt{49}}{\sqrt{100}} = s$$

Step 4   Simplify the numerator and denominator.

$$\pm\frac{\sqrt{49}}{\sqrt{100}} = s$$

$$\pm\frac{7}{10} = s$$

Step 5   Use reasoning to decide the length of each side of the park.

The length of the park cannot be negative, so only the positive square root, $\frac{7}{10}$, makes sense.

Solution   The length of each side of the park is $\frac{7}{10}$ mile.

A number that is the cube of an integer is called a **perfect cube**. For example, 27 is a perfect cube because $27 = 3^3$.

A number that is used as a factor 3 times is the **cube root** of the product. For example, 2 is the cube root of 8 because $2 \cdot 2 \cdot 2$ or 2^3 equals 8. The symbol $\sqrt[3]{}$ indicates the cube root of a number. The cube root of a positive number is always positive.

$$\sqrt[3]{64} = 4 \qquad \sqrt[3]{(-216)} = -6 \qquad \sqrt[3]{1} = 1 \qquad \sqrt[3]{x^3} = x$$

You can solve equations of the form $x^3 = p$ by taking the cube root of each side.

Example 4

Crate Company builds wooden boxes of all sizes. The drawing below shows the volume of one of its cube-shape boxes. What is the edge length, s, of the box?

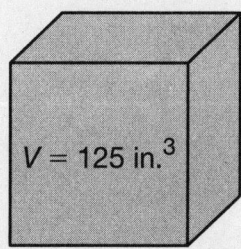

$V = 125$ in.^{3}

Strategy   Write and solve an equation by finding the cube root.

Step 1   Write an equation. Use the formula for the volume of a cube.

$$V = s^3$$

Substitute 125 for V.

$$125 = s^3$$

Step 2   Find the cube root.

$$125 = s^3$$
$$\sqrt[3]{125} = \sqrt[3]{s^3}$$
$$\sqrt[3]{125} = s$$

Step 3   Simplify the radical.

$$\sqrt[3]{125} = s$$
$$\sqrt[3]{5 \cdot 5 \cdot 5} = s$$
$$5 = s$$

Solution   The edge length of each side of the box is 5 inches.

If a number is not a perfect cube, then its cube root is irrational. For example, 10 is not a perfect cube, so $\sqrt[3]{10}$ is irrational. To estimate the cube root of a number that is not a perfect cube, use the cube root of the nearest perfect cube.

Example 5

Find the solution of $x^3 = 75$. Then estimate its value.

Strategy   **Find the cube root of each side of the equation. Then estimate the value of the cube root.**

Step 1   Find the cube root of each side of the equation.

$$x^3 = 75$$
$$\sqrt[3]{x^3} = \sqrt[3]{75}$$
$$x = \sqrt[3]{75}$$

Step 2   Estimate the value of $\sqrt[3]{75}$ to the nearest integer by finding the closest perfect cubes.

The closest perfect cube less than 75 is 64. The closest perfect cube greater than 75 is 125. Since 75 is closer to 64 than to 125, $\sqrt[3]{75}$ is closer to 4 than to 5.

$$x \approx 4$$

Step 3   To get a closer estimate of $\sqrt[3]{75}$, cube decimals to the tenths place, and compare them to 75.

$$4.2^3 = 74.088$$
$$4.3^3 = 79.507$$

75 is closer to 74.088, so $\sqrt[3]{75} \approx 4.2$.

Solution   **The solution of $x^3 = 75$ is $\sqrt[3]{75}$ or approximately 4.2.**

To find the cube root of a rational number in the form $\frac{a}{b}$, where $b \neq 0$, find the cube root of the numerator, a, and the cube root of the denominator, b. Then simplify. For example, $\sqrt[3]{\frac{1}{8}} = \frac{\sqrt[3]{1}}{\sqrt[3]{8}}$, or $\frac{1}{2}$.

Example 6

What are the solutions of $x^3 = \frac{729}{1,000}$?

Strategy   **Find the cube root of each side of the equation, and simplify.**

Step 1   Take the cube root of each side.

$$x^3 = \frac{729}{1,000}$$
$$\sqrt[3]{x^3} = \sqrt[3]{\frac{729}{1,000}}$$
$$x = \sqrt[3]{\frac{729}{1,000}}$$

Step 2   To find $\sqrt[3]{\dfrac{729}{1,000}}$, take the cube root of the numerator and the cube root of the denominator.

$$x = \sqrt[3]{\dfrac{729}{1,000}}$$

$$= \dfrac{\sqrt[3]{729}}{\sqrt[3]{1,000}}$$

Step 3   Simplify the numerator and denominator.

$$x = \dfrac{\sqrt[3]{729}}{\sqrt[3]{1,000}}$$

$$= \dfrac{9}{10}$$

Solution   The solution of $x^3 = \dfrac{729}{1,000}$ is $\dfrac{9}{10}$.

② COACHED EXAMPLE

A contractor is painting a square wall in a bedroom. The area of the wall is 196 square feet. What is the length of each side of the wall?

Write an equation. Use the formula for the area of a square.

$A = s^2$

Substitute _____ for _____.

$s^2 =$ _____

Find the square root of each side of the equation.

$$s^2 = 196$$

$$\sqrt{\rule{2cm}{0pt}} = \pm\sqrt{\rule{2cm}{0pt}}$$

$$\rule{2cm}{0pt} = \rule{1.5cm}{0pt}$$

Simplify the radical.

$s = \pm\sqrt{196}$

$s =$ _____

Use reasoning to decide the length of the wall. The length of the wall cannot be

_____, so only the _____ square root, _____, makes sense.

The length of each side of the wall is _____ feet.

1 Select True or False for each statement.

    A. 1 is a perfect square.   ○ True   ○ False

    B. 1 is a perfect cube.   ○ True   ○ False

    C. -1 is a perfect square.   ○ True   ○ False

    D. $\sqrt{1}$ is irrational.   ○ True   ○ False

2 Draw a line from each equation to its solution(s).

    A. $x^2 = \dfrac{1}{64}$ •   • $\dfrac{1}{10}$

    B. $x^3 = \dfrac{1}{64}$ •   • $\dfrac{1}{4}$

    C. $x^2 = \dfrac{1}{100}$ •   • $\pm\dfrac{1}{8}$

    D. $x^3 = \dfrac{1}{1,000}$ •   • $\pm\dfrac{1}{10}$

3 Select a value that is between 9 and 10. Circle all that apply.

    A. $\sqrt{80}$ **E.** $\sqrt[3]{750}$

    B. $\sqrt{89}$ **F.** $\sqrt[3]{999}$

    C. $\sqrt{101}$ **G.** $\sqrt[3]{1,010}$

    D. $\sqrt[3]{725}$

4 Compare the value of each expression to $\sqrt[3]{125}$. Write the expression in the correct box.

| $\sqrt{25}$ | $\sqrt[3]{\dfrac{216}{8}}$ | 12^2 | $\sqrt{125}$ | $(1)^7$ | $\sqrt[3]{\dfrac{1,000}{125}}$ |

Less Than $\sqrt[3]{125}$	Equal to $\sqrt[3]{125}$	Greater Than $\sqrt[3]{125}$

5 Josh cut a square sheet of paper along a diagonal to make two congruent triangles. The area of one triangle is 60.5 in.^{2} Find the length of one side, s, of the square. Show your work.

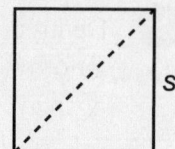

6 Use numbers from the box to represent the approximate locations on the number line.

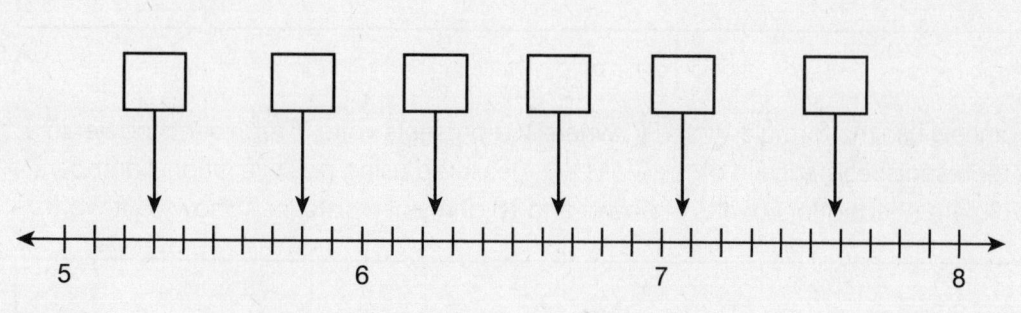

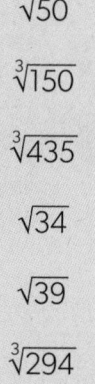

$\sqrt{50}$

$\sqrt[3]{150}$

$\sqrt[3]{435}$

$\sqrt{34}$

$\sqrt{39}$

$\sqrt[3]{294}$

7 Li used square roots and cube roots to write equations equal to 10. Use items from the box to write two different equations that Li could have written.

$10 =$ _____ $+$ _____

$10 =$ _____ $-$ _____

$\sqrt[3]{27}$

$\sqrt{49}$

$\sqrt{1}$

$\sqrt[3]{64}$

$\sqrt[3]{8}$

$\sqrt{121}$

8 Darius created a geometric square design for art class. The area of the inside square with side length *s* is equal to 50% of the total area of the design. What is *s* rounded to the nearest tenth of an inch? Explain how you found your answer.

8 in.

9 Electrical engineers use the formula $V = \sqrt{PR}$, where *V* represents volts, *P* represents power in watts, and *R* represents resistance in ohms. Volts are measured using positive rational numbers. How many volts are needed for 8 watts of power and 18 ohms of resistance? Show your work.

10 Every positive real number has both a positive and a negative square root. Does every positive real number also have both a positive and negative cube root? Show your work or explain how you found your answer.

11 For each equation in the table, indicate with an "X" whether the equation has 1 solution or 2 solutions.

Equation	1 Solution	2 Solutions
$x^2 = \frac{49}{121}$		
$x^2 = 121$		
$x^3 = 512$		

12 Sasha is solving equations of the form $x^2 = p$.

Part A

For what value(s) of p will the equation $x^2 = p$ have 2 real number solutions? Explain your reasoning.

Part B

For what value(s) of p will the equation $x^2 = p$ have 1 real number solution? Explain your reasoning.

Part C

For what value(s) of p will the equation $x^2 = p$ have 0 real number solutions? Explain your reasoning.

Understanding Scientific Notation

The distance from Earth to Mars on a certain day of the year is about 40,000,000 miles. The length of a common dust mite is about 0.04 centimeter. You can use scientific notation to write very large numbers or very small numbers, such as these, in a shorter form.

A number is in **scientific notation** if the first factor, or **coefficient**, is greater than or equal to 1 and less than 10. The second factor must be a power of 10. A **power of 10** is a number in the form 10^n, where n is an integer.

Standard Form	Scientific Notation
40,000,000	4×10^7
0.04	4×10^{-2}

When you write a large number in scientific notation, you move the decimal point n places to the left to find the coefficient. Then write the second factor as 10^n.

Example 1

Write 800,000,000,000 in scientific notation.

Strategy   Write the number as the product of a coefficient and 10^n.

Step 1   Move the decimal point to the left to find the coefficient.

$$800{,}000{,}000{,}000 \rightarrow 8.00{,}000{,}000{,}000.$$

The coefficient is 8.

Step 2   Multiply the coefficient by 10^n.

The value of n is the number of places the decimal point was moved to create the coefficient.

The decimal point was moved **11 places to the left**, so 11 is the exponent of 10.

8×10^{11}

Solution $800{,}000{,}000{,}000 = 8 \times 10^{11}$

Similarly, when you write a small number in scientific notation, you move the decimal point n places to the right to find the coefficient. Then write the second factor as 10^{-n}.

Example 2

Write 0.0005 in scientific notation.

Strategy   **Write the number as the product of a coefficient and 10^{-n}.**

Step 1   Move the decimal point to the right to find the coefficient.

$$0.0005 \rightarrow 0.0005.$$

The coefficient is 5.

Step 2   Multiply the coefficient by 10^{-n}.

The decimal point was moved **4 places to the right**, so use **−4** as the exponent of 10.

5×10^{-4}

Solution $0.0005 = 5 \times 10^{-4}$

When you multiply a number by 10^n, where n is positive, the decimal point of the number moves n places to the right. You can use this to help you write a number that is in scientific notation as a number in standard form.

Example 3

The population of the United States is about 3×10^8. Write this number in standard form.

Strategy   **Find the product of the coefficient and the power of 10.**

Step 1   Multiply 3 by 10^8. Insert zeros as necessary.

The exponent is **8**, so move the decimal point **8 places to the right**.

$$3 \times 10^8 = 3.00000000.$$

Step 2   Write the number in standard form.

300,000,000

Solution   **The population of the United States is about 300,000,000.**

When you multiply a number by 10^n, where n is negative, the decimal point of the number moves n places to the left. You can also use this to help you write a number that is in scientific notation as a number in standard form.

Example 4

Human hair grows at an average rate of about 4×10^{-2} centimeter per day. Write this rate in standard form.

Strategy **Find the product of the coefficient and the power of 10.**

Step 1 Multiply 4 by 10^{-2}. Insert zeros as necessary.

The exponent is -2, so move the decimal point **2 places to the left**.

$$4 \times 10^{-2} = 0.04.$$

Step 2 Write the number in standard form.

0.04

Solution **Human hair grows at an average rate of about 0.04 centimeter per day.**

Comparing two numbers written in scientific notation is similar to the way you compare two whole numbers. One way to compare two numbers is to express how many times as much one number is than the other. For example, 508 is about 20 times as much as 25.

Example 5

About how many times greater is 4×10^5 than 9×10^3?

Strategy **Rewrite the greater number so that its power of 10 is the same as the power of 10 of the lesser number. Then compare the coefficients.**

Step 1 Rewrite 4×10^5 so that its power of 10 is the same as the power of 10 in 9×10^3.

Subtract the exponents of the powers of 10, $5 - 3 = 2$.

Move the decimal point of the coefficient **2 places to the right**. Insert zeros as necessary.

$4 \times 10^5 = 400 \times 10^3$

Step 2 Compare the numbers by estimating how many times greater one coefficient is than the other.

400×10^3

9×10^3

$400 \div 9$ is about $400 \div 10$, or 40. So, 400×10^3, or 4×10^5, is about 40 times greater than 9×10^3.

Solution 4×10^5 is about 40 times greater than 9×10^3.

Example 6

During 1 year, about 2×10^7 U.S. students were enrolled in college. That same year, about 4×10^6 U.S. students were enrolled in private schools in grades 1 through 12. For that year, about how many times more U.S. students were enrolled in college than in private schools?

Strategy   Rewrite the greater number so that its power of 10 is the same as the power of 10 of the lesser number. Then compare the coefficients.

Step 1   Rewrite 2×10^7 so its power of 10 is the same as the power of 10 in 4×10^6.

Subtract the exponents, $7 - 6 = 1$.

Move the decimal point of the coefficient **1 place to the right**. Insert zeros as necessary.

$2 \times 10^7 = 20 \times 10^6$

Step 2   Compare the numbers by finding how many times greater 20 is than 4.

$\mathbf{20 \times 10^6}$

$\mathbf{4 \times 10^6}$

$20 \div 4$ is 5. So, 20×10^6, or 2×10^7, is 5 times greater than 4×10^6.

Solution   About 5 times more students were enrolled in college than in private schools.

② COACHED EXAMPLE

At sea level, the speed of sound is about 3×10^2 meters per second. The speed of light is about 3×10^8 meters per second. About how many times faster is the speed of light than the speed of sound at sea level?

Rewrite $3 \times 10^{\underline{}}$ so it has the same power of 10 as $3 \times 10^{\underline{}}$.

Subtract the exponents.

_____ − _____ = _____

Move the decimal point _____ places to the _____. Insert zeros if necessary.

$3 \times 10^8 =$ _____

Compare the coefficients.

_____ $\times 10^2$

3×10^2

_____ ÷ _____ = _____

So, _____ $\times 10^2$, or 3×10^8, is about _____ times greater than 3×10^2.

The speed of light is about _____ meters per second faster than the speed of sound at sea level.

1 Select True or False for each statement.

A. 2×10^4 is in scientific notation. ○ True ○ False

B. 0.9×10^{-3} is in scientific notation. ○ True ○ False

C. 8×5^2 is in scientific notation. ○ True ○ False

D. If you write 70,000 in scientific notation, the coefficient will be 70. ○ True ○ False

E. If you write 0.003 in scientific notation, the second factor will be 10^{-3}. ○ True ○ False

2 Which numbers are less than 1,000? Circle all that apply.

A. 8×10^2

B. 9×10^3

C. 1×10^1

D. 5×10^1

E. 3×10^4

F. 6×10^2

G. 7×10^3

3 Circle numbers that show how to rewrite the number in scientific notation.

$$0.0100 = \boxed{\begin{matrix} 0.1 \\ 1 \\ 10 \\ 100 \end{matrix}} \times \boxed{\begin{matrix} 10^{-4} \\ 10^{-3} \\ 10^{-2} \\ 10^{-1} \end{matrix}}$$

4 When writing each number in scientific notation, will the power of 10 be 10^{-3}? Select Yes or No.

A. 0.0020 ○ Yes ○ No

B. 2,000 ○ Yes ○ No

C. 0.008 ○ Yes ○ No

D. 0.100 ○ Yes ○ No

E. 10.000 ○ Yes ○ No

5 During 1 year, the cost of airing a 30-second commercial during a championship football game was $4 million.

Part A

What is $4 million written in standard form?

Part B

To write $4 million in scientific notation, will the power of 10 be positive or negative. Explain your reasoning.

Part C

Write $4 million in scientific notation.

6 In 2012, the estimated population of California was about 4×10^7. The estimated population of Alaska was about 7×10^5. About how many times greater was the estimated population of California than the estimated population of Alaska in 2012? Explain how you found your answer.

7 Use numbers from the box to write each number in scientific notation.

$$2 \times 10^{\underline{\hspace{1cm}}} = 0.020000$$

$$40,000 = \underline{\hspace{1.5cm}} \times 10^{\underline{\hspace{1cm}}}$$

$$\underline{\hspace{1.5cm}} \times 10^{-6} = 0.000004$$

$$0.0002 = \underline{\hspace{1.5cm}} \times 10^{\underline{\hspace{1cm}}}$$

−4
−2
2
4

8 Circle the power of 10 or number that makes each equation true.

10^5		0.2
$2 \times$ 10^6 $= 20,000,000$		2 $\times 10^{-3} = 0.00200$
10^7		200

9 Use powers of 10 from the box to complete the table of equivalent expressions.

Number	Equivalent Expression
20 million	
20 ten thousandths	
20 hundredths	
20 tens	

2×10^{-7}
2×10^{-4}
2×10^{-2}
2×10^{-1}
2×10^{1}
2×10^{2}
2×10^{4}
2×10^{7}

10 The mass of a certain grain of rice is about 3×10^{-2} grams. The mass of a certain grain of salt is about 6×10^{-5} grams.

Part A

Which has a greater mass: the grain of rice or the grain of salt? Explain how you found your answer.

Part B

How many times greater is the mass of the larger grain than the smaller grain? Explain how you found your answer.

Using Scientific Notation

A number expressed in **scientific notation** is written as the product of two factors. The first factor is a number greater than or equal to 1 and less than 10, and the second factor is a power of 10.

$$4.32 \times 10^3 = 4.32 \times 10 \times 10 \times 10 = 4,320$$

Numbers expressed in scientific notation can be added and subtracted. The numbers can be written in standard form, and then the operation can be performed.

Addition	Subtraction
$2.3 \times 10^4 + 6.11 \times 10^5$	$6.11 \times 10^5 - 2.3 \times 10^4$
$23,000 + 611,000$	$611,000 - 23,000$
$634,000$	$588,000$
6.34×10^5	5.88×10^5

Using this method requires an additional step of writing the answer in scientific notation. You will learn more efficient methods that involve using the properties of operations.

Example 1

Add: $6.12 \times 10^3 + 8.305 \times 10^3$.

Strategy   **Use the distributive property to rewrite the expression.**

Step 1   The second factor of each addend is 10^3. Use the distributive property to factor out 10^3.

$$6.12 \times 10^3 + 8.305 \times 10^3 = 10^3(6.12 + 8.305)$$

Step 2   Add the numbers inside the parentheses. Use the commutative property of multiplication to write the answer as a number times a power of 10.

$$6.12 \times 10^3 + 8.305 \times 10^3 = 10^3(6.12 + 8.305)$$
$$= 10^3(14.425)$$
$$= 14.425 \times 10^3$$

Step 3   Write 14.425×10^3 in scientific notation.

Use multiples of 10 to move the decimal point so that the first factor has a value greater than or equal to 1 and less than 10.

$$14.425 \times 10^3 = 14.425 \times 10 \times 10 \times 10$$
$$= 1.4425 \times 10 \times 10 \times 10 \times 10$$
$$= 1.4425 \times 10^4$$

Solution $6.12 \times 10^3 + 8.305 \times 10^3 = 1.4425 \times 10^4$

Example 2

Subtract: $2.81 \times 10^8 - 3.6 \times 10^5$.

Strategy   **Rewrite the numbers so they have the same power of 10, and then use the distributive property.**

Step 1   Rewrite 2.81×10^8 so that it has an exponent of 5.

Use the associative property of multiplication to regroup factors of 10 with the coefficient to make 10^5.

$$2.81 \times 10^8 = 2.81 \times 10 \times 10 \times 10 \times 10 \times 10 \times 10 \times 10 \times 10$$
$$= (2.81 \times 10 \times 10 \times 10)(10 \times 10 \times 10 \times 10 \times 10)$$
$$= 2,810 \times 10 \times 10 \times 10 \times 10 \times 10$$
$$= 2,810 \times 10^5$$

Step 2   Use the distributive property to factor out 10^5 from each expression.

$$2.81 \times 10^8 - 3.6 \times 10^5 = 2,810 \times 10^5 - 3.6 \times 10^5$$
$$= 10^5 (2,810 - 3.6)$$

Step 3   Subtract the values inside the parentheses.

$$10^5 (2,810 - 3.6) = 2,806.4 \times 10^5$$

Step 4   Rewrite $2,806.4 \times 10^5$ using scientific notation.

The decimal point of 2,806.4 must move 3 places to the left to change the value to a number between 1 and 10.

$$2,806.4$$

When moving the decimal point to the left, increase the value of the exponent by the number of places the decimal point is moved.

$$2,806.4 \times 10^5 = 2.8064 \times 10^8$$

Solution $2.81 \times 10^8 - 3.6 \times 10^5 = 2.8064 \times 10^8$

To multiply or divide numbers expressed in scientific notation, use the laws of exponents.

> **Product of powers:** To multiply powers with the same base, add the exponents.
>
> $x^a \cdot x^b = x^{(a + b)}$
>
> **Quotient of powers:** To divide powers with the same base, subtract the exponents.
>
> $\dfrac{x^b}{x^a} = x^{(b-a)}$

Example 3

Multiply: $(8.2 \times 10^5)(3.61 \times 10^{-3})$.

Strategy   Use the laws of exponents to simplify.

Step 1   Use the commutative property to rewrite the expression. Then find the product of 8.2 and 3.61.

$$(8.2 \times 10^5)(3.61 \times 10^{-3}) = (8.2)(10^5)(3.61)(10^{-3})$$
$$= (8.2)(3.61)(10^5)(10^{-3})$$
$$= (29.602)(10^5)(10^{-3})$$

Step 2   Use the product of powers property to multiply 10^5 and 10^{-3}.

10^5 and 10^{-3} have the same base of 10, so add the exponents.

$$(10^5)(10^{-3}) = 10^{5 + (-3)} = 10^2$$

Step 3   Check if the product is written in scientific notation. If not, use multiples of 10 to move the decimal point.

$$29.602 \times 10^2 = 29.602 \times 10 \times 10$$
$$= 2.9602 \times 10 \times 10 \times 10$$
$$= 2.9602 \times 10^3$$

Solution $(8.2 \times 10^5)(3.61 \times 10^{-3}) = 2.9602 \times 10^3$

Example 4

Divide: $\dfrac{-1.334 \times 10^5}{2.3 \times 10^{-5}}$.

Strategy Use the laws of exponents to simplify.

Step 1 Use the commutative property to rewrite the expression. Then find the quotient of -1.334 and 2.3.

$$\frac{-1.334 \times 10^5}{2.3 \times 10^{-5}} = \frac{-1.334}{2.3} \times \frac{10^5}{10^{-5}}$$

$$= -0.58 \times \frac{10^5}{10^{-5}}$$

Step 2 Use the quotient of powers property to divide 10^5 by 10^{-5}.

10^5 and 10^{-5} have the same base of 10, so subtract the exponents.

$$\frac{10^5}{10^{-5}} = 10^{5-(-5)} = 10^{10}$$

Step 3 Check if the quotient is written in scientific notation. If not, use multiples of 10 to move the decimal point.

$$-0.58 \times 10^{10} = -0.58 \times 10 \times 10 \times 10 \times 10 \times 10 \times 10 \times 10 \times 10 \times 10 \times 10$$

$$= -5.8 \times 10 \times 10 \times 10 \times 10 \times 10 \times 10 \times 10 \times 10 \times 10$$

$$= -5.8 \times 10^9$$

Solution $\dfrac{-1.334 \times 10^5}{2.3 \times 10^{-5}} = -5.8 \times 10^9$

Example 5

The mass of Earth is 5.9726×10^{24} kg. The mass of Venus is 4.8676×10^{24} kg. How many times greater is the mass of Earth than the mass of Venus?

Strategy Divide the mass of Earth by the mass of Venus. Then simplify using the laws of exponents.

Step 1 Write the division statement.

$$\frac{\text{Earth's mass}}{\text{Venus' mass}} = \frac{5.9726 \times 10^{24}}{4.8676 \times 10^{24}}$$

Step 2 Use the commutative property to rewrite the expression. Then find the quotient of 5.976 and 4.8676. Round your answer to the nearest ten-thousandth.

$$\frac{5.9726 \times 10^{24}}{4.8676 \times 10^{24}} = \frac{5.9726}{4.8676} \times \frac{10^{24}}{10^{24}}$$

$$\approx 1.2270 \times \frac{10^{24}}{10^{24}}$$

Step 3   Use the laws of exponents to divide 10^{24} by 10^{24}.

$$\frac{10^{24}}{10^{24}} = 10^{24-24} = 10^0$$

Any number to the power of zero is 1, so $10^0 = 1$.

Solution   The mass of Earth is about 1.2270×1 or 1.2270 times greater than that of Venus.

Example 6

Justin estimated the mass of a grain of sugar as 6.25×10^{-4} gram. Based upon Justin's estimate, what is the mass of 500 grains of sugar?

Strategy   **Write an expression. Then use a calculator to evaluate.**

Step 1   Write the expression.

The mass of 500 grains of sugar is about $500 \times (6.25 \times 10^{-4})$ grams.

Step 2   Use a calculator to evaluate the expression. Many calculators use the key labeled "EE" or "EXP" to show scientific notation.

Solution   **Based upon Justin's estimate, the mass of 500 grains of sugar is 0.3125 gram.**

---

② COACHED EXAMPLE

Divide: $\dfrac{1.28 \times 10^{-3}}{-6.4 \times 10^4}$

Rewrite the expression using the _____.

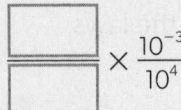 $\times \dfrac{10^{-3}}{10^4}$

Divide the decimals.

_____ $\times \dfrac{10^{-3}}{10^4}$

Use the _____ to divide the factors with exponents.

Since the bases are the same, _____ the exponents.

$\dfrac{10^{-3}}{10^4} = 10^{(\underline{\quad})} = 10^{\underline{\quad}}$

Rewrite the quotient in scientific notation.

$-0.2 \times 10^{-7} =$ _____ $\times 10^{\underline{\quad}}$

$\dfrac{1.28 \times 10^{-3}}{-6.4 \times 10^4} =$ _____

1 Does each expression have a value of 5×10^{-3}? Select Yes or No.

A. $3.1 \times 10^{-6} + 1.9 \times 10^3$ ○ Yes ○ No

B. $6 \times 10^{-3} + 1 \times 10^{-3}$ ○ Yes ○ No

C. $4 \times 10^{-3} + 1 \times 10^{-3}$ ○ Yes ○ No

D. $3.1 \times 10^{-3} + 1.9 \times 10^{-3}$ ○ Yes ○ No

2 Use numbers from the box to make the equation true.

$$(3.5 \times 10^{\underline{\quad}})(2.1 \times 10^{\underline{\quad}}) = 7.35 \times 10^8$$

2
3
4
5
6

3 Circle the addends that make the equation true.

1.5×10^2	2.5×10^{-1}	
5×10^3	1×10^2	$= 2.5 \times 10^4$
2.5×10^{-1}	2×10^4	

(with a $+$ between the two columns)

4 Select True or False for each equation.

A. $3.4608 \times 10^7 \div 7.21 \times 10^3 = 4.8 \times 10^3$ ○ True ○ False

B. $9.844 \times 10^3 \div 2.3 \times 10^5 = 7.544 \times 10^{-2}$ ○ True ○ False

C. $1.98448 \times 10^7 \div 3.14 \times 10^7 = 6.32 \times 10^{-1}$ ○ True ○ False

D. $7.356 \times 10^{-4} \div 6.13 \times 10^{-2} = 1.2 \times 10^{-6}$ ○ True ○ False

5 Draw a line from each expression to its value.

A. $7.92 \times 10^3 + 8.1 \times 10^4$ •

B. $3.1 \times 10^4 - 2.8 \times 10^4$ •

C. $(8.6 \times 10^5)(3.2 \times 10^2)$ •

D. $9.223 \times 10^5 \div 4.01 \times 10^2$ •

• 2.752×10^8

• 3×10^3

• 8.892×10^4

• 2.3×10^3

6 Light travels at a speed of 1.86×10^5 miles per second. The Earth has a circumference of 2.4901×10^4 miles. If an object could travel at the speed of light, how long would it take to circle Earth? Write your answer to the nearest hundredth second. Show your work.

7 Which expression has the same value as -2.34×10^8? Circle all that apply.

A. -23.4×10^7

B. -0.234×10^9

C. $(-1.17 \times 10^8)(2 \times 10^8)$

D. $(1.17 \times 10^6)(-2 \times 10^2)$

E. $\dfrac{(4.914 \times 10^6)}{(2.1 \times 10^2)}$

F. $\dfrac{(4.914 \times 10^{10})}{(2.1 \times 10^2)}$

8 To multiply 3.1×10^{-3} and 1.28×10^{-4}, Malik first rewrote the first factor as shown below.

$3.1 \times 10^{-3} = 0.31 \times 10^{-4}$

Part A

Why is it **not** necessary for Malik to complete this step?

Part B

Find the product of the two factors. Show your work.

9 Complete the equation to make a true statement.

$8.3 \times 10^4 - (\underline{\hspace{1cm}}) \times 10^3 = 5.7 \times 10^4$

10 A grain of sand weighs about 1×10^{-6} gram. Researchers at the University of Hawaii estimate there are 7.5×10^{18} grains of sand on all the beaches of the Earth. How much do all of those grains of sand weigh? Write your answer in scientific notation.

_____ grams

11 In 2012, the population of China was about 1.351×10^9, and the population of Japan was about 1.276×10^8. Based upon these estimates, approximately how many more people lived in China than in Japan in 2012? Write your answer in scientific notation.

_____ people

12 Miriam and Priya are subtracting numbers written in scientific notation.

Miriam's expression

$$1.4 \times 10^3 - 2.83 \times 10^4$$

Priya's expression

$$0.14 \times 10^4 - 2.83 \times 10^4$$

Part A

Without completing the subtraction, how can you determine that Miriam and Priya's answers will have the same value? Explain.

Part B

Which expression would you rather use to subtract? Why?

Part C

Complete the subtraction. Show your work.

Understanding Proportional Relationships

① GETTING THE IDEA

A **proportion** is an equation stating that two ratios are equal. For example, $\frac{2}{3} = \frac{4}{6}$ is a proportion. When two ratios are equal, they have a **proportional relationship**.

Suppose a person drives a car at a constant speed of 50 miles per hour. The graph below shows the length of time and the distance traveled. In this example, time and distance have a proportional relationship. The longer the person drives the car, the farther the person will travel.

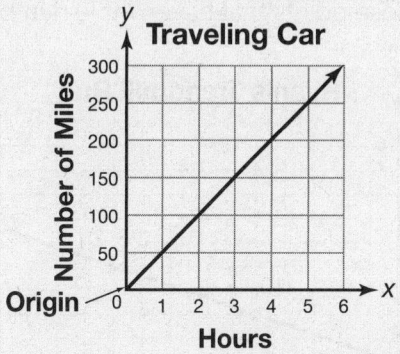

Notice the data start at the point (0, 0). This point is called the **origin**. All equations representing proportional relationships pass through the origin and form a straight line.

A **rate of change** is a comparison of two quantities that are changing. In this example, the rate of change between distance traveled and time is 50 miles traveled every 1 hour, or $\frac{50}{1} = 50$.

A **unit rate** is a ratio of measurements in which the second measurement is 1 unit. So, the unit rate for the speed of the car above is the same as the rate of change.

$$\frac{50 \text{ mi}}{1 \text{ hour}} = 50 \text{ miles per hour}$$

You may remember that the **slope** of a line is a ratio. It describes a comparison between the change in x-values and the change in y-values.

$$\text{slope} = \frac{\text{rise}}{\text{run}} = \frac{\text{change in } y\text{-coordinates}}{\text{change in } x\text{-coordinates}}$$

Using the points (0, 0) and (1, 50), you can calculate the slope of the line as $\frac{50 - 0}{1 - 0} = 50$.

Notice that the rate of change, unit rate, and slope of a proportional relationship are all the same.

Example 1

Ryan is running on a treadmill. The graph below shows the proportional relationship between the time he has run and his distance. What is Ryan's speed as a unit rate?

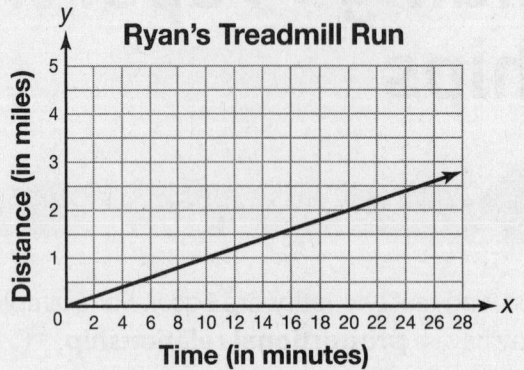

Strategy   Determine the slope of the line, and write it as a ratio of two measurements.

Step 1   Identify two points on the line.

If possible, choose points that have whole number values.

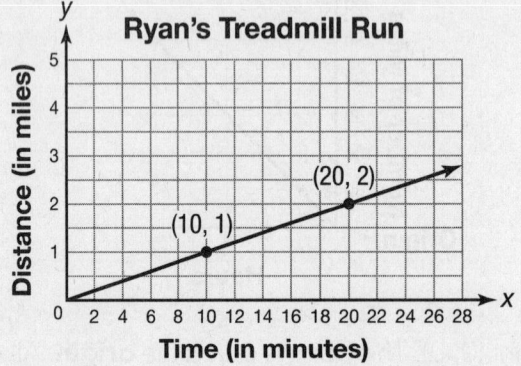

Step 2   Use the coordinates of the two points to find the slope.

$$\text{slope} = \frac{\text{change in } y\text{-coordinates}}{\text{change in } x\text{-coordinates}}$$

$$= \frac{2 - 1}{20 - 10}$$

$$= \frac{1}{10}$$

Step 3   Use the slope to write the unit rate.

$$\text{slope} = \frac{\text{vertical change}}{\text{horizontal change}}$$

The vertical change is represented by the y-coordinates.

The y-coordinates represent the distance in miles.

The horizontal change is represented by the x-coordinates.

The x-coordinates represent the time in minutes.

So, a slope of $\frac{1}{10}$ represents Ryan running 1 mile in 10 minutes, or $\frac{1 \text{ mile}}{10 \text{ minutes}}$.

A unit rate always has a denominator of 1. Write an equivalent fraction with a denominator of 1.

$$\frac{1 \text{ mile} \div 10}{10 \text{ minutes} \div 10} = \frac{0.1 \text{ mile}}{1 \text{ minute}}$$

Solution   Ryan's speed as a unit rate is $\frac{0.1 \text{ mile}}{1 \text{ minute}}$, or 0.1 mile per minute.

When the equation of a proportional relationship is written in the form $y = mx$, the slope of the relationship is the value of m. The slope can be used to identify the unit rate.

Example 2

Allyson mows lawns to make extra money. The equation $30x - 2y = 0$ compares the amount of money Allyson earns, y, to the number of lawns she mows, x. How much does Allyson earn for each lawn she mows?

Strategy   Find the unit rate by rewriting the equation in the form $y = mx$.

Step 1   Use the properties of equality to solve for y.

$$30x - 2y = 0$$
$$30x - 2y + \mathbf{2y} = 0 + \mathbf{2y} \qquad \text{Add } 2y \text{ to both sides.}$$
$$\frac{30x}{2} = \frac{2y}{2} \qquad \text{Divide both sides by 2.}$$
$$15x = y$$

Step 2   Determine the slope of the equation.

The value of m in the equation $y = mx$ is the slope.

In the equation $15x = y$, the value of m is 15, so the slope is 15.

Step 3   Use the slope to write the unit rate.

The y-coordinates represent the amount of money Allyson earns.

The x-coordinates represent the number of lawns Allyson mows.

So, a slope of $\frac{15}{1}$ represents a unit rate of $15 per lawn.

Solution   Allyson earns $15 for every lawn she mows.

Example 3

For the past month, Mr. Stumm recorded the number of days he went to work each week. He also recorded the number of tollbooths he drove through during those days. Mr. Stumm drove the same route to and from work each day. How many tollbooths does Mr. Stumm drive through each day?

Number of Days	Number of Tollbooths
3	12
6	24
7	28

Strategy   Use the table to find the unit rate of the data.

Step 1   Choose two ordered pairs from the table. Find the slope.

$(3, 12)$ and $(6, 24)$

$$\text{slope} = \frac{24 - 12}{6 - 3}$$

$$= \frac{12}{3}$$

$$= \frac{4}{1}, \text{ or } 4$$

Step 2   Use the slope to write the unit rate.

$$\text{slope} = \frac{4}{1}, \text{ or } 4$$

The y-coordinates represent the number of tollbooths.

The x-coordinates represent the number of days.

The unit rate is 4 tollbooths per day.

Solution   Mr. Stumm goes through 4 tollbooths per day.

Example 4

Javier and Sarah are baking muffins. Each baker used a different way to show the relationship between the total number of muffins baked, y, and the number of batches made, x. Who baked more muffins per batch?

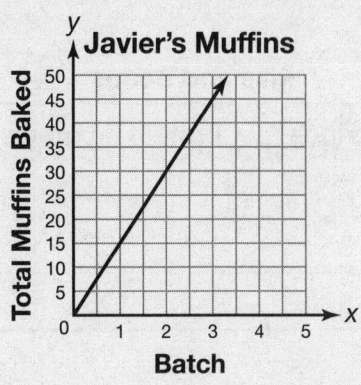

Sarah's Muffins

$$y = 16x$$

Strategy   Compare the unit rate in the graph and the equation.

Step 1   Use the graph to find Javier's unit rate.

Find the coordinates of two points.

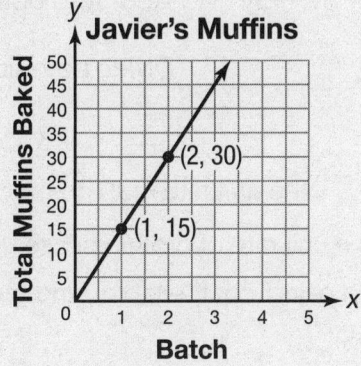

Use the points to find the slope.

$$\text{slope} = \frac{30 - 15}{2 - 1}$$

$$= \frac{15}{1}, \text{ or } 15$$

Javier's unit rate is 15 muffins per batch.

Step 2   Use the equation to find Sarah's unit rate.

When the equation is in the form $y = mx$, the value of m is the slope.

$m = 16$, or $\frac{16}{1}$

Sarah's unit rate is 16 muffins per batch.

Step 3   Compare the unit rates.

        Javier   Sarah

15 muffins per batch $\;\bigcirc<\;$ 16 muffins per batch

Solution   Sarah bakes more muffins per batch than Javier.

Example 5

Amar is making grilled chicken with rice and beans. The relationship between the number of grams of protein, y, and the number of servings, x, is given below for the two recipes. Which food has more grams of protein per serving?

Chicken

$$0 = 270x - 3y$$

Rice and Beans

Servings	Protein (in grams)
2	42
3	63
5	105

Strategy   Compare the unit rates in the equation and table.

Step 1   Use the equation to find the unit rate of protein per serving for the grilled chicken.

Solve for y.

$$0 = 270x - 3y$$

$0 + \mathbf{3y} = 270x - 3y + \mathbf{3y}$ Add 3y to both sides.

$\dfrac{3y}{3} = \dfrac{270x}{3}$ Divide both sides by 3.

$y = 90x$

Since $m = 90$, or $\dfrac{90}{1}$, the unit rate is 90 grams of protein per serving of chicken.

Step 2   Use the table to find the unit rate of protein per serving for the rice and beans.

Write two ordered pairs from the table. Find the slope.

(3, 63) and (5, 105)

$\text{slope} = \dfrac{105 - 63}{5 - 3}$

$= \dfrac{42}{2}$

$= \dfrac{21}{1}$, or 21

Since $m = \dfrac{21}{1}$, or 21, the unit rate is 21 grams of protein per serving of rice and beans.

Step 3   Compare the unit rates.

            Chicken   **Rice and Beans**

90 grams of protein per serving $\left(>\right)$ 21 grams of protein per serving

Solution   **There is more protein in 1 serving of chicken than in 1 serving of rice and beans.**

Example 6

Betty and SuLyn are comparing the number of "likes" they each receive on their pages on a social media site. They tracked the total number of likes they received for 5 days. They each recorded their "likes" in different ways and determined the relationships were proportional. Who received more "likes" per day?

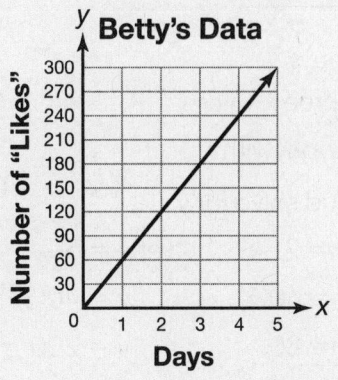

SuLyn's Data

Days	Number of "Likes"
1	55
2	110
3	165
4	220
5	275

Strategy   Compare the unit rate in the graph and table.

Step 1   Use the graph to find the unit rate for Betty.

Use two points on the line to find the slope.

(4, 240) and (2, 120)

$$\text{slope} = \frac{240 - 120}{4 - 2} = \frac{120}{2} = 60$$

Since $m = \frac{60}{1}$, the unit rate for Betty's "likes" is 60 "likes" per day.

Step 2   Use the table to find the unit rate for SuLyn.

Write two ordered pairs from the table. Find the slope.

(3, 165) and (5, 275)

$$\text{slope} = \frac{275 - 165}{5 - 3} = \frac{110}{2} = 55$$

Since $m = \frac{55}{1}$, the unit rate for SuLyn's "likes" is 55 "likes" per day.

Step 3   Compare the unit rates.

          Betty   **SuLyn**

60 "likes" per day $>$ 55 "likes" per day

Solution   Betty received more "likes" per day than SuLyn.

Example 7

The equation $y = 40x$ represents the height, in feet, of a hot air balloon, y, after x minutes. Draw a graph to represent the equation.

Strategy Find and graph points that are on the line.

Step 1 Create a table to find points on the line.

Label the columns x and y. Write at least three x-values.

Keep the values small so they are easy to work with.

Substitute each value into the equation, and solve for y.

Let $x = 0$.	Let $x = 1$.	Let $x = 2$.	Let $x = 5$.
$y = 40(0)$	$y = 40(1)$	$y = 40(2)$	$y = 40(5)$
$y = 0$	$y = 40$	$y = 80$	$y = 200$

Time (x) (in minutes)	Balloon's Height (y) (in feet)
0	0
1	40
2	80
5	200

Step 2 Label the axes of a coordinate graph, and write a title. Then graph the ordered pairs from the table, and connect the points.

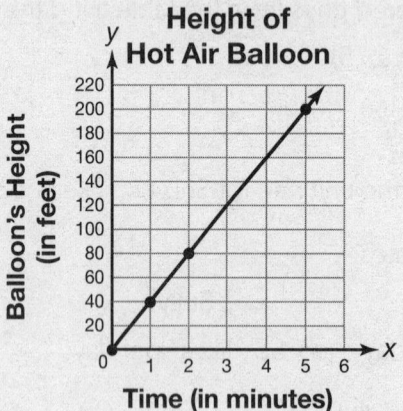

Solution The graph above represents the equation $y = 40x$, the height of the hot air balloon over time.

Enzo and Nick are in a fishing competition. They each recorded the total number of fish caught, y, and the time spent fishing, x, in different ways. Who caught more fish per hour?

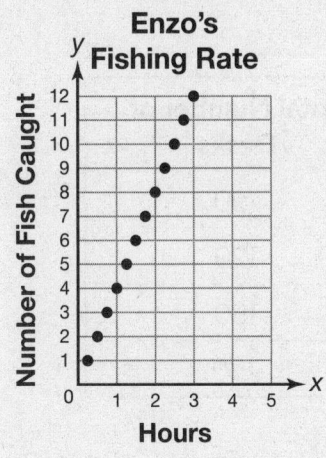

Enzo's Fishing Rate

Nick's Fishing Rate
$y = 3x$

To find Enzo's unit rate, find the _____ of the line.

Identify two points on the line.

(1, _____) and (2, _____)

slope = $\dfrac{\boxed{} - \boxed{}}{\boxed{} - \boxed{}}$ = _____

Since m = _____, Enzo caught _____ fish per hour.

Find Nick's unit rate.

The equation $y = 3x$ is in the form _____, so m = _____.

Nick caught _____ fish per hour.

_____ caught more fish per hour than _____.

1 At Copper Hill Elementary School, each classroom has the same number of desks. The table below shows the total number of desks and the number of classrooms. Select True or False for each statement.

Number of Classrooms	Total Number of Desks
3	90
4	120
6	180
9	270

A. Each classroom has 9 desks. ○ True ○ False

B. The unit rate is 30 desks per 1 classroom. ○ True ○ False

C. The relationship between classrooms and desks is a proportional relationship. ○ True ○ False

D. In 2 classrooms, there are 100 desks. ○ True ○ False

2 Use numbers from the box to write the slope of the equation $4x - 2y = 0$.

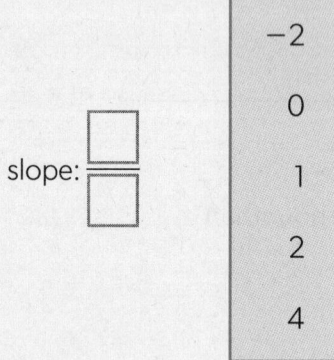

slope: ☐/☐

-2
0
1
2
4

3 Select the equation that has a unit rate of $\frac{3}{4}$. Circle all that apply.

A. $3x - 4y = 0$

B. $4x + y = 0$

C. $9x - 12y = 0$

D. $12x + 9y = 0$

E. $15x - 20y = 0$

4 In the graph below, x represents the time in seconds, and y represents the number of pages printed by a printer. Circle the number that makes the sentence true.

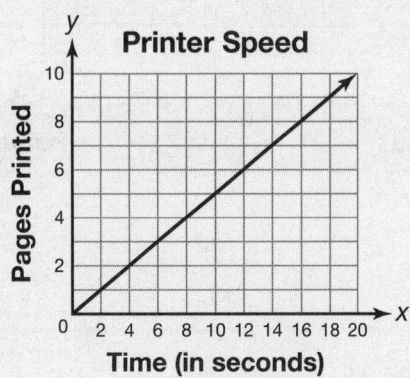

The printer has a unit rate of

$\frac{1}{2}$
2
4

page(s) per second.

5 Compare the equation $y = \frac{1}{4}x$ to the table. Do they have the same slope? Explain.

x	y
0	0
3	$\frac{3}{4}$
5	$1\frac{1}{4}$
8	2

6 Decide if each point is on the line $y = 2x$. Write the point in the correct box.

| A(2, 4) | B(0, 3) | C(1, 2) | D(3, 6) | E(10, 5) | F(1.5, 3) |

Points on Line	Points NOT on Line

7 Kelly is knitting a blanket. She can knit 6 rows per minute. Look at each rate. Is it equivalent to 6 rows per minute? Select Yes or No.

A. 18 rows in 3 minutes ○ Yes ○ No

B. 12 rows in 6 minutes ○ Yes ○ No

C. 4 rows in 24 minutes ○ Yes ○ No

D. 48 rows in 8 minutes ○ Yes ○ No

E. 60 rows in 10 minutes ○ Yes ○ No

8 The equation $y = 5x$ describes Santiago's reading rate. Let x be the number of minutes and y be the total number of pages Santiago has read. Graph the equation.

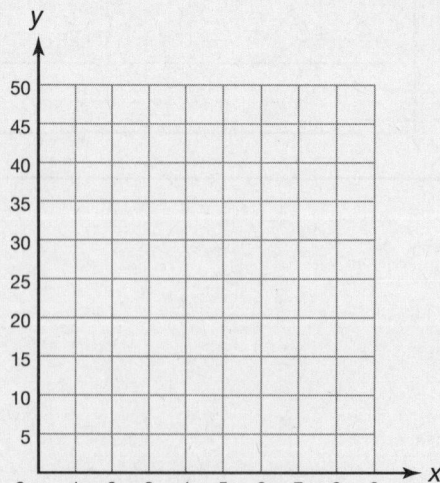

9 Nia is making invitations to her graduation party. She can make 22 invitations per hour. Nia wants to know how many invitations she can finish during the times shown in the table. Complete the table.

Nia's Invitations

Number of Hours	Total Number of Invitations Made
1	
2	
3	
6	

10 Garret and Margo are taking pictures on their school trip. The graph shows the total number of pictures Garret took based upon the number of hours he was on the trip. The table shows the number of pictures Margo took based upon the number of hours she was on the trip.

Garret's Pictures

Margo's Pictures

Number of Hours	Number of Pictures
3	150
4	200
6	300

Part A

Explain how you know that Garret and Margo took the same number of pictures per hour.

Part B

Evan took more pictures per hour than Garret or Margo. He took fewer than 100 pictures per hour. Fill in the table so that Evan's unit rate is greater than Garret's and Margo's.

Evan's Pictures

Number of Hours	Number of Pictures

Relating Slope and *y*-Intercept to Linear Equations

① GETTING THE IDEA

An equation is a **linear equation** when all of its points lie on a line. When a line passes through the origin, the equation of the line can be written in the form $y = mx$, where m represents the **slope** of the line.

Recall that the slope of the line is the change in the *y*-coordinates divided by the change in the *x*-coordinates. The slope of a line can be positive or negative.

Positive Slope

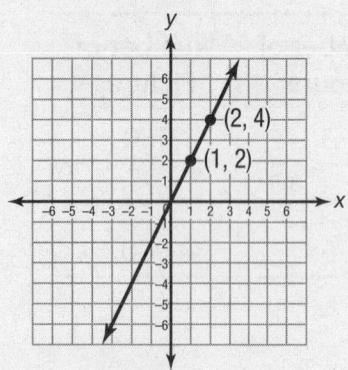

$$m = \frac{4 - 2}{2 - 1} = \frac{2}{1} = 2$$

$$y = \mathbf{2}x$$

Negative Slope

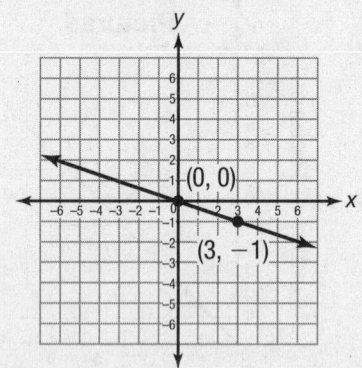

$$m = \frac{0 - (-1)}{0 - 3} = \frac{1}{-3} = -\frac{1}{3}$$

$$y = -\frac{\mathbf{1}}{\mathbf{3}}x$$

You can use similar triangles to show that the slope of a non-vertical line is the same between any two points on the line.

Geometric figures are **similar** when they are the same shape but not necessarily the same size. The lengths of corresponding sides of similar figures are proportional.

$$\frac{CB}{FE} = \frac{AC}{DF} = \frac{BA}{ED}$$

$$\frac{8}{4} = \frac{6}{3} = \frac{10}{5}$$

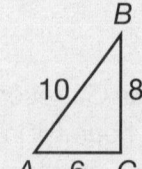

Triangles *ABC* and *DEF* are similar triangles because they have the same shape and the lengths of their corresponding sides are proportional.

Example 1

Is the slope of the line from point X to point Y the same as the slope of the line from point M to point N?

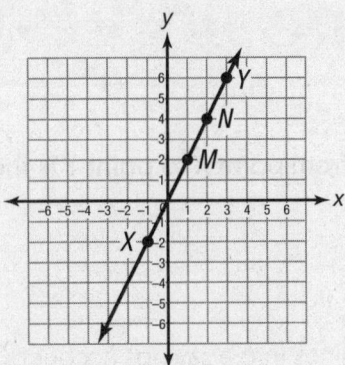

Strategy   Draw similar triangles to show the slopes are the same.

Step 1   Use each pair of points to construct a right triangle.

Use the grid lines to form right angles.

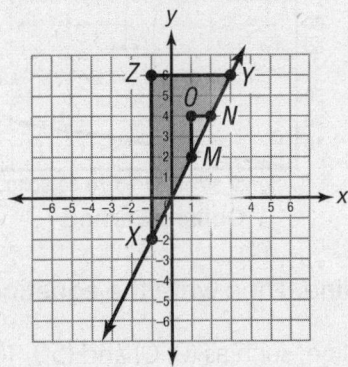

Step 2   Find the lengths of the horizontal and vertical sides of $\triangle XYZ$ and $\triangle MNO$.

$\triangle XYZ$ $\triangle MNO$

$XZ = 8$ $MO = 2$

$ZY = 4$ $ON = 1$

Step 3   Compare the ratios of the corresponding side lengths to prove the triangles are similar.

$\frac{XZ}{ZY} \stackrel{?}{=} \frac{MO}{ON}$

$\frac{8}{4} \stackrel{?}{=} \frac{2}{1}$

$2 = 2$

The ratios are the same, so the triangles are similar.

Step 4 Use the coordinates of the points to find the slopes of the lines.

Slope of line from $X(-1, -2)$ to $Y(3, 6)$ Slope of line from $M(1, 2)$ to $N(2, 4)$

$$m = \frac{6 - (-2)}{3 - (-1)}$$
$$= \frac{8}{4} = \frac{2}{1}, \text{ or } 2$$

$$m = \frac{4 - 2}{2 - 1}$$
$$= \frac{2}{1}, \text{ or } 2$$

Solution The slope of the line from point X to point Y is the same as the slope of the line from point M to point N.

Example 2

Julianne deposits a fraction of her earnings into a savings account. The line graphed below shows the total savings in her account based upon her earnings. Write an equation for the line.

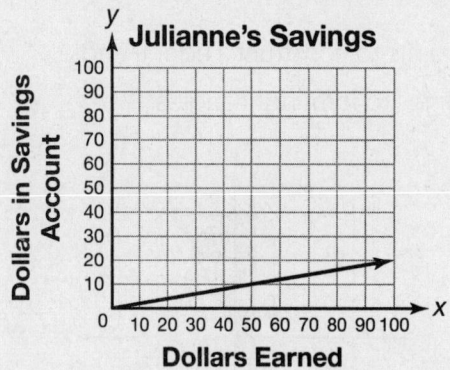

Strategy Find the slope of the line. Then write the equation in the form $y = mx$.

Step 1 Use any points on the line, such as $(0, 0)$ and $(50, 10)$, to find the slope, m.

$$\text{Slope} = \frac{\text{change in } y\text{-coordinates}}{\text{change in } x\text{-coordinates}}$$

$$= \frac{10 - 0}{50 - 0}$$

$$= \frac{10}{50}$$

$$= \frac{1}{5}$$

$$m = \frac{1}{5} = 0.20$$

Step 2 Write an equation in the form $y = mx$.

$$y = \frac{1}{5}x$$

Solution The equation of the line is $y = \frac{1}{5}x$ or $y = 0.20x$.

An equation in the form $y = mx + b$ is called the **slope-intercept form of a line**. It can be used to write the equation of a line that does not pass through the origin.

$$y = mx + b$$

slope y-intercept

The **y-intercept** is the y-coordinate of the point at which the line passes through the y-axis—that is, where $x = 0$. The y-intercept can be positive or negative.

Example 3

Write an equation for the line graphed below.

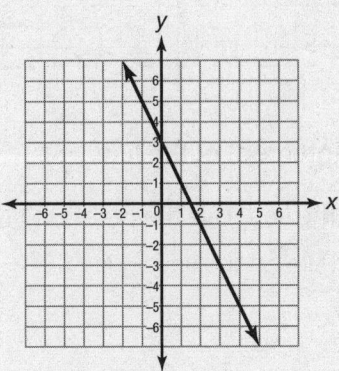

Strategy　　Find the slope and y-intercept of the line.

Step 1　　Identify two points on the line. Use the points to find the slope of the line.

$(-1, 5)$ and $(1, 1)$ lie on the line.

$$m = \frac{5 - 1}{-1 - 1}$$

$$= \frac{4}{-2}$$

$$= -2$$

Step 2　　Find the point where the line crosses the y-axis.

The line crosses the y-axis at the point $(0, 3)$, so the y-intercept is 3.

$$b = 3$$

Step 3　　Use the values of m and b to write an equation in the form $y = mx + b$.

$$y = -2x + 3$$

Solution　　The equation of the line is $y = -2x + 3$.

Example 4

Write an equation for the line graphed below.

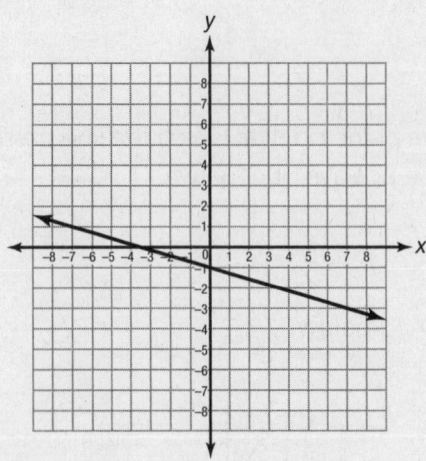

Strategy   **Find the slope and *y*-intercept of the line.**

Step 1   Identify two points on the line. Use the points to find the slope of the line.

$(-7, 1)$ and $(0, -1)$ lie on the line.

$$m = \frac{-1 - 1}{0 - (-7)}$$

$$= \frac{-2}{7}$$

Step 2   Find the point where the line crosses the *y*-axis.

The line crosses the *y*-axis at the point $(0, -1)$, so the *y*-intercept is -1.

$$b = -1$$

Step 3   Use the values of *m* and *b* to write an equation in the form $y = mx + b$.

$$y = \frac{-2}{7}x + (-1) \text{ or } y = -\frac{2}{7}x - 1$$

Solution   **The equation of the line is $y = -\frac{2}{7}x - 1$.**

Is the slope of the line between points *A* and *C* the same as the slope of the line between points *C* and *E*?

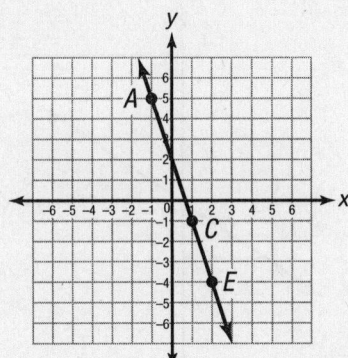

Construct two similar, _____ triangles: △*ABC* and △*CDE*.

Find the lengths of the legs of the triangles.

△*ABC*	△*CDE*
BC = _____	*DE* = _____
AB = _____	*CD* = _____

Compare the ratios of the corresponding side lengths to prove the triangles are similar.

$$\frac{BC}{AB} \overset{?}{=} \frac{DE}{CD}$$

_____ $\overset{?}{=}$ _____

_____ = _____

The ratios are the _____, so the triangles are _____.

Find the slope of the line from *A*(−1, 5) to *C*(1, −1).

slope = $\dfrac{\boxed{} - \boxed{}}{\boxed{} - \boxed{}}$ = $\dfrac{\boxed{}}{\boxed{}}$ = $\boxed{}$

The slope of the line from *A*(−1, 5) to *C*(1, −1) is _____.

Find the slope of the line from *C*(1, −1) to *E*(2, −4).

slope = $\dfrac{\boxed{} - \boxed{}}{\boxed{} - \boxed{}}$ = $\dfrac{\boxed{}}{\boxed{}}$ = $\boxed{}$

The slope of the line from *C*(1, −1) to *E*(2, −4) is _____.

The slope of the line from point *A* to point *C* is _____ **the slope of the line from point *C* to point *E*.**

1 Select the equation that could represent the line. Circle all that apply.

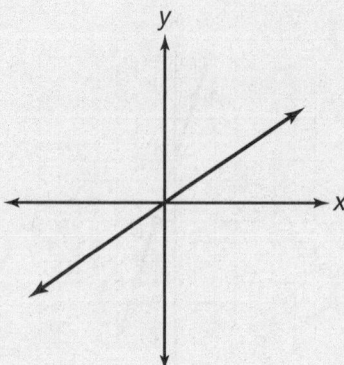

A. $y = \frac{2}{3}x$

B. $y = -\frac{3}{5}x$

C. $y = 4x$

D. $y = -3x + 2$

E. $y = \frac{1}{2}x + 1$

2 Michael wrote the equation $y = 0.1x + 5$ to find the total cost of his phone bill, y, based on the number of texts he sends per month, x. Circle the number that shows the slope and the y-intercept of the equation of the line.

$m =$

| $\frac{1}{10}$ |
| $\frac{1}{5}$ |
| 1 |
| 5 |

$b =$

| $\frac{1}{10}$ |
| $\frac{1}{5}$ |
| 1 |
| 5 |

3 Erwin graphed the line shown. Brandon graphed the line $y = \frac{1}{3}x + 1$. Brandon says both lines have the same y-intercept. Do you agree? Why or why not?

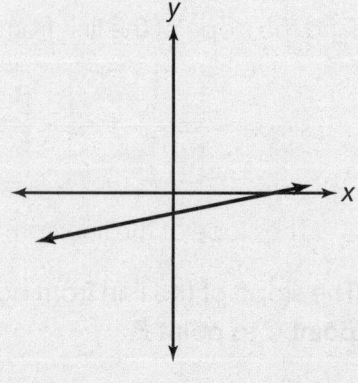

4 Draw a line from each graph to its equation.

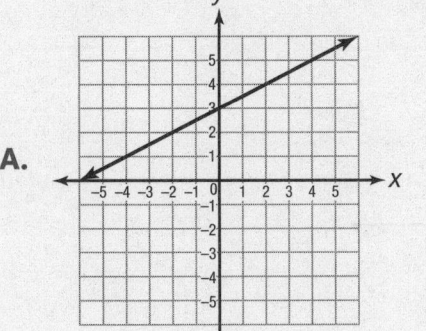

A. •

• $y = -3x + 1$

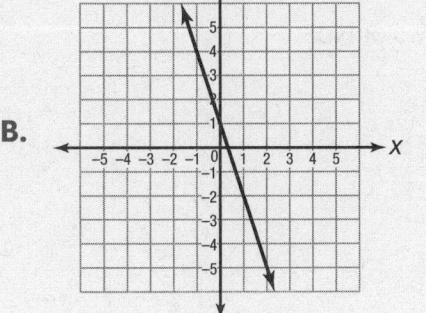

B. •

• $y = -x - 3$

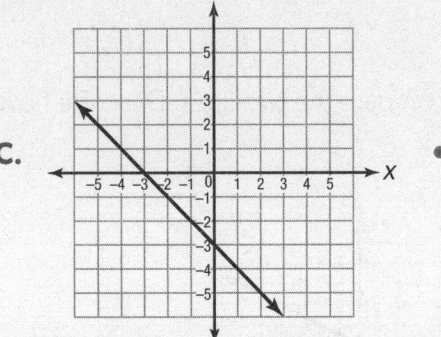

C. •

• $y = \frac{1}{2}x + 3$

5 Use the graph of the line below.

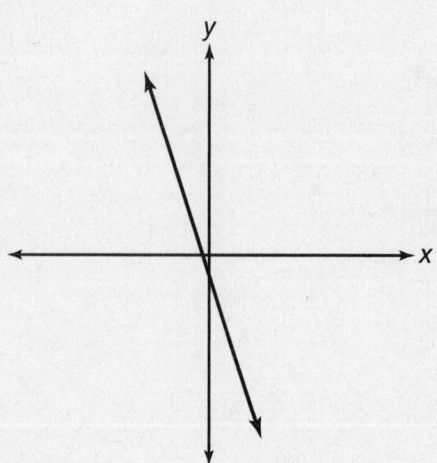

Could the given value be the slope of the line? Select Yes or No.

A. $m = -4$ ○ Yes   ○ No

B. $m = -\dfrac{1}{2}$ ○ Yes   ○ No

C. $m = -\dfrac{1}{8}$ ○ Yes   ○ No

D. $m = \dfrac{1}{4}$ ○ Yes   ○ No

E. $m = 3$ ○ Yes   ○ No

6 Write the equation for each line shown below. Then compare the two lines. Describe how they are similar and how they are different.

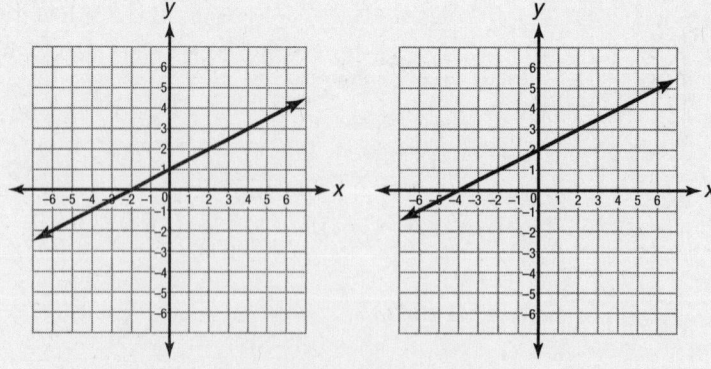

_____   _____

_____

Sarah is completing a science experiment. She finds that when she boils 4 ounces of a solution, it becomes a solid that has a mass of 2 grams. When she boils 8 ounces of a solution, it becomes a solid that has a mass of 3 grams. She records the data as the points (4, 2) and (8, 3).

Part A

Graph the two points Sarah wrote. Draw the line that contains the points.

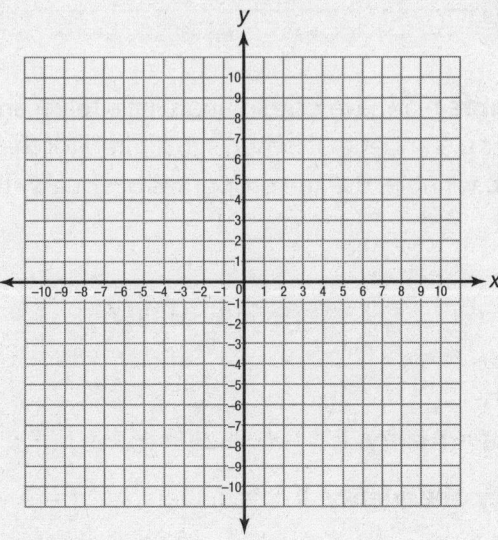

Part B

Write the equation that represents the line.

_____

Part C

When Sarah continued the experiment, she found that 12 ounces of the solution will form a solid that has a mass of 4 grams. She recorded the data as point (12, 4). Is the slope of the line between the points (4, 2) and (8, 3) the same as the slope of the line between the points (4, 2) and (12, 4)? Explain your answer.

Solving Linear Equations in One Variable

 GETTING THE IDEA

A **linear equation** in one **variable** may have one solution, infinitely many solutions, or no solutions. A **solution** to a linear equation is a number that, when substituted for the variable, makes the equation true. To solve an equation in one variable, use the properties of equality to isolate the variable on one side of the equation.

Properties of Equality

For all real numbers a, b, and c:

Addition property of equality: If $a = b$, then $a + c = b + c$.

Subtraction property of equality: If $a = b$, then $a - c = b - c$.

Multiplication property of equality: If $a = b$, then $ac = bc$.

Division property of equality: If $a = b$ and $c \neq 0$, then $\frac{a}{c} = \frac{b}{c}$.

You can check your solution to a linear equation by substituting the value of the variable back into the original equation. If a true sentence results, the solution is correct.

Example 1

Solve for x. $2(3x + 0.5) = 25$

Strategy   Use the properties of equality to isolate the variable.

Step 1   Simplify the expression on the left side of the equation by applying the distributive property.

$$2(3x + 0.5) = 25$$
$$2 \cdot 3x + 2 \cdot 0.5 = 25$$
$$6x + 1 = 25$$

Step 2   Use the subtraction property of equality. Subtract 1 from both sides of the equation.

$$6x + 1 = 25$$
$$6x + 1 - 1 = 25 - 1$$
$$6x = 24$$

Step 3   Use the division property of equality. Divide both sides by 6 to solve for x.

$$6x = 24$$
$$\frac{6x}{6} = \frac{24}{6}$$
$$x = 4$$

Step 4   Check the solution by substituting 4 for x into the original equation.

$$2(3x + 0.5) = 25$$
$$2(3 \cdot 4 + 0.5) \stackrel{?}{=} 25$$
$$2(12 + 0.5) \stackrel{?}{=} 25$$
$$2(12.5) \stackrel{?}{=} 25$$
$$25 = 25 \checkmark$$

Solution   **The equation $2(3x + 0.5) = 25$ has one solution. The solution is $x = 4$.**

Example 2

Solve for k. $4 - 2k = -5(k + 7)$

Strategy   **Use the properties of equality to isolate the variable.**

Step 1   Simplify the expression on the right side of the equation by applying the distributive property.

$$4 - 2k = -5(k + 7)$$
$$4 - 2k = -5 \cdot k + (-5) \cdot 7$$
$$4 - 2k = -5k - 35$$

Step 2   Use the addition property of equality. Add $5k$ to both sides of the equation, and then combine like terms.

$$4 - 2k = -5k - 35$$
$$4 - 2k + 5k = -5k - 35 + 5k$$
$$4 + 3k = -35$$

Step 3   Use the subtraction property of equality. Subtract 4 from both sides of the equation, and then combine like terms.

$$4 + 3k = -35$$
$$4 + 3k - 4 = -35 - 4$$
$$3k = -39$$

Step 4   Use the division property of equality. Isolate the variable by dividing both sides by 3, and then simplify.

$$3k = -39$$
$$\frac{3k}{3} = -\frac{39}{3}$$
$$k = -13$$

Step 5 Check the solution by substituting -13 for k into the original equation.

$$4 - 2k = -5(k + 7)$$
$$4 - 2(-13) \overset{?}{=} -5(-13 + 7)$$
$$4 + 26 \overset{?}{=} -5(-6)$$
$$30 = 30 \checkmark$$

Solution **The equation $4 - 2k = -5(k + 7)$ has one solution. The solution is $k = -13$.**

Some equations have no solutions. If you try to solve an equation that has no solution, the equation will be transformed into a number sentence that is false.

Example 3

Solve for y. $\frac{3}{4}(4y + 8) = 5 + 3y$

Strategy **Use the properties of equality to isolate the variable.**

Step 1 Apply the distributive property.
$$\frac{3}{4}(4y + 8) = 5 + 3y$$
$$3y + 6 = 5 + 3y$$

Step 2 Subtract $3y$ from both sides of the equation.
$$3y + 6 = 5 + 3y$$
$$3y + 6 - 3y = 5 + 3y - 3y$$
$$6 = 5$$

Step 3 Interpret the resulting equation.

$6 = 5$

This is not a true statement, so there is no solution to the equation

$\frac{3}{4}(4y + 8) = 5 + 3y$.

Solution **The equation $\frac{3}{4}(4y + 8) = 5 + 3y$ has no solution.**

Some equations are true no matter what the value of the variable. These equations have infinitely many solutions. If you try to solve an equation that has infinitely many solutions, the equation will be transformed into a number sentence that is true.

Example 4

Solve for c. $10c - 6(2c - 1) = -2(c - 3)$

Strategy   Use the properties of equality to isolate the variable.

Step 1   Apply the distributive property to simplify each side of the equation. Then combine like terms.

$$10c - 6(2c - 1) = -2(c - 3)$$
$$10c - 12c + 6 = -2c + 6$$
$$-2c + 6 = -2c + 6$$

Step 2   Add $2c$ to both sides of the equation.

$$-2c + 6 = -2c + 6$$
$$-2c + 6 + 2c = -2c + 6 + 2c$$
$$6 = 6$$

Step 3   Interpret the resulting equation.

$$6 = 6$$

This is a true statement, so the original equation has infinitely many solutions.

Solution   The equation $10c - 6(2c - 1) = -2(c - 3)$ has infinitely many solutions.

Example 5

Mr. Williams is buying tickets for the school musical. Adult tickets cost $3 more than student tickets. He buys 7 student tickets and 6 adult tickets, and he spends a total of $83. What is the price of one adult ticket?

Strategy   Write and solve an equation that models the situation.

Step 1   Identify the variable.

Let x represent the price of a student ticket.

Since adult tickets cost $3 more than student tickets, let $x + 3$ represent the price of an adult ticket.

Step 2   Write an equation to model the situation.

Since x represents the price of a student ticket, the cost of 7 student tickets is $7x$.

Since $x + 3$ represents the price of an adult ticket, the cost of 6 adult tickets is $6(x + 3)$.

7 student tickets	plus	6 adult tickets	costs	$83
↓	↓	↓	↓	↓
$7x$	$+$	$6(x + 3)$	$=$	83

The equation is $7x + 6(x + 3) = 83$.

Step 3   Solve the equation using the properties of equality and the distributive property, and by combining like terms.

$$7x + 6(x + 3) = 83$$
$$7x + 6x + 18 = 83$$
$$13x + 18 = 83$$
$$13x + 18 - 18 = 83 - 18$$
$$13x = 65$$
$$\frac{13x}{13} = \frac{65}{13}$$
$$x = 5$$

Step 4   Interpret your result.

Since x represents the price of a student ticket, the price of a student ticket is $5.

Since $x + 3$ represents the price of an adult ticket, the price of an adult ticket is $8.

Solution   **The price of one adult ticket is $8.**

② COACHED EXAMPLE

Solve for x. $4(1 + 3x) = 5(x - 2)$

Apply the distributive property to both sides of the equation.

$$4(1 + 3x) = 5(x - 2)$$
$$4 + \underline{\hspace{1cm}}x = \underline{\hspace{1cm}}x - \underline{\hspace{1cm}}$$

Move the variable term from the right side of the equation to the left side by subtracting _____ from both sides. Then simplify each side.

$$4 + 12x - \underline{\hspace{1cm}} = 5x - 10 - \underline{\hspace{1cm}}$$
$$4 + \underline{\hspace{1cm}}x = \underline{\hspace{1cm}}$$

Isolate the term containing the variable by subtracting _____ from both sides of the equation.

$$4 + \underline{\hspace{1cm}}x - \underline{\hspace{1cm}} = -10 - \underline{\hspace{1cm}}$$
$$\underline{\hspace{1cm}}x = \underline{\hspace{1cm}}$$

Isolate the variable by dividing both sides of the equation by _____.

$$\underline{\hspace{1cm}}x \div \underline{\hspace{1cm}} = \underline{\hspace{1cm}} \div \underline{\hspace{1cm}}$$
$$x = \underline{\hspace{1cm}}$$

Check that the solution makes the original equation true.

$$4(1 + 3(\underline{\hspace{1cm}})) \stackrel{?}{=} 5(\underline{\hspace{1cm}} - 2)$$

The solution to $4(1 + 3x) = 5(x - 2)$ is _____.

1 Compare the solution of each equation to 0. Write the equation in the correct box.

$5(d + 2) = 3(d - 6)$	$-6m = 2(3m - 1)$	$\frac{2}{3}(3y + 6) = 0$
$-4 = \frac{1}{2}p - 7$	$15 - (4z + 3) = 12$	$0.4(3.2x + 2) - x = 2x + 1.8$

Solution Is Less Than 0	Solution Is Equal to 0	Solution Is Greater Than 0

2 Which equation has at least one solution? Circle all that apply.

A. $2x - 1 = 2$ D. $\frac{4}{5}m = 1 - \frac{1}{5}m$

B. $3(y + 1) = 3y$ E. $10 + 0.5w = \frac{1}{2}w - 10$

C. $5p - (3 + p) = 6p + 1$ F. $4a + 3(a - 2) = 8a - (6 + a)$

3 Jamal is building a rectangular deck. The length of the deck will be 1 foot longer than twice the width. The deck will be attached to Jamal's house on one of its longer sides, and a railing will be attached to the other sides. Jamal calculates that he will need 49 feet of railing. What are the dimensions of the deck? Show your work.

4 Is each equation equivalent to $-4(3x + 2) = x + 2(x - 1)$? Select Yes or No.

A. $-12x + 2 = 3x - 1$ ○ Yes ○ No

B. $3x + 2 = x + 2(x - 1) + 4$ ○ Yes ○ No

C. $-12x - 8 = 2x - 2$ ○ Yes ○ No

D. $-8 = 15x - 2$ ○ Yes ○ No

E. $-15x = -10$ ○ Yes ○ No

F. $x = -\frac{2}{5}$ ○ Yes ○ No

5 Select True or False for each statement.

A. If $\frac{4}{3}h = 12$, then $h = 16$.   ○ True ○ False

B. If $-\frac{2}{5}r = -20$, then $r = 50$.   ○ True ○ False

C. If $\frac{1}{2} = -\frac{3}{7}q$, then $q = -1\frac{1}{6}$.   ○ True ○ False

D. If $\frac{3}{8} = 24c$, then $c = 9$.   ○ True ○ False

6 Eight more than twice a number is equal to ten less than five times the number.

Part A

Let n represent the number. Write an equation that can be used to find n.

Part B

Solve your equation for n. Show your work.

7 The following equation is true for all values of x. Write the number that completes the equation. Show your work.

$$5y + 2(3y - 1) = \underline{\qquad} y - (y + 2)$$

8 Explain why the equation $10x - 1 = 10x + 4$ has no solution.

9 For each linear equation in the table, indicate with an "X" whether the equation has no solution, one solution, or infinitely many solutions.

Equation	No Solution	One Solution	Infinitely Many Solutions
$8(a + 2) = 5a + 16 + 3a$			
$6m + 2 - 4m = 2(m + 2)$			
$3(z + 3) = 7 + 3z + 6 - z$			

10 Emma substitutes 3 for x in a one-variable linear equation and finds that it makes the equation true. She then substitutes 5 for x in the same linear equation and finds that 5 also makes the equation true. What can you conclude about the number of solutions of the equation? Explain your reasoning.

11 Amelia is making bags of snack mix for a class party. The snack mix includes dried fruit, cashews, and peanuts. The dried fruit costs $8.25 per pound, the cashews cost $5.99 per pound, and the peanuts cost $3.99 per pound. Amelia buys 2 more pounds of peanuts than she does cashews and 1 pound of dried fruit. If her total bill is $41.18, how many pounds of peanuts does she buy? Show your work.

12 Liam is solving the equation $12a - 4(5a - 1) = 2(3a + 6) - 4a$. The result of each step of his solution is shown below.

$$12a - 4(5a - 1) = 2(3a + 6) - 4a$$

$$12a - 20a + 4 = 6a + 12 - 4a$$

$$-8a + 4 = 2a + 12$$

$$-6a + 4 = 12$$

$$-6a = 8$$

$$a = -\frac{4}{3}$$

Part A

Circle the step in which Liam's first error occurred. Describe the error.

Part B

Solve the equation correctly. Show your work.

Solving Systems of Two Linear Equations Graphically

1 GETTING THE IDEA

A **system of linear equations** is a set of two or more linear equations that have the same variables.

To solve a system of linear equations graphically, graph each equation, and see if the graphs intersect. If they do, identify the point of intersection. The x- and y-values of the **point(s) of intersection** represent the solution(s) of the system of equations.

Parallel lines have the same slope but different y-intercepts. Parallel lines do not intersect. Therefore, there is no solution of the system of equations of parallel lines.

Coincident lines have the same slope and the same y-intercept. The lines lie on top of each other. The solution of the system of equations is infinite since it includes all of the points on the lines.

The graph of a system of linear equations shows if the system has one solution, no solution, or infinitely many solutions.

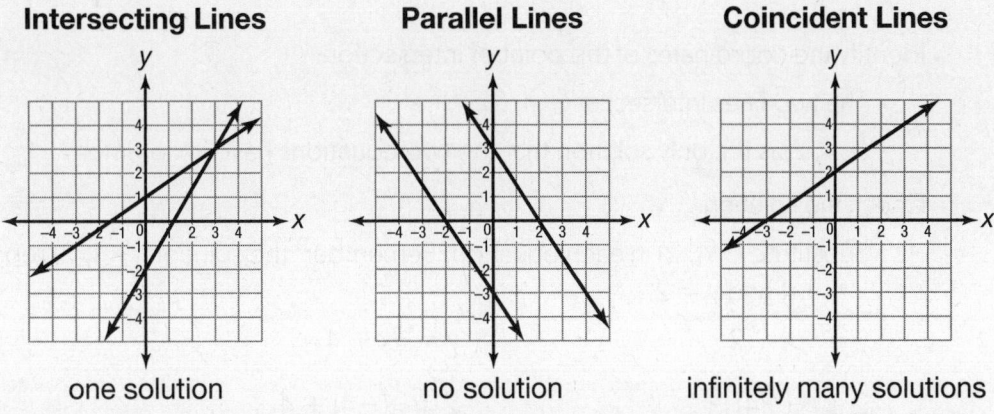

Intersecting Lines	Parallel Lines	Coincident Lines
one solution	no solution	infinitely many solutions

Example 1

Solve the system of linear equations graphically.

$$y = -x - 2$$
$$y = \frac{1}{2}x + 4$$

Strategy   Graph each equation, and identify the coordinates of the point of intersection.

Step 1 Graph $y = -x - 2$.

Compare the equation to $y = mx + b$.

$m = -1$, so the slope is -1.

$b = -2$, so the y-intercept is -2.

Plot the y-intercept at $(0, -2)$. Since the slope is -1 (or $-\frac{1}{1}$), count 1 unit down and 1 unit to the right to find another point that lies on the line. Plot the new point. Then draw the line.

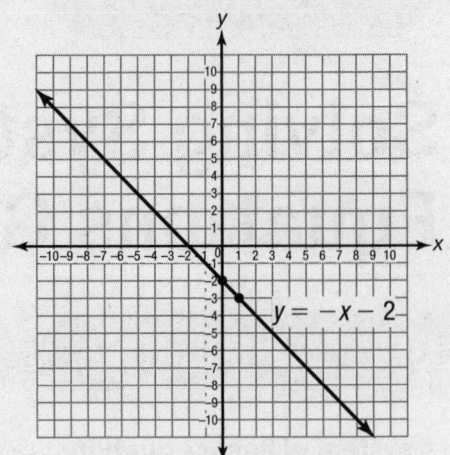

Step 2 Graph $y = \frac{1}{2}x - 4$ on the same coordinate plane.

Compare the equation to $y = mx + b$.

$m = \frac{1}{2}$, so the slope is $\frac{1}{2}$.

$b = 4$, so the y-intercept is 4.

Plot the y-intercept at $(0, 4)$. Since the slope is $\frac{1}{2}$, count 1 unit up and 2 units to the right to find another point that lies on the line. Plot the new point. Then draw the line.

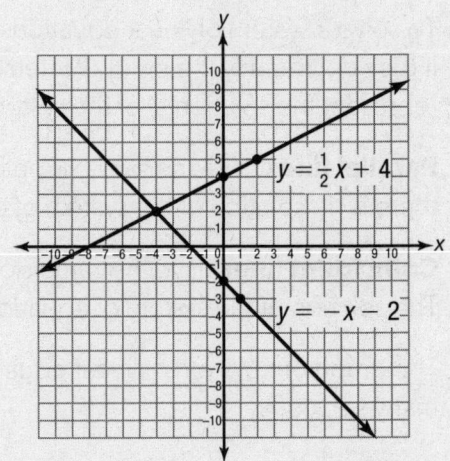

Step 3 Identify the coordinates of the point of intersection.

The two lines intersect at $(-4, 2)$.

$(-4, 2)$ is the only solution that the two equations have in common.

Step 4 Check the solution.

Substitute $(-4, 2)$ in each equation. Remember, the solution $(-4, 2)$ represents $x = -4$ and $y = 2$.

$y = -x - 2$ $\qquad\qquad\qquad$ $y = \frac{1}{2}x + 4$

$2 \overset{?}{=} -(-4) - 2$ $\qquad\qquad$ $2 \overset{?}{=} \frac{1}{2}(-4) + 4$

$2 \overset{?}{=} 4 - 2$ $\qquad\qquad\quad$ $2 \overset{?}{=} -2 + 4$

$2 = 2$ ✓ $\qquad\qquad\qquad$ $2 = 2$ ✓

Solution The solution of the system of equations is $(-4, 2)$.

Example 2

Solve the system of linear equations graphically.

$2x + y = 6$

$4x + 2y = 0$

Strategy   **Graph each equation. Then interpret the graph to describe the solution.**

Step 1   Graph $2x + y = 6$.

Solve the equation for y. Then identify the slope and the y-intercept.

$$2x + y = 6$$

$$2x - \mathbf{2x} + y = 6 - \mathbf{2x} \qquad \text{Subtract } 2x \text{ from both sides.}$$

$$y = -2x + 6$$

$m = -2$, so the slope is -2.

$b = 6$, so the y-intercept is 6.

Plot the y-intercept at (0, 6). Since the slope is $-2 \left(\text{or } -\frac{2}{1}\right)$, count 2 units down and 1 unit to the right to find another point that lies on the line. Plot the new point. Then draw the line.

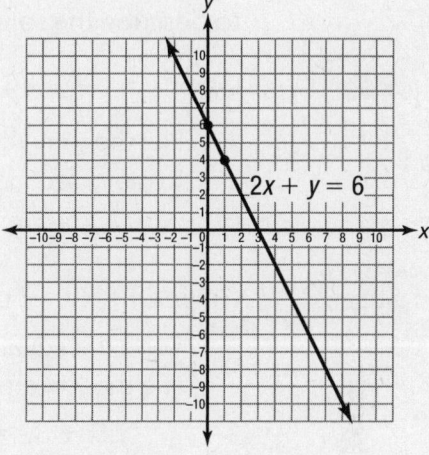

Step 2   Graph $4x + 2y = 0$ on the same coordinate plane.

Solve the equation for y. Then identify the slope and the y-intercept.

$$4x + 2y = 0$$

$$4x - \mathbf{4x} + 2y = 0 - \mathbf{4x} \qquad \text{Subtract } 4x \text{ from both sides.}$$

$$2y = -4x$$

$$\frac{2y}{2} = \frac{-4x}{2} \qquad \text{Divide both sides by 2.}$$

$$y = -2x$$

$m = -2$, so the slope is -2.

$b = 0$, so the y-intercept is 0.

Plot the y-intercept at (0, 0). Since the slope is $-2 \left(\text{or } -\frac{2}{1}\right)$, count 2 units down and 1 unit to the right to find another point that lies on the line. Plot the new point. Then draw the line.

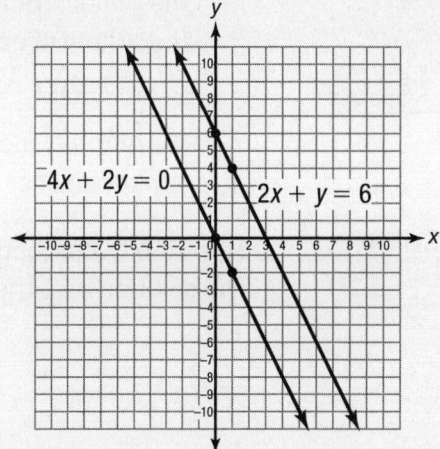

Step 3   Interpret the graph.

The graph of the system is a pair of parallel lines. Parallel lines do not intersect, so the equations have no solutions in common.

Solution   **The system of equations has no solution.**

Example 3

Solve the system of linear equations graphically.

$$y = -\frac{2}{3}x + 1$$
$$2x + 3y = 3$$

Strategy   **Graph each equation. Then interpret the graph to describe the solution.**

Step 1   Graph $y = -\frac{2}{3}x + 1$.

Plot the y-intercept at $(0, 1)$. Use the slope to plot a second point and draw the line.

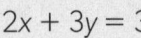

Step 2   Graph $2x + 3y = 3$ on the same coordinate plane.

Solve the equation for y to identify the slope and the y-intercept.

$$2x + 3y = 3$$

$2x - 2x + 3y = 3 - 2x$ Subtract $2x$ from both sides.

$3y = -2x + 3$ Use the commutative property of addition.

$\dfrac{3y}{3} = \dfrac{-2x + 3}{3}$ Divide both sides by 3.

$$y = -\frac{2}{3}x + 1$$

$m = -\frac{2}{3}$, so the slope is $-\frac{2}{3}$.

$b = 1$, so the y-intercept is 1.

The y-intercept and the slope are the same as those for the first line. The system of equations is coincident lines.

Step 3   Interpret the graph.

The graph of the system is a pair of coincident lines, so there are infinitely many solutions.

Solution   **Since the two equations represent the same line, there are infinitely many solutions. The solutions are the coordinates of all of the points that lie on the line.**

Fiona bought two sunflower plants. One plant is 8 inches tall and is growing at a rate of 3 inches per week. The other plant is 12 inches tall and is growing at a rate of 2 inches per week. This situation can be modeled using the following system of equations. In the equations, x represents the number of weeks, and y represents the height of the plant in inches.

$$y = 3x + 8$$
$$y = 2x + 12$$

If the plants continue to grow at the same rates, when will they be exactly the same height?

Solve the system of equations graphically to find the point where the lines intersect. At this point, the plants will be the same height.

The slope of the equation $y = 3x + 8$ is _____. The y-intercept is _____.
Graph and label this line on the coordinate plane below.

The slope of the equation $y = 2x + 12$ is _____. The y-intercept is _____.
Graph and label this line on the coordinate plane below.

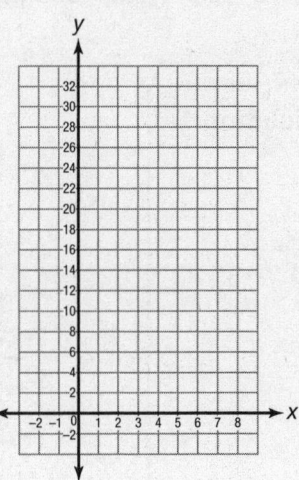

The solution to the system of equations is the point where _____.

Look at your graph. The solution is (_____ , _____).

In the problem, x represents the number of _____, and y represents the

_____ of the plant.

Both plants will be _____ tall at week _____.

The plants will be exactly the same height during week _____.

1 For each system of equations, indicate whether the system has no solution, one solution, or infinitely many solutions by placing an "X" in the correct column.

System of Equations	No Solution	One Solution	Infinitely Many Solutions
$4x - 6y = 10$ $6x - 9y = 15$			
$y = -\dfrac{3}{2}x + 3$ $3x + 2y = 3$			
$4x + 3y = 12$ $3x - 4y = -12$			

2 Use the graph to find the solution of each system of equations. If no solution exists, write "no solution."

System of Equations	Solution
$x - 4y = 8$ $3x + 2y = 10$	
$y = -\dfrac{3}{2}x - 2$ $2x - y = -5$	
$3x + 2y = 10$ $y = -\dfrac{3}{2}x - 2$	

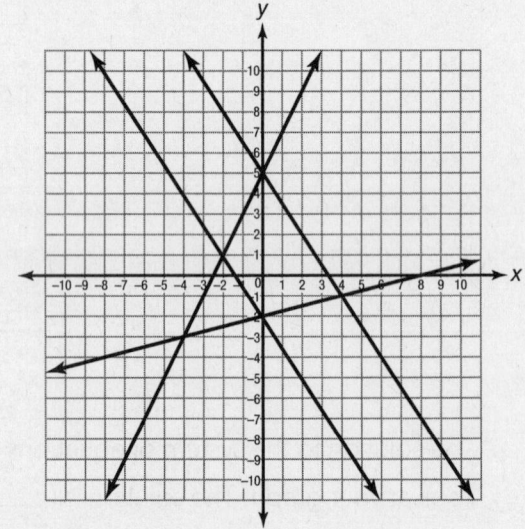

3 Select a system of equations that has no solution. Circle all that apply.

A. $6x + 3y = 12$
$6x - 3y = 12$

C. $6x + 3y = 12$
$-6x - 3y = 12$

B. $6x + 3y = 12$
$6x - 3y = -12$

D. $6x + 3y = 12$
$-6x - 3y = -12$

4 Consider the system of linear equations below.

$$y = -x + 1$$
$$y = \frac{2}{3}x - 4$$

Part A

Graph the system of equations on the coordinate plane.

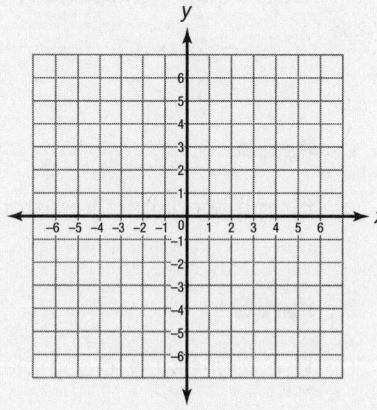

Part B

What is the solution to the system of equations? Explain how your graph justifies your answer.

Part C

Substitute your answer to Part B into both of the original equations to show that it makes both equations true and is the solution to the system.

5 The first equation in a system of two linear equations is $4x + 2y = 10$. The graph of the second equation passes through $(0, -3)$. If the system of equations has no solution, what is the second equation? Write your answer in slope-intercept form. Explain your reasoning.

6 Patrick and Zander are runners. Patrick runs 12 miles a week. Zander runs 7 miles a week. They are both starting training for a marathon. Patrick will increase his running distance by 2 miles each week. Zander will increase his running distance by 3 miles each week. This situation can be modeled using the following system of equations. In the equations, *x* represents the number of weeks each boy spends training, and *y* represents the number of miles each boy runs per week.

$$y = 2x + 12$$
$$y = 3x + 7$$

Part A

Graph and label the system of equations.

Part B

Use your graph to complete the sentence below.

During week _____, Patrick and Zander both run

exactly _____ miles.

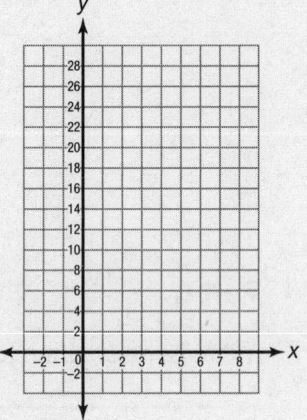

7 Jamal says that if the graphs of two linear equations both pass through the origin, then the system of equations has infinitely many solutions. Is Jamal correct? Use words and an example to justify your answer. You may use the coordinate plane to help you solve the problem.

8.EE.8.b, 8.EE.8.c

Solving Systems of Two Linear Equations Algebraically

1 GETTING THE IDEA

You can solve a **system of linear equations** algebraically. Using the **substitution** method, you solve one equation for one of the variables, and then substitute the expression equal to the variable into the second equation.

Example 1

Solve the system of linear equations by substitution.

$$x - 2y = 7$$
$$3x + 4y = -9$$

Strategy Substitute an expression representing one variable into the second equation.

Step 1 Since the simplest variable to solve for is x in the first equation, solve the first equation for x.

$$x - 2y = 7$$
$$x - 2y + 2y = 7 + 2y$$
$$x = 7 + 2y$$

Step 2 Substitute the expression equal to x into the second equation.

Since $x = 2y + 7$, substitute $2y + 7$ for x into the second equation. Then solve the equation for y.

$$3x + 4y = -9$$
$$3(2y + 7) + 4y = -9$$
$$6y + 21 + 4y = -9$$
$$10y + 21 = -9$$
$$10y + 21 - 21 = -9 - 21$$
$$10y = -30$$
$$\frac{10y}{10} = \frac{-30}{10}$$
$$y = -3$$

Step 3 Substitute the value of y into one of the original equations. Then solve for x.

$$x - 2y = 7$$
$$x - 2(-3) = 7$$
$$x + 6 = 7$$
$$x + 6 - 6 = 7 - 6$$
$$x = 1$$

The solution is $(1, -3)$.

Step 4 Check the solution.

Substitute $(1, -3)$ into both of the original equations.

$$x - 2y = 7 \qquad\qquad 3x + 4y = -9$$
$$\mathbf{1} - 2(\mathbf{-3}) \stackrel{?}{=} 7 \qquad\qquad 3(\mathbf{1}) + 4(\mathbf{-3}) \stackrel{?}{=} -9$$
$$1 + 6 \stackrel{?}{=} 7 \qquad\qquad 3 - 12 \stackrel{?}{=} -9$$
$$7 = 7 \checkmark \qquad\qquad -9 = -9 \checkmark$$

Solution The solution to the system of equations is $(1, -3)$.

You can also solve a system of two linear equations using the **elimination** method. In this method, you add or subtract the two equations to eliminate one of the variables.

Example 2

Solve the system of linear equations by elimination.

$$5x + 4y = 7$$
$$x + 4y = -5$$

Strategy Add or subtract the equations to eliminate one of the variables.

Step 1 Since both equations contain $4y$, subtract the equations to eliminate y.

Remember to carry the subtraction sign through to all terms.

$$
\begin{array}{ll}
5x + 4y = 7 & \qquad\;\; 5x + 4y = 7 \\
\underline{-\,(x + 4y = -5)} \;\rightarrow & \underline{\;\; -\,x - 4y = 5} \\
& \qquad 4x \qquad\;\; = 12 \\
& \qquad \dfrac{4x}{4} = \dfrac{12}{4} \\
& \qquad\quad x = 3
\end{array}
$$

Step 2 Substitute the value of x into one of the original equations. Then solve for y.

$$x + 4y = -5$$
$$3 + 4y = -5$$
$$3 - 3 + 4y = -5 - 3$$
$$4y = -8$$
$$\frac{4y}{4} = \frac{-8}{4}$$
$$y = -2$$

The solution is $(3, -2)$.

Step 3 Check the solution.

Substitute $(3, -2)$ into both of the original equations.

$5x + 4y = 7$	$x + 4y = -5$
$5(3) + 4(-2) \stackrel{?}{=} 7$	$3 + 4(-2) \stackrel{?}{=} -5$
$15 - 8 \stackrel{?}{=} 7$	$3 - 8 \stackrel{?}{=} -5$
$7 = 7 \checkmark$	$-5 = -5 \checkmark$

Solution The solution to the system of equations is $(3, -2)$.

For some systems, you may need to multiply one or both of the equations by a number (or numbers). Try to get the coefficient of one variable in both equations to be the same number with opposite signs, for example, 6 and -6. When you add the equations, the variable will be eliminated.

Example 3

Solve the system of linear equations algebraically. Check your solution by graphing the equations.

$$6x + 3y = 14$$
$$3x + 2y = 10$$

Strategy Multiply one equation by a number that will eliminate a variable when you add the equations.

Step 1 Multiply the second equation by -2.

When the equations are added, the x terms will be eliminated.

$$-2(3x + 2y) = -2(10)$$
$$-6x - 4y = -20$$

Step 2 Add the equations to eliminate x.

$$6x + 3y = 14$$
$$+ \quad -6x - 4y = -20$$
$$\overline{-y = -6}$$
$$y = 6$$

Step 3 Substitute the value of *y* into one of the original equations, and solve for *x*.

Substitute $y = 6$ into the second equation, and solve for *x*.

$$3x + 2y = 10$$
$$3x + 2(6) = 10$$
$$3x + 12 = 10$$
$$3x + 12 - 12 = 10 - 12$$
$$3x = -2$$
$$\frac{3x}{3} = \frac{-2}{3}$$
$$x = -\frac{2}{3}$$

The solution is $\left(-\frac{2}{3}, 6\right)$.

Step 4 Check the solution by graphing.

Write each equation in slope-intercept form, $y = mx + b$. Then graph the equations. Identify the coordinates of the point of intersection.

$$6x + 3y = 14 \qquad\qquad 3x + 2y = 10$$
$$6x + 3y - 6x = 14 - 6x \qquad 3x + 2y - 3x = 10 - 3x$$
$$3y = -6x + 14 \qquad\qquad 2y = -3x + 10$$
$$\frac{3y}{3} = \frac{-6x}{3} + \frac{14}{3} \qquad\qquad \frac{2y}{2} = \frac{-3x}{2} + \frac{10}{2}$$
$$y = -2x + 4\frac{2}{3} \qquad\qquad y = -\frac{3}{2}x + 5$$

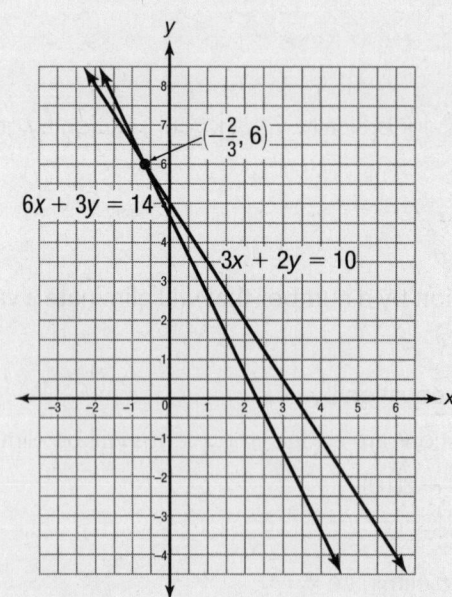

The graph confirms that the solution, $\left(-\frac{2}{3}, 6\right)$, is reasonable.

Solution The solution to the system of equations is $\left(-\frac{2}{3}, 6\right)$.

Sometimes, you can solve a system of equations by thinking about how the equations are related.

Example 4

Solve the system of linear equations by inspection.

$5x + y = 3$

$5x + y = 2$

Strategy **Inspect the equations. Look for similarities.**

Step 1 Examine the structure of the equations.

Both equations contain $5x + y$.

The equations have different constants on the right side of the equation.

Step 2 Use reasoning to analyze the equations.

The first equation says that $5x + y$ is equal to 3.

The second equation says that $5x + y$ is equal to 2.

It is not possible for $5x + y$ to be equal to two different numbers at the same time.

Step 3 Determine the solution of the system.

No ordered pair of values will make both of these equations true.

There is no solution.

Solution **There is no solution to the system of linear equations.**

If you subtract the equations in Example 4, both x and y are eliminated. The result is $0 = 1$. This is false. This indicates that the system of equations has no solution. When solving a system of equations algebraically, if a true statement results such as $0 = 0$, the system of equations has infinitely many solutions.

Example 5

Keisha and Joanna are buying jam and pies at a farm stand. Mrs. Barrymore sells all jars of jam for one price; it doesn't matter what flavor is in the jar. She also sells all of her pies for the same price. Keisha pays $37.50 for 5 jars of jam and 2 pies. Joanna pays $40.50 for 4 jars of jam and 3 pies. Write and solve a system of equations that can be used to determine the cost of one jar of jam and the cost of one pie.

Strategy **Write and solve two equations in the same two variables.**

Step 1 Identify the variables.

The variables are the price of one jar of jam and the price of one pie.

Let j represent the price of one jar of jam.

Let p represent the price of one pie.

Step 2 Write two equations to model the situation.

Since 5 jars of jam and 2 pies cost \$37.50, $5j + 2p = 37.50$.

Since 4 jars of jam and 3 pies cost \$40.50, $4j + 3p = 40.50$.

The system of equations is:

$5j + 2p = 37.50$

$4j + 3p = 40.50$

Step 3 Solve the system of equations.

To solve by elimination, multiply the first equation by 3 and the second equation by -2. When the equations are added, p will be eliminated.

$3(5j + 2p) = 3(37.50)$ $\rightarrow$ $15j + 6p = 112.50$

$-2(4j + 3p) = -2(40.50)$ $\rightarrow$ $-8j - 6p = -81.00$

Add the two new equations.

$$
\begin{array}{r}
15j + 6p = 112.50 \\
+\ \ -8j - 6p = -81.00 \\
\hline
7j \quad\ \ = 31.50
\end{array}
$$

$$\frac{7j}{7} = \frac{31.50}{7}$$

$$j = 4.50$$

Substitute 4.50 for j into the first original equation to find p.

$$5j + 2p = 37.50$$

$$5(4.50) + 2p = 37.50$$

$$22.50 + 2p = 37.50$$

$$22.50 + 2p - 22.50 = 37.50 - 22.50$$

$$2p = 15.00$$

$$\frac{2p}{2} = \frac{15.00}{2}$$

$$p = 7.50$$

Step 4 Interpret the result.

Since $j = 4.50$, the cost of one jar of jam is \$4.50.

Since $p = 7.50$, the cost of one pie is \$7.50.

Solution **The cost of a jar of jam is \$4.50. The cost of a pie is \$7.50.**

A jar of dimes and quarters contains 52 coins. The value of the coins is $8.65. Write and solve a system of equations that can be used to find the number of each type of coin.

Let d represent the number of dimes, and let q represent the number of quarters.

Since the total number of coins is 52, Equation 1 is: $d +$ _____ $=$ _____

Since the total value of the coins is $8.65, Equation 2 is: _____$d +$ _____ $= 8.65$

The system of equations is:

Equation 1: _____

Equation 2: _____

To solve the system of equations by substitution, solve Equation 1 for d.

$d + q = 52$

$d + q -$ _____ $= 52 -$ _____

$d = 52 -$ _____

Substitute the expression for d into Equation 2, and solve for q.

$0.10d + 0.25q = 8.65$

$0.10($_____$) + 0.25q = 8.65$

_____ $-$ _____ $+ 0.25q = 8.65$

_____ $+$ _____ $= 8.65$

_____ $=$ _____

$q =$ _____

Substitute the value of q back into Equation 1, and solve for d.

$d +$ _____ $= 52$

$d =$ _____

Interpret your answer: There are _____ quarters and _____ dimes.

Check your answer. Does the collection of coins have a value of $8.65?

The jar contains _____ quarters and _____ dimes.

1 In the system of linear equations below, a and b are integers. The solution of the system is $(2, -4)$. Find the values of a and b.

$$ax + 2y = -2$$

$$ax + by = 10$$

$a = $ _____, $b = $ _____

2 To solve the system of equations below, Elena begins by multiplying the first equation by 5.

$$2x + 3y = 14$$

$$7x + 5y = 16$$

Part A

Elena wants to eliminate a variable by adding the equations together. By what integer could Elena multiply the second equation? _____

Part B

Solve the system of equations algebraically. You may use Elena's strategy or one of your own. Show your work.

The solution is (_____, _____).

3 Explain why the system of equations $-2x + y = 6$ and $y - 2x = 4$ has no solution.

4 Given $2x + y = 8$ and $3x - y = 17$, Sven solved the system of equations by substitution. The result of each step of his solution is shown.

$$2x + y = 8 \qquad\qquad 3x - y = 17$$
$$y = 8 - 2x \qquad 3x - 8 - 2x = 17$$
$$x - 8 = 17$$
$$x = 25$$

Part A

Circle the step in which Sven's first error occurred. Describe the error.

Part B

Solve the system of equations correctly. Show your work.

The solution is (_____, _____).

5 The two systems of equations below have the same solution. Find the values of a and b.

System 1	System 2
$3x - 4y = -7$	$ax + 5y = 0$
$-3x + 2y = 11$	$-4x + by = 6$

$a =$ _____, $b =$ _____

6 The system of equations below has infinitely many solutions. What is the value of c? Explain your reasoning.

$x - y = 8$

$y - x = c$

7 Write and solve a system of equations to solve the following problem. Show your work.

The Walker and Baldwin families ordered lunch at the refreshment stand at the football game. The Walker family ordered 4 hot dogs, 3 veggie burgers, and 7 orders of French fries, and paid $36. The Baldwin family ordered 6 hot dogs, 2 veggie burgers, and 8 orders of French fries, and paid $39. If an order of French fries costs $1.75, what are the prices of a hot dog and a veggie burger?

The price of a hot dog is $_____, and the price of a veggie burger is $_____.

8 The perimeter of a rectangular garden is 100 feet. The length of the garden is 8 feet longer than twice the width.

Part A

Write a system of two linear equations that represents this situation. Let *l* represent the length of the garden, and let *w* represent the width.

Part B

Find the length and the width of the garden. Show your work.

The length is _____ feet, and the width is _____ feet.

9 Write and solve a system of equations to solve the following problem. Show your work.

Jackie has 24 dimes and 13 quarters. Pilar has the same amount of money as Jackie, but she has only nickels and quarters. If Pilar has 53 coins, how many nickels and how many quarters does she have?

Pilar has _____ nickels and _____ quarters.

10 The graph shows the prices of two stocks over a 7-week period.

Part A

Write the system of equations represented by the graph.

Stock A: _____

Stock B: _____

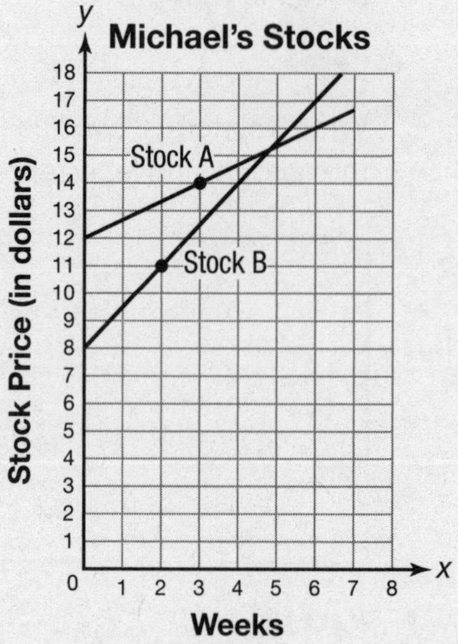

Michael's Stocks

Part B

Solve the system of equations represented by the graph to find when the prices of the stocks were the same. What was the price of the stock at that time? Use an algebraic method, and show your work.

The stocks were the same price at _____ weeks. The price of each stock was $_____.

Part C

How does the graph help you check your answer to Part B for reasonableness?

DOMAIN 2 REVIEW

1 The equation $y = 33x$ describes the number of minutes x it takes a printer to print y pages in black and white. The table shows the number of minutes x it takes a printer to print y pages in color. Which kind of page can the printer print faster? Explain.

Number of Minutes, x	Number of Pages, y
2	52
5	130
8	208
15	390

2 Compare the value of each expression to 25. Write the number in the correct box.

$$5^2 \cdot 2^0 \qquad 3^4 \cdot 2^2 \qquad \frac{5^6}{5^4} \qquad 3^6 \cdot 3^{-3} \qquad 3^3 - 2^1 \qquad \frac{5^3}{2^2}$$

Less Than 25	Equal to 25	Greater Than 25

3 In 2011, Americans used 1.86×10^{11} kilowatt-hours to light their homes. They used 4.6×10^{10} kilowatt-hours to run their computers and computer equipment. Circle the number that correctly completes the statement.

2.5

The amount of electricity used for lighting is about   3   times the amount used for computers.

4

4 Look at the line graphed to the right. Write an equation of a different line that has the same y-intercept as the line shown, but has a slope that is two times the slope of the given line.

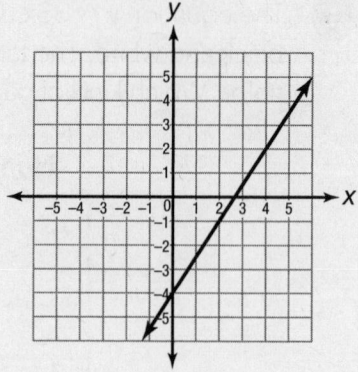

_____

5 Use numbers from the box to write each number in scientific notation.

$3 \times 10^{—} = 3,000$

$0.000004 = \underline{\hspace{2cm}} \times 10^{—}$

$\underline{\hspace{2cm}} \times 10^{6} = 4,000,000$

$0.006 = \underline{\hspace{2cm}} \times 10^{—}$

−6
−4
−3
3
4
6

6 The equation $y = 15x$ describes Anna's biking rate. Let x be the number of hours and y be the total number of miles Anna has biked. Graph the equation.

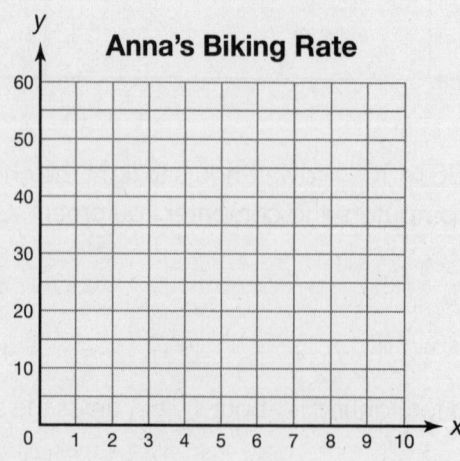

Anna's Biking Rate

7 Beth made wristbands and belts for a craft sale. She sold 30 of these items. Each wristband sold for $5.50. Each belt sold for $8.75. If Beth made $204 at the craft sale, how many wristbands did she sell? How many belts did she sell? Write and solve a system of equations to solve the problem. Show your work.

Beth sold _____ wristbands and _____ belts.

8 Jana needs to rent a moving van for one day. Reliable Rentals charges $20 for the day and $0.50 for each mile. Dependable Rentals charges $10 for the day and $0.80 for each mile. Jana wrote and solved the equation below to find the number of miles for which the costs of renting from the companies will be the same. She used m to represent the number of miles.

$$20 - 0.5m = 10 + 0.8m$$
$$20 = 10 + 1.3m$$
$$10 = 1.3m$$
$$m = \frac{10}{1.3} = \frac{100}{13} = 7\frac{9}{13}$$

The costs will be equal if the van is driven about 8 miles.

Part A

Look at Jana's equation and her solution. Circle the first error that appears in Jana's work. Describe the error.

Part B

Solve the problem correctly. Show your work.

9 Select True or False for each equation.

A. $7.4 \times 10^3 + 4.6 \times 10^2 = 7.86 \times 10^3$ ○ True ○ False

B. $8.35 \times 10^5 - 3.1 \times 10^3 = 8.04 \times 10^4$ ○ True ○ False

C. $6.21 \times 10^2 + 9.2 \times 10^5 = 9.2621 \times 10^4$ ○ True ○ False

D. $1.456 \times 10^4 - 2.1 \times 10^3 = 1.246 \times 10^4$ ○ True ○ False

10 Draw a line from each equation to the line it represents.

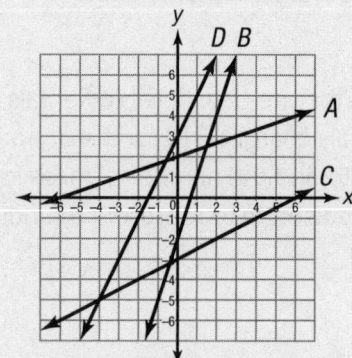

A. $y = \frac{1}{2}x - 3$ •   • line A

B. $y = 2x + 3$ •   • line B

C. $y = \frac{1}{3}x + 2$ •   • line C

D. $y = 3x - 2$ •   • line D

11 Complete the equation so that it has infinitely many solutions.

$6w + 3(4w - 2) =$ _____(_____$w - 3)$

12 A cube, with side length s, has a volume of 216 cubic centimeters. The equation $s^3 = 216$ shows the volume of a cube. What is the side length of the cube in centimeters?

13 Mia has $40 in a savings account. She will start adding $5 to her account each week. Juan has $15 in a savings account. He will start adding $10 to his account each week.

Part A

Let x represent the number of weeks each person adds money to his or her savings account. Let y represent the total number of dollars in the account. Write a system of two linear equations to represent the situation.

_____

Part B

Graph the system of equations you wrote in Part A.

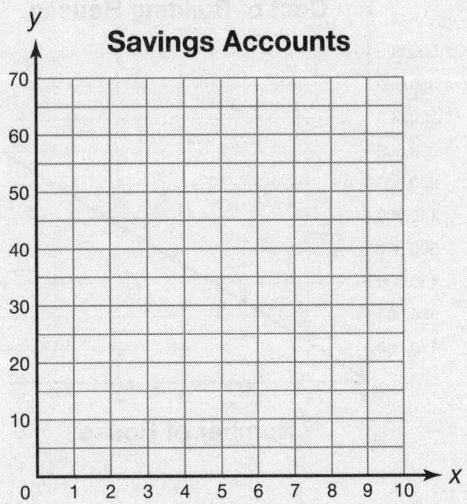

Part C

Use your graph to complete the sentence below.

After _____ weeks, Mia and Juan will both have $_____ in their accounts.

14 Which system of equations has (4, 1) as its solution? Circle all that apply.

A. $-3x + 8y = -4$
$3x - 7y = 5$

D. $3x + 2y = 14$
$2x + 3y = 7$

B. $y = -2x + 9$
$2x + y = 4$

E. $x + y = 5$
$4y = x$

C. $y = \frac{3}{4}x - 2$
$y = \frac{1}{2}x - 1$

Allston Construction

Allston Construction Company builds and sells houses. The president, Mrs. Allston, is analyzing the company's income and expenses.

Part A To build a house, the company must spend money on materials, labor, and land. The amount of money in dollars, y, that it costs to build x number of houses is represented by the equation $y = 180,000x$ and the graph below.

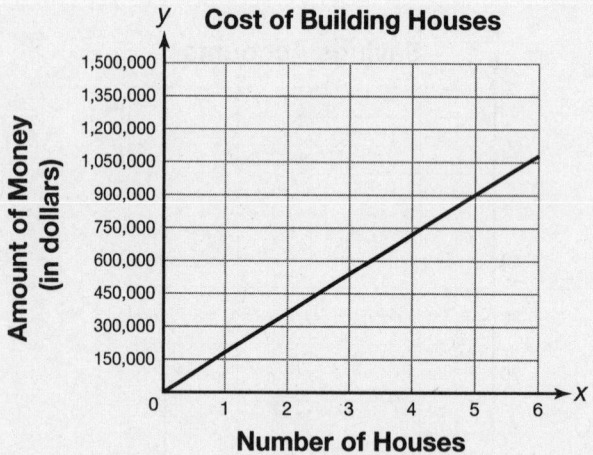

The amount of money in dollars, y, that the company takes in from selling x number of houses is given by the equation $y = 240,000x$. Graph this equation on the coordinate plane above. Does it cost the Allston Construction Company more money to build a house than the house sells for? How much does it cost to build a house?

Part B The company also spends $120,000 each year on advertising. This means that the total costs for selling x houses in a year is given by the equation $y = 180,000x + 120,000$.

Find out how many houses the company needs to build and sell in order to break even, so that the company's income for the year is equal to its costs for the year.

Part C Similar houses that the company built in another town are not selling as well. Mrs. Allston decides to sell one house for $180,000 in order to cover the construction costs. She finds that every time a house sells, she can sell the next house for $4,800 more. The profit, p, for selling x houses in this situation is given by the equation $p = 4,800x^2 - 120,000$. How many houses must the company sell in this situation in order to break even?

Part D Seeds must be planted in each lot to grow grass. Each square foot of lawn requires 3,000 grass seeds. The houses' lawns each measure 9,800 square feet. Write each of these numbers in scientific notation. Then find the number of seeds needed for one house's lawn.

DOMAIN 3

Functions

Introducing Functions

① GETTING THE IDEA

A **relation** is a set of ordered pairs. The x-coordinates in a relation are the **inputs**, and the y-coordinates are the **outputs**.

inputs   **outputs**

{(**1**, 2), (**3**, 9), (**5**, 8), (**14**, 10)}   {(1, **2**), (3, **9**), (5, **8**), (14, **10**)}

A **function** is a relation in which each input has exactly one output. The relation above is a function.

Example 1

Determine whether the relation shown in the table is a function.

Input, x	Output, y
−5	−6
4	10
0	−4
−2	1
4	5

Strategy   Look for inputs with the same value.

Step 1   Look at the x-values in the table. Are any of the values the same?

There are two inputs with a value of 4.

Step 2   Look at the corresponding y-values. If these outputs are different, the relation is not a function.

The outputs for 4 are 10 and 5. The outputs are different.

Input, x	Output, y
−5	−6
4	10
0	−4
−2	1
4	5

Solution   The relation is not a function because the input 4 has two different outputs.

A relation or function can also be represented by a graph.

Example 2

The graph shows the ages compared to the heights of trees in a park. Determine whether the relation given by the graph is a function.

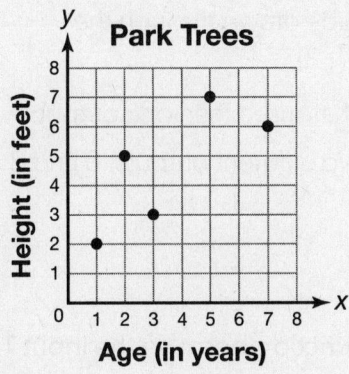

Strategy   Look for points with the same *x*-coordinates.

Step 1   Write the coordinates of the points.

(1, 2), (2, 5), (3, 3), (5, 7), (7, 6)

Step 2   Look at the *x*-coordinates, or inputs. If the inputs are all different, the relation is a function.

The inputs are 1, 2, 3, 5, and 7. The inputs are all different.

Solution   **The relation is a function because each input has only one output.**

When a relation is represented by a graph, the *vertical line test* can be used to determine whether the relation is a function or not a function. The **vertical line test** says that if a vertical line can be drawn so that it passes through more than one point on the graph, then the relation is not a function. If two points are along a vertical line, they have the same *x* value. The vertical line test works because a function must have a unique *y* value for every *x* value.

Example 3

Determine whether the relation represented by the graph is a function.

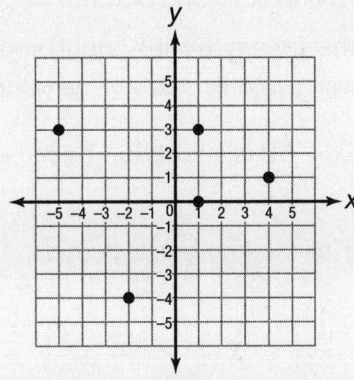

Strategy	Use the vertical line test.

Step 1 Determine whether a vertical line can be drawn through more than one point on the graph.

A vertical line can be drawn through the points (1, 0) and (1, 3).

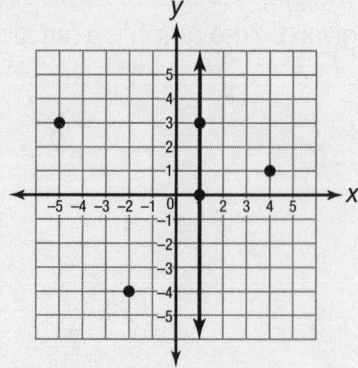

Step 2 Identify the input that has more than one output.

The input 1 has two different outputs, 0 and 3.

Solution The relation is not a function because the input 1 has two different outputs.

A relation or function can also be represented by an equation.

Example 4

Ming rents a truck for $50 per day. He must also pay $0.75 for each mile driven. The equation $y = 0.75x + 50$ represents this situation, where x is the number of miles and y is the total cost in dollars. Determine whether the relation $y = 0.75x + 50$ is a function.

Strategy Create a table of x–y values.

Step 1 Choose the inputs. Because x represents the number of miles, use 0 and positive values that are easy to compute.

Step 2 Calculate the outputs. Record the outputs in the table.

$x = 0: y = 0.75(0) + 50 = 0 + 50 = 50$

$x = 10: y = 0.75(10) + 50 = 7.50 + 50 = 57.50$

$x = 20: y = 0.75(20) + 50 = 15 + 50 = 65$

$x = 30: y = 0.75(30) + 50 = 22.50 + 50 = 72.50$

$x = 40: y = 0.75(40) + 50 = 30 + 50 = 80$

Number of Miles, x	Total Cost, y
0	50.00
10	57.50
20	65.00
30	72.50
40	80.00

Step 3 Check that each input has exactly one output.

The table shows that for any x-value (input) you choose, the equation $y = 0.75x + 50$ will give only one y-value (output).

Solution The relation $y = 0.75x + 50$ is a function because every input has only one output.

Some graphs of relations represent an infinite number of points.

Example 5

Determine whether the relation represented by the graph is a function.

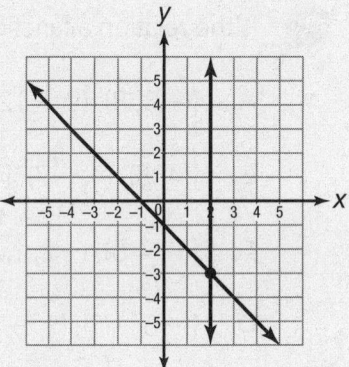

Strategy   Use the vertical line test to determine if the relation is a function.

Step 1   Determine whether a vertical line can be drawn through more than one point on the graph.

Any vertical line drawn through this graph passes through only one point on the graph.

Step 2   Identify any inputs that have more than one output.

There are no inputs that have more than one output.

Solution   The relation is a function because each input has only one output.

---

② COACHED EXAMPLE

Laura recorded the gallons of gasoline she bought and the amount she paid. The inputs are the numbers of gallons of gasoline. The outputs are the amounts paid. Is the relation represented by her table a function?

Gas Purchased (in gallons)	6.5	3	5.1	2.9	4.8
Amount Paid (in dollars)	23.70	10.77	18.82	10.77	17.28

Look at the inputs in the table.

The inputs are _____.

Are any of the inputs the same? _____

If the inputs are all different, the relation is a function.

Is the relation a function? _____

The relation given in the table _____ **a function because** _____
_____.

1 Is the relation a function? Select Yes or No.

A. $\{(-3, 8), (9, -12), (0, 0), (4, -1), (3, 8)\}$ ○ Yes ○ No

B. $\{(4, 5), (4, -7), (4, 2), (4, 0), (4, 9)\}$ ○ Yes ○ No

C. $\{(8, 4.5), (-2, 1.2), (5, 0.3), (-1, 4.5), (9, 2.5)\}$ ○ Yes ○ No

D. $\{(-6, -1), (5, -1), (0, -1), (-2, -1), (3, -1)\}$ ○ Yes ○ No

2 Drew earns \$9.50 an hour at his job. The equation $y = 9.5x$ represents this situation. The number of hours Drew works is represented by x, and y represents the total amount of money Drew earns in dollars. Does the equation $y = 9.5x$ represent a function? Use a table to explain your reasoning.

3 Write five ordered pairs in the table to represent a relation that is not a function.

x	y

4 Draw a line on the graph that represents a relation, but not a function. Explain your reasoning.

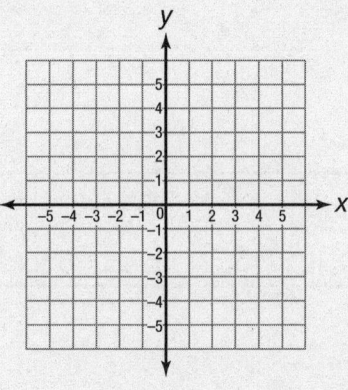

5 Plot a point on the graph so that the relation is not a function. Then write the ordered pair.

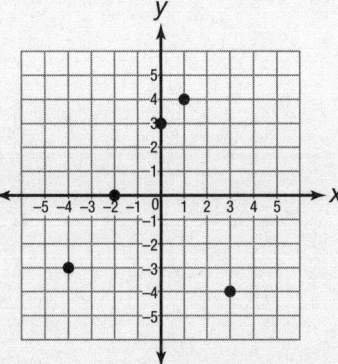

(_____ , _____)

6 The table represents a function. Use a number from the box to complete the table.

x	1		−2	0	−5	8	−15
y	2	−8	−1	15	5	−6	12

1
0
−2
−5
−8
−15

7 Gail claims that because the output 4 has two inputs in the table, the table does not represent a function. Is she correct? Explain.

x	y
−10	4
5	2
0	4
10	8
−20	−2

8 The graph shows the lengths and weights of fish in a lake that were caught and released. Isabelle caught a fish that was 8 inches long and weighed 9 pounds. Add this fish to the graph. Does the graph represent a function? Explain.

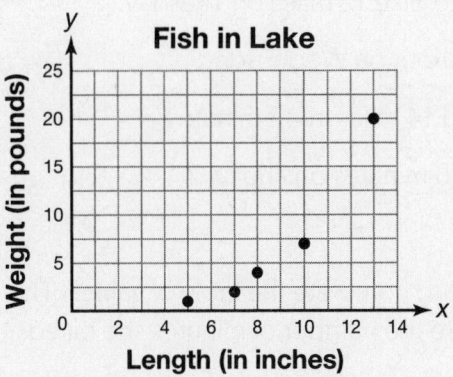

9 Select a graph that represents a function. Circle all that apply.

A.
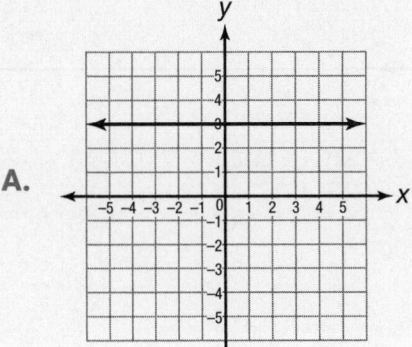

C.
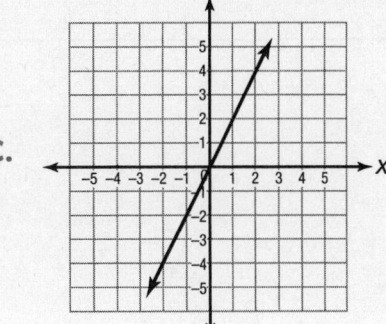

B.
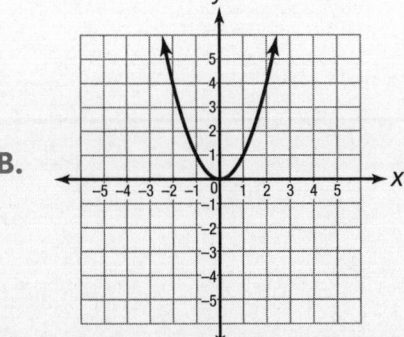

D.
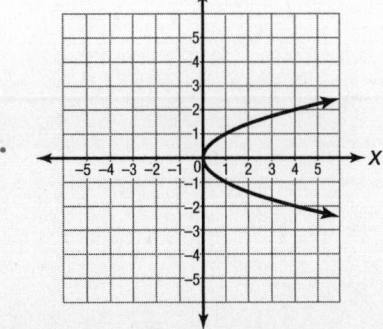

10 Leah rode her bike 5 days last week.

- On Monday, she biked 15 miles in 45 minutes.

- It took her 40 minutes to bike 12 miles on Tuesday.

- She biked 18 miles in 1 hour on Wednesday.

- On Thursday, she biked 14 miles in 42 minutes.

- She biked 16 miles in 48 minutes on Friday.

Part A

Use the information above to complete the table of values. The inputs are the distances Leah biked. The outputs are the number of minutes she biked.

Distance Biked (in miles)					
Time Biked (in minutes)					

Part B

Is the relation in the table a function? Explain.

LESSON 13

Comparing Functions

1 GETTING THE IDEA

A **rate of change** is a rate that describes how one quantity changes in relation to another quantity. The **slope** of a line is a rate of change.

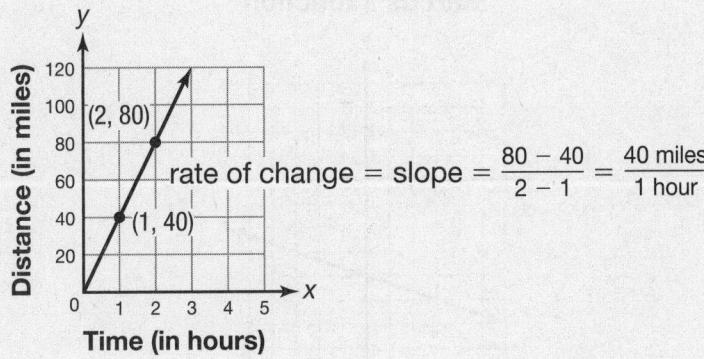

rate of change = slope = $\dfrac{80-40}{2-1}=\dfrac{40\ miles}{1\ hour}$

The slope-intercept form of the equation for the line shown on the graph is $y = 40x$. Remember, the **slope-intercept form** is $y = mx + b$, where m is the slope of the line and b is the **y-intercept**.

Example 1

The table and the equation both represent linear functions. Which function has a greater rate of change?

Function A

x	2	4	5	8	10
y	21	17	15	9	5

Function B

$y = -3x - 9$

Strategy   Find the rate of change for each function.

Step 1   Find the rate of change for Function A.

Because the function is linear, it has a constant rate of change. Choose any two ordered pairs from the table to find the slope, or rate of change.

Rate of change = $\dfrac{15-17}{5-4}=-\dfrac{2}{1}=-2$

Step 2   Find the rate of change for Function B.

Since the slope is a rate of change, identify the slope from the equation.

$y = -3x - 9$

$m = -3$

The rate of change for Function B is -3.

Step 3	Compare the rates of change.

Function A   Function B

-2 $>$ -3

Solution   Function A has the greater rate of change.

Example 2

Marcus graphed the function shown. Anna wrote the function given by the equation $y = 4x - 2$. Which function has the greater y-intercept?

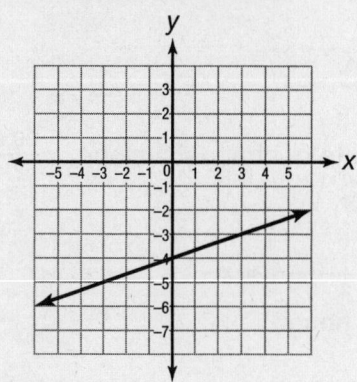

Marcus's function

Strategy   Find each y-intercept.

Step 1   Find the y-intercept of Marcus's function.

The graph crosses the y-axis at the point $(0, -4)$. The y-intercept is -4.

Step 2   Find the y-intercept of Anna's function.

$y = 4x - 2$

$b = -2$

The y-intercept is -2.

Step 3   Compare the y-intercepts.

Anna   Marcus

-2 $>$ -4

Solution   Anna's function has the greater y-intercept.

Functions also have an **x-intercept**. The x-intercept is the point at which a function crosses the x-axis.

Example 3

Shawn and Mei leave an amusement park at the same time. Both drive home at a constant speed. The table shows the function that models Shawn's trip home. The graph shows the function that models Mei's trip home. Who got home first?

Shawn's Drive Home

Time Spent Driving (in hours), x	0	5
Distance from Home (in miles), y	180	0

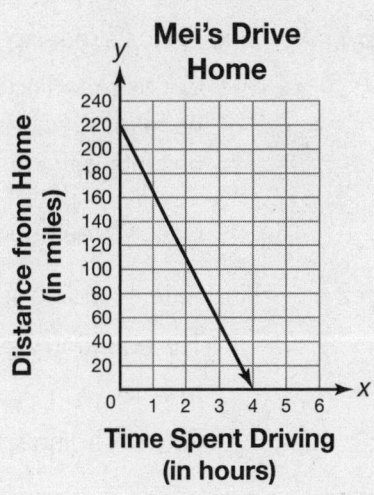

Strategy	Compare the x-intercepts.
Step 1	Find the number of hours it took Shawn to get home.
	Shawn is home when the distance $y = 0$. According to the table, $y = 0$ when $x = 5$.
	Because x is the number of hours spent driving, it took Shawn 5 hours to get home.
Step 2	Find the number of hours it took Mei to get home.
	On Mei's graph, the x-intercept is $x = 4$.
	Because x is the number of hours spent driving, it took Mei 4 hours to get home.
Step 3	Compare the two times.

Mei's Time   Shawn's Time

4     $<$ 5

Solution	**Mei got home first.**

Rates of change can be found in many real-world situations. Speed is a rate of change that describes how a distance or other quantity changes with respect to time.

Example 4

Carlos and Kate are reading the same book for class. Carlos has read 30 pages so far and plans to read 15 pages each day to finish the book. Kate's plan for reading the book can be represented by the equation $y = 18x + 20$, where x is the number of days and y is the total number of pages read. Who plans to read the remaining pages of the book faster?

Strategy   Find each person's reading speeds.

Step 1   Find Carlos's reading speed. Write this rate as a unit rate.

Carlos's reading speed is a rate of change and describes how the number of pages he reads changes with respect to the number of days. Carlos's reading speed as a unit rate is the number of pages he plans to read each day.

$$\text{Carlos's reading speed} = \frac{15 \text{ pages}}{1 \text{ day}}$$

Step 2   Find Kate's reading speed. Write the rate as a unit rate.

The equation $y = 18x + 20$ is in slope-intercept form.

$m = 18$

$$\text{Kate's reading speed} = \frac{18 \text{ pages}}{1 \text{ day}}$$

Step 3   Compare the reading speeds.

Kate's Reading Speed   **Carlos's Reading Speed**

$$\frac{18 \text{ pages}}{1 \text{ day}} > \frac{15 \text{ pages}}{1 \text{ day}}$$

Solution   Kate plans to read the remaining pages faster.

Julie is comparing cell phone plans that charge by the month. Let x represent the number of minutes over 200 minutes, and let y represent the total cost in dollars. Plan A is represented by the equation $y = 0.2x + 20$. Plan B is represented in the graph. Which plan charges more per minute over the 200 minutes that are included?

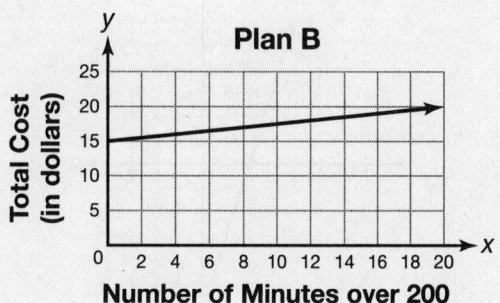

Find the unit rate of change for Plan A.

The unit rate of change is $\dfrac{\$\boxed{}}{1\ \text{minute}}$ because _____.

Find the unit rate of change for Plan B.

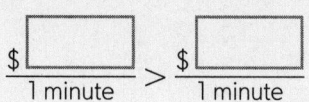

Compare the unit rates.

$\dfrac{\$\boxed{}}{1\ \text{minute}} > \dfrac{\$\boxed{}}{1\ \text{minute}}$

Plan _____ **charges more per minute over 200 minutes.**

1 Which function's graph does not have a greater *x*-intercept than the graph of the function shown?

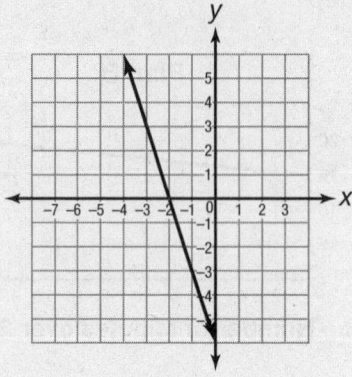

A. $y = 4x$

B. $y = 2x - 6$

C. $y = \frac{1}{3}x + 2$

D. $y = x - 4$

2 Compare the functions. Which function has the lesser rate of change?

Evan's function

$y = -2x + 5$

Liz's function

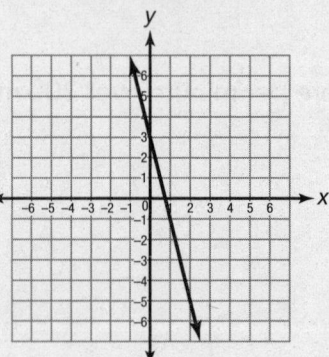

3 Ella and Li leave the library at the same time to walk home. Both walk at a constant speed. Which person got home first? Explain.

Li's function

Time Spent Walking (in minutes), x	0	32
Distance from Home (in miles), y	0.75	0

Ella's function

$y = -0.02x + 0.75$, where x represents the time spent walking in minutes and y represents the distance from home in miles

4 Jen wrote a function given by the equation $y = 0.1x - 5$. Which table represents a linear function with the same rate of change as Jen's function? Circle all that apply.

A.

x	0	10
y	−5	−4

C.

x	20	50
y	3	0

B.

x	−4	−8
y	−5.4	−5.8

D.

x	1	30
y	−4.9	−2

5 Amy is running a marathon to raise money for a charity. Tom is sponsoring Amy. He will pay $10 plus an additional $4 per mile. Leah is also sponsoring Amy. The amount she will pay is given by the linear function shown in the table. Who is paying more per mile? Explain.

Number of Miles, x	5	10
Amount Paid (in dollars), y	30	55

6 Beth opened a savings account with $50. She puts $10 into the account each week. Juan also opened a savings account. The amount he is saving is shown in the graph.

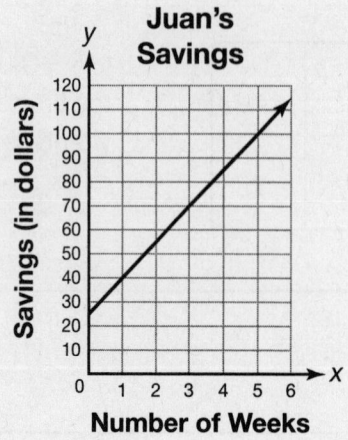

Juan's Savings

Part A

Who is saving more each week? Explain.

Part B

Who started with more money in his or her account? Explain.

7 Greg is buying a bike on a payment plan. The equation $y = -20x + 600$ models the amount he has left to pay, where x is the number of weeks and y is the amount of money owed in dollars. Lin is also buying a bike on a payment plan. The bike costs $500. She will pay $25 each week.

Part A

What is the y-intercept of Greg's equation?

_____

Part B

Explain what the y-intercept represents in the problem situation.

Part C

Whose bike will be paid off first? Explain how you know.

Linear and Nonlinear Functions

A **linear function** is a function whose graph is a straight line. Equations of linear functions can be written in the form $y = mx + b$. From this form of the equation, you can identify the **slope** m and the **y-intercept** b of the line that represents the function.

Example 1

Does the equation $2x + 3y = -15$ represent a linear function? If it does, identify the slope and the y-intercept of the graph that represents the function.

Strategy   **Determine if the equation can be written in the form $y = mx + b$.**

Step 1   Solve the equation for y.

$$2x + 3y = -15$$

$$2x - 2x + 3y = -15 - 2x$$

$$3y = -2x - 15$$

$$\frac{3y}{3} = \frac{-2x - 15}{3}$$

$$y = -\frac{2}{3}x - 5$$

Step 2   Compare the equation to $y = mx + b$. If the function is linear, identify the slope and y-intercept.

The equation can be written in the form $y = mx + b$, so it represents a linear function.

$$y = mx + b$$
$$\downarrow \qquad \downarrow$$
$$y = -\frac{2}{3}x - 5$$

The slope m is $-\frac{2}{3}$. The y-intercept b is -5.

Solution   **The equation $2x + 3y = -15$ represents a linear function. The slope of the graph of the function is $-\frac{2}{3}$ and the y-intercept is -5.**

Functions whose graphs do not form a straight line, such as the one in Example 2, are classified as **nonlinear functions**.

Example 2

Does the equation $y - 2x^3 = 4$ represent a linear function? If it does, identify the slope and the y-intercept of the graph that represents the function.

Strategy   Determine if the equation can be written in the form $y = mx + b$.

Step 1   Solve the equation for y.

$$y - 2x^3 = 4$$
$$y - 2x^3 + 2x^3 = 4 + 2x^3$$
$$y = 2x^3 + 4$$

Step 2   Compare the equation to $y = mx + b$. If the function is linear, identify the slope and y-intercept.

The equation cannot be written in the form $y = mx + b$ because it contains x^3. Therefore, it does not represent a linear function.

Solution   The equation $y - 2x^3 = 4$ **does not represent a linear function.**

Example 3

For each graph below, determine whether it represents a linear function or a nonlinear function.

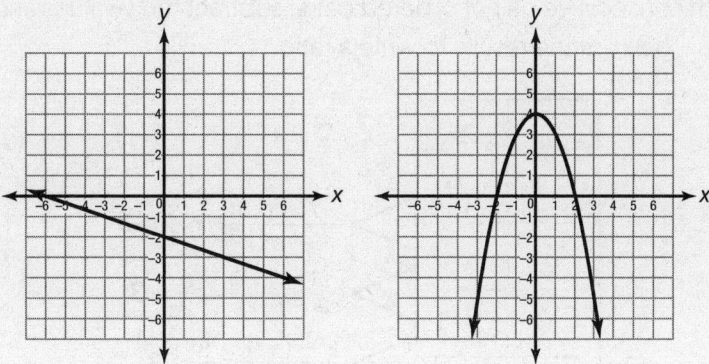

Strategy   Use the definitions of linear function and nonlinear function.

Step 1   Check the first graph.

The graph is a straight line.

Therefore, the graph represents a linear function.

Step 2   Check the second graph.

The graph is not a straight line.

Therefore, the graph represents a nonlinear function.

Solution   The first graph represents a linear function. The second graph represents a nonlinear function.

If you are given a table of values for a function, you can determine whether the function is linear or nonlinear by comparing the ratio of the change in *y*-values to the change in *x*-values. If this ratio is the same for all pairs of ordered pairs in the table, then the function is linear. If not, then it is nonlinear.

Example 4

Is the function represented by the values in the table linear or nonlinear?

x	y
−3	−10
−2	−7
0	−1
1	2
3	8

Strategy **Compare the ratios of the change in *y*-values to the change in *x*-values.**

Step 1   For each consecutive pair of ordered pairs, subtract the *y*-values and subtract the *x*-values. Then use the results to write a ratio.

x	y
−3	−10
−2	−7
0	−1
1	2
3	8

$$\frac{-7 - (-10)}{-2 - (-3)} = \frac{3}{1} = 3$$

$$\frac{-1 - (-7)}{0 - (-2)} = \frac{6}{2} = 3$$

$$\frac{2 - (-1)}{1 - 0} = \frac{3}{1} = 3$$

$$\frac{8 - 2}{3 - 1} = \frac{6}{2} = 3$$

Step 2   Compare the ratios and interpret the result.

The ratios are equal. Therefore, the function is linear.

Solution   **The function represented by the values in the table is linear.**

Example 5

Is the function represented by the values in the table linear or nonlinear?

x	y
−4	8
−3	4
0	0
3	−4
4	−8

Strategy   Compare the ratios of the change in y-values to the change in x-values.

Step 1   For each consecutive pair of ordered pairs, subtract the y-values and subtract the x-values. Then use the results to write a ratio.

$$\frac{4-8}{-3-(-4)} = \frac{-4}{1} = -4$$

$$\frac{0-4}{0-(-3)} = -\frac{4}{3}$$

$$\frac{-4-0}{3-0} = -\frac{4}{3}$$

$$\frac{-8-(-4)}{4-3} = \frac{-4}{1} = -4$$

Step 2   Compare the ratios and interpret the result.

Since the ratios are not equal, the function is nonlinear.

Solution   **The function represented by the values in the table is nonlinear.**

---

② COACHED EXAMPLE

Does the equation $y = x^2 + 9$ represent a linear function or a nonlinear function? Explain your reasoning.

Linear functions can be written in the form $y =$ _____.

Compare the equation $y = x^2 + 9$ to the one you wrote above.

What is different about the forms of the two equations? _____

Since the equation $y = x^2 + 9$ contains _____, the equation represents

a _____ function.

The equation $y = x^2 + 9$ represents a _____ function because

_____.

1 Jason drew the graph below. Which statement about Jason's graph is true? Circle all that apply.

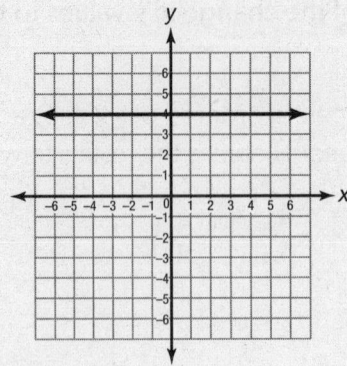

A. The graph represents a function.

B. The graph represents a linear function.

C. The slope of the graph is 1.

D. The *y*-intercept of the graph is 4.

E. The equation of the line is $x = 4$.

2 Does the table represent a linear function or a nonlinear function? Explain how you know.

x	y
2	$\frac{1}{2}$
3	$\frac{1}{3}$
4	$\frac{1}{4}$
5	$\frac{1}{5}$
6	$\frac{1}{6}$

3 Does the equation represent a linear function? Select Yes or No.

A. $y = x$　　　　　　○ Yes　○ No

B. $0.8x + 1.5y = -6$　○ Yes　○ No

C. $x = \frac{3}{2}$　　　　　　○ Yes　○ No

D. $y = 2x + x^2$　　　○ Yes　○ No

E. $y - 5 = 0$　　　　○ Yes　○ No

F. $y = \sqrt{x} + 1$　　　○ Yes　○ No

4 The table represents a linear function. Find the values of a and b.

x	y
a	15
-3	11
0	5
2	b
7	-9

$a =$ _____, $b =$ _____

5 Look at each function. Is it a linear function or a nonlinear function? Select Linear or Nonlinear.

A. the number of minutes m to cook c cups of rice　　○ Linear　○ Nonlinear

B. the volume V of a cube with side length s　　○ Linear　○ Nonlinear

C. the distance walked after m minutes at r feet per minute　　○ Linear　○ Nonlinear

D. the cost C for t tickets to the museum　　○ Linear　○ Nonlinear

E. the value v of a car that depreciates at 15% annually　　○ Linear　○ Nonlinear

6 Antonio uses a function to determine the height of a football from the time it is kicked to the time it lands on the ground. Is the function linear or nonlinear? Use words, numbers, or models to justify your answer.

7 A linear function is represented by a graph that passes through the origin and has a slope of $\frac{4}{5}$. Determine if each point is on the graph or not on the graph of this linear function. Write the ordered pair in the correct box.

$\left(-\frac{4}{5}, -1\right)$ $(15, 12)$ $\left(-2, -\frac{8}{5}\right)$ $\left(1, \frac{4}{5}\right)$ $(-4, -5)$ $\left(\frac{1}{2}, \frac{2}{5}\right)$

On the Graph	Not on the Graph

8 Mariko says that the graph that passes through $(-3, -3)$, $(-3, 0)$, and $(-3, 3)$ represents a linear function. Is she correct? Explain your reasoning.

9 The table shows the growth rate of a pine tree.

Part A

Complete the table. Use the formula for area: $A = \pi\left(\dfrac{d}{2}\right)^2$.

Age of Tree (in years)	Diameter of Tree (in inches)	Area of Cross Section (in square inches)
14	6	_____π
21	9	20.25π
28	12	_____π
35	15	56.25π
42	18	_____π
49	21	110.25π

Part B

Is the relationship between the diameter and the age of the tree a linear function? Explain.

Part C

Is the relationship between the area of the cross section and the age of the tree a linear function? Explain.

8.F.4

Using Functions to Model Relationships

 GETTING THE IDEA -

Two quantities, x and y, are said to have a **linear relationship** if $y = mx + b$ for all ordered pairs (x, y) in the relationship. For example, if t is the time it takes to drive d miles when driving 40 miles per hour, t and d have a linear relationship, because the linear function $d = 40t$ describes the relationship. The value of m (in this example, 40) is the **rate of change** of the function.

The graph of a linear relationship is a straight line. The **initial value** of a function is the y-value when $x = 0$, which is the **y-intercept**. The equation of the line can be written in **slope-intercept form**, $y = mx + b$.

Example 1

Geri's Gym is running a special for new members. The fee for joining the gym has been reduced to $25. Members then pay $19.99 per month to use the gym. Write an equation in slope-intercept form to represent this situation. Identify the initial value and the rate of change of the function.

Strategy   Identify the initial value and the rate of change in the situation. Then use these values to write an equation in the form $y = mx + b$.

Step 1   Identify the initial value.

The initial value is the fee for joining the gym, which is $25.

So, $b = 25$.

Step 2   Identify the rate of change.

The rate of change is the monthly fee, which is $19.99 per month.

So, $m = 19.99$.

Step 3   Write the equation.

Substitute the values for m and b in the equation $y = mx + b$.

$y = 19.99x + 25$

Solution   **The equation $y = 19.99x + 25$ represents the situation. The initial value is $25. The rate of change is $19.99 per month.**

Example 2

A plumber charges a fee of $50 to diagnose a problem, and $70 per hour for labor to fix it. Write an equation in slope-intercept form to represent this situation. Identify the initial value and the rate of change. Then graph the function.

Strategy   Write an equation in the form $y = mx + b$, and draw its graph.

Step 1   Identify the initial value.

The initial value is the flat fee, which is $50.

So, $b = 50$.

Step 2   Identify the rate of change.

The rate of change is the hourly fee for labor, which is $70 per hour.

So, $m = 70$.

Step 3   Write the equation.

Substitute the values for m and b in the equation $y = mx + b$.

$y = 70x + 50$

Step 4   Graph the equation.

The y-intercept is 50. The slope is 70, or $\frac{70}{1}$.

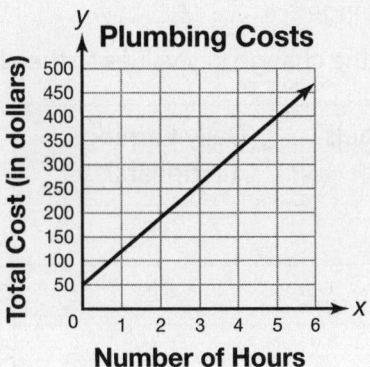

Solution   The equation $y = 70x + 50$ represents the situation. The initial value is $50. The rate of change is $70 per hour. The graph is shown above.

If you are given a table of ordered pairs that satisfy a linear relationship, you can find the rate of change by finding the ratio of the change in y-values to the change in x-values.

Example 3

Pierre picks apples at his aunt's orchard on Saturdays during the apple harvest. His aunt pays him a daily wage, plus an additional amount for each bushel of apples he picks. The table below shows his daily earnings, y, if he picks x bushels of apples.

Pierre's Apple Picking

Number of Bushels of Apples, x	Daily Earnings (in dollars), y
1	38
2	46
3	54
4	62
5	70

Write a linear function that models this situation. Identify the initial value and the rate of change. Then graph the function.

Strategy   Write an equation in the form $y = mx + b$, and draw its graph.

Step 1   Identify the rate of change.

Find the ratio of the change in y-values to the change in x-values.

Number of Bushels of Apples, x	Daily Earnings (in dollars), y
1	38
2	46
3	54
4	62
5	70

$$\frac{46 - 38}{2 - 1} = 8$$

$$\frac{54 - 46}{3 - 2} = 8$$

$$\frac{62 - 54}{4 - 3} = 8$$

$$\frac{70 - 62}{5 - 4} = 8$$

The rate of change is $8 per bushel. So, $m = 8$.

Step 2   Identify the initial value.

The initial value is the value of the function when $x = 0$. Subtract the rate of change for 1 hour from the earnings for 1 hour: $38 - 8 = 30$.

So, $b = 30$.

Step 3   Write the equation.

Substitute the values for m and b in the equation $y = mx + b$.

$y = 8x + 30$

Step 4   Graph the equation.

The *y*-intercept is 30. The slope is 8, or $\frac{8}{1}$.

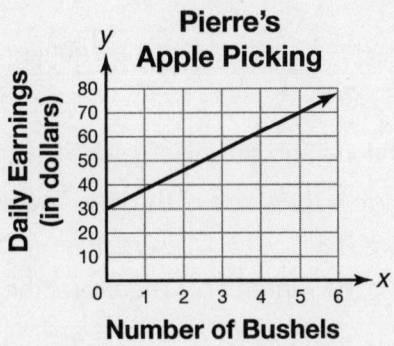

Pierre's Apple Picking

Solution   The function $y = 8x + 30$ models the situation. The initial value is \$30. The rate of change is \$8 per bushel. The graph is shown in Step 4.

Since the rate of change of a function is the ratio of the change in *y*-values to the change in *x*-values, the rate of change is also the slope of the line that represents the function.

Example 4

A pool is being drained so that it can be repaired. The graph shows the amount of water in the pool during the time it takes to drain it completely. Write the function that is represented by the graph. Identify the rate of change and the initial value.

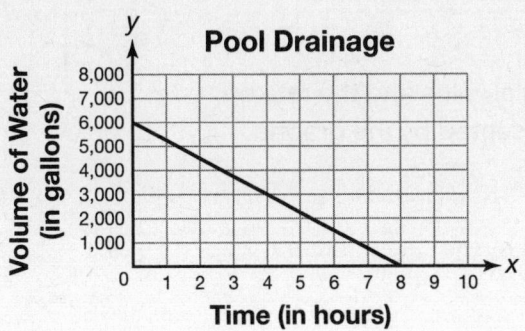

Pool Drainage

Strategy   Find the slope and *y*-intercept of the line, and use these values to write an equation in the form $y = mx + b$.

Step 1   Find the slope of the line.

Find the ratio of the change in *y*-values to the change in *x*-values between two points on the line.

Use (0, 6,000) and (4, 3,000).

$$\frac{3,000 - 6,000}{4 - 0} = \frac{-3,000}{4} = -750$$

So, $m = -750$.

Step 2   Find the *y*-intercept of the line.

Read the graph. The *y*-intercept is 6,000.

Step 3   Write the equation.

Substitute the values for *m* and *b* in the equation $y = mx + b$.

$y = -750x + 6,000$

Step 4   Identify the rate of change and the initial value.

The rate of change is the slope of the line. Therefore, the rate of change is -750 gallons per hour.

The initial value is the *y*-intercept. Therefore, the initial value is 6,000 gallons.

Solution   The function represented by the graph is $y = -750x + 6,000$. The rate of change is -750 gallons per hour. The initial value is 6,000 gallons.

② COACHED EXAMPLE

A chef is roasting a large turkey. She knows the turkey must cook long enough to bring the internal temperature to 180°F. After the turkey has been in the oven for 3 hours, the chef inserts a meat thermometer into the turkey and monitors the internal temperature over the next 30 minutes. The graph shows the data.

Identify and interpret the initial value and the rate of change of the function represented by the graph.

Roasting Turkey

Look at the graph.

The initial value is represented by the _____-intercept.

The initial value is _____ .

This is the internal temperature of the turkey when _____.

The rate of change is represented by the _____.

Use two points on the graph to calculate the rate of change: (_____, _____) and (10, 140).

The rate of change is _____ per _____.

What does the rate of change indicate to the chef? _____

The initial value is _____, which means that the _____.

The rate of change is _____, which means that the _____.

1 At a home improvement store, customers can rent a small cargo truck to transport any large items they purchase. The store charges $20 as a rental fee plus $7.50 per hour to rent the truck.

Part A

Identify the initial value and the rate of change for the function that represents the situation.

The initial value is _____. The rate of change is _____.

Part B

Write an equation, in slope-intercept form, that represents the situation.

_____

Part C

Explain how you can use the equation from Part A to determine the total cost of renting the truck for 5 hours.

2 The linear relationship represented by the table has an initial value of 88 and a rate of change of −6. Complete the table.

x	y
2	
	64
	46
9	
	10

3 Shana is hiking down into a canyon. The table shows her elevation above the canyon floor at different hours during the course of the hike. A linear function represents the relationship between the number of hours Shana has hiked and her elevation.

Number of Hours	Elevation (in feet)
1	3,500
3	2,100
4.5	1,050
5	700

Part A

What is the initial value of the function? Explain how you know.

Part B

What does the initial value of the function represent in terms of the situation?

4 Water is leaking out of a red cylindrical tank into a blue cylindrical tank that has been placed beneath the table on which the red tank stands. The height of the water in the red tank at time t can be represented by a linear function. The height of the water in the blue tank at time t can also be represented by a linear function. Under what condition would the rates of change of the two functions be negatives of each other? Explain your reasoning.

5 Mario sells used cars. He earns a base salary of *s* dollars per week. He also earns a commission of *c* dollars for each car that he sells. Use numbers, variables, and symbols from the box to write an equation that shows the linear relationship between Mario's weekly earnings, *y*, and the number of cars, *x*, that he sells in a week.

$$y = \underline{\hspace{1cm}} \ \underline{\hspace{1cm}} \ \underline{\hspace{1cm}} \ \underline{\hspace{1cm}}$$

+

−

100

c

x

s

6 An airplane is flying at 9,000 feet. It begins descending at a rate of 500 feet per minute.

Part A

Write an equation in slope-intercept form that shows the relationship between the number of minutes, *x*, and the height of the plane, *y*.

_____

Part B

On the grid, draw a graph of the equation that represents this situation.

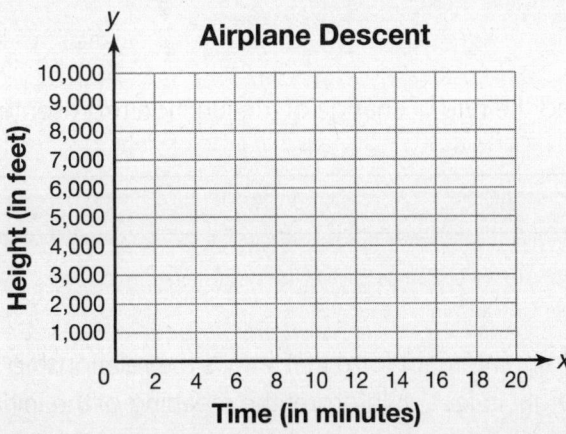

Airplane Descent

Height (in feet) / Time (in minutes)

7 A manufacturer of screened sweatshirts includes a shipping charge of $5.99 on all online orders. Customers also pay 2.5% tax on their purchases. There is a linear relationship between c, the cost of the items purchased, and t, the total cost including shipping and tax. Select True or False for each statement about the function that represents the relationship between c and t.

A. The function can be represented by the equation $c = 0.025t + 5.99$. ○ True ○ False

B. The function can be represented by the equation $t = 1.025c + 5.99$. ○ True ○ False

C. The initial value of the function is 0.025. ○ True ○ False

D. The initial value of the function is $5.99. ○ True ○ False

E. The rate of change is 2.5%. ○ True ○ False

8 The graph shows the height of a balloon during the first 30 seconds after it is released.

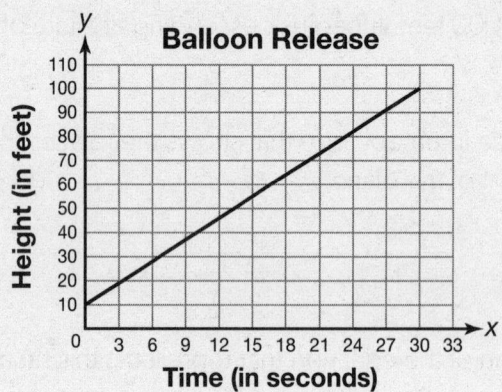

Part A

Find the initial value and the rate of change of the function represented by the graph.

The initial value is _____.

The rate of change is _____.

Part B

Write an equation in slope-intercept form that shows the relationship between the number of seconds, x, and the height in feet, y. Interpret the meaning of the initial value and the rate of change in terms of the situation.

_____

_____

Describing Functional Relationships from Graphs

① GETTING THE IDEA

The graph of a **linear function** is a line. If the line rises from left to right, the function is said to be an increasing function. If it falls from left to right, the function is said to be a decreasing function.

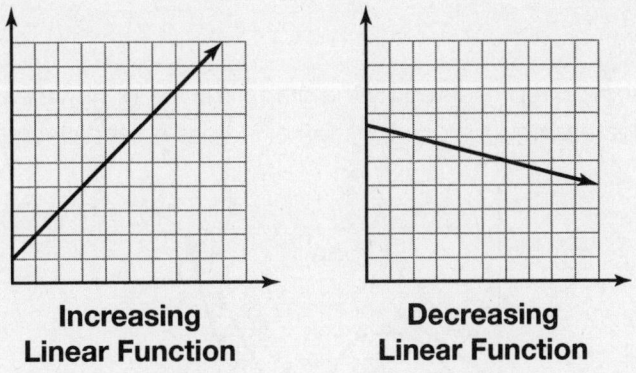

Increasing Linear Function

Decreasing Linear Function

The graphs of **nonlinear functions** may be increasing, decreasing, or a combination of increasing and decreasing.

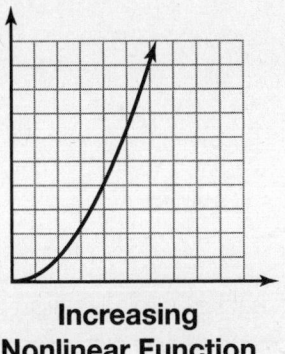

Increasing Nonlinear Function

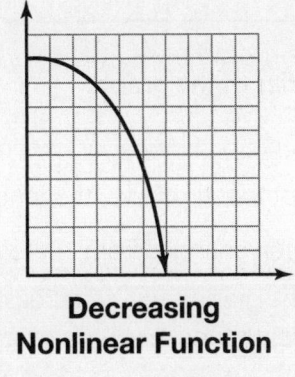

Decreasing Nonlinear Function

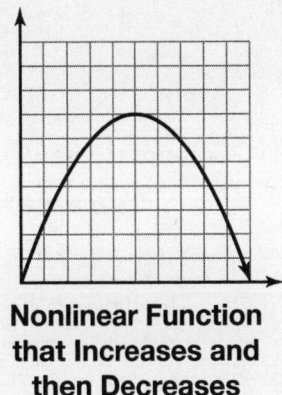

Nonlinear Function that Increases and then Decreases

Example 1

Determine whether the function represented by the graph is linear or nonlinear. Then tell whether the function is increasing or decreasing, or a combination of increasing and decreasing.

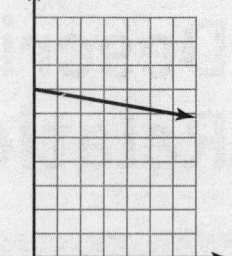

Strategy   Analyze the characteristics of the graph.

Step 1   Determine whether the function is linear or nonlinear.

Since the graph is a straight line, the function is linear.

Step 2   Determine whether the function is increasing or decreasing.

Since the graph falls from left to right, the function is decreasing.

Solution   This function is linear and is decreasing.

Example 2

Determine whether the function represented by the graph is linear or nonlinear. Then tell whether the function is increasing or decreasing, or a combination of increasing and decreasing.

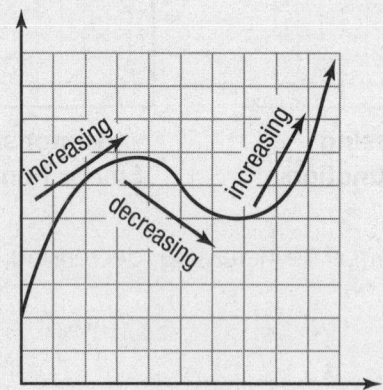

Strategy   Analyze the characteristics of the graph.

Step 1   Determine whether the function is linear or nonlinear.

Since the graph is not a straight line, the function is nonlinear.

Step 2   Determine how the function changes from left to right.

Starting on the left, the graph rises, or increases. It reaches a relative high point and then falls, or decreases. It then reaches a relative low point and increases again.

Solution   The graph represents a nonlinear function that has a combination of increasing and decreasing sections.

Example 3

The graph below shows the height of a log boat during a 3-minute log flume ride.

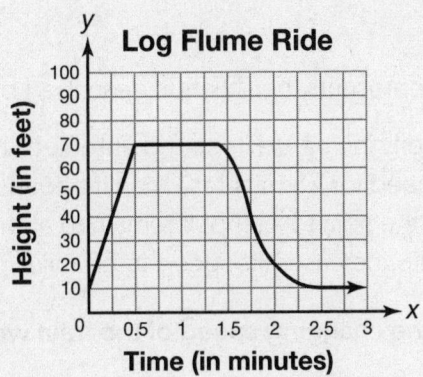

Describe the function represented by the graph.

Strategy Analyze the characteristics of the graph.

Step 1 Determine whether the function is linear or nonlinear.

Since the graph is not a straight line, the function is nonlinear.

Step 2 Determine the points where the function changes.

At first, the graph is a straight line segment that is increasing.

After 0.5 minute, the graph is a horizontal line segment (neither increasing nor decreasing).

At about 1.5 minutes, the graph changes to a curve that decreases.

For the last 0.75 minute, the graph is a horizontal line segment (neither increasing nor decreasing).

Step 3 Determine what the shape of the graph in each section indicates about the situation.

For the first 0.5 minute, the height of the log boat is steadily increasing. The log boat is being pulled to the top of the ride.

For the next minute, the height of the log boat is not changing. The log boat is moving across a level part of the ride.

For about the next 0.75 minute, the graph indicates that the height of the log boat is decreasing. The log boat is going down the water chute.

For the last 0.75 minute of the ride, the graph indicates that the height of the log boat is not changing. The log boat is moving across a level part at the bottom of the ride.

Solution **The graph represents a nonlinear function. The function is increasing when the log boat is being pulled up the ride, is constant as the log boat moves across the top of the ride, is decreasing as the log boat descends down the water chute, and is constant at the end of the ride.**

You can sketch the graph of a real-world function by considering when changes occur and how they affect the situation.

Example 4

Draw a graph of the function that represents the situation described below.

When a train left the station, it steadily increased its speed. It took 10 minutes to reach its top speed of 60 miles per hour. It rode at this speed for 25 minutes. Then it began slowing down to stop at the next station. It took 10 minutes to bring the train to a stop. It remained at the station for 5 minutes and then pulled away. Again, the train steadily increased its speed to 60 miles per hour over a 10-minute period.

Strategy   **Think about how the changing speed of the train will look on a graph.**

Step 1   Set up the graph.

Decide what the x-and y-coordinates represent.

The x-coordinate represents time in minutes and the y-coordinate represents speed in miles per hour. The total time is 60 minutes. The speed ranges from 0 to 60 miles per hour.

Step 2   Determine the characteristics of each part of the trip. Use that information to draw each part of the graph.

The initial speed is 0 miles per hour.

The speed increases steadily over the first 10 minutes to reach a speed of 60 miles per hour.

Since this part of the function is increasing at a constant rate, draw a straight line segment that rises from (0, 0) to (10, 60).

The train travels at a constant speed (60 miles per hour) for 25 minutes.

Since the train's speed does not change during this time, draw this part of the graph as a horizontal line segment from (10, 60) to (35, 60).

The train then slows down steadily over the next 10 minutes until its speed is 0 miles per hour.

Since this part of the function is decreasing at a constant rate, draw a straight line segment that falls from (35, 60) to (45, 0).

The train remains stationary (0 miles per hour) for 5 minutes.

Draw this part of the graph as a horizontal line segment from (45, 0) to (50, 0).

The train then speeds up steadily over the next 10 minutes to reach a speed of 60 miles per hour.

Since this part of the function is increasing at a constant rate, draw a straight line segment that rises from (50, 0) to (60, 60).

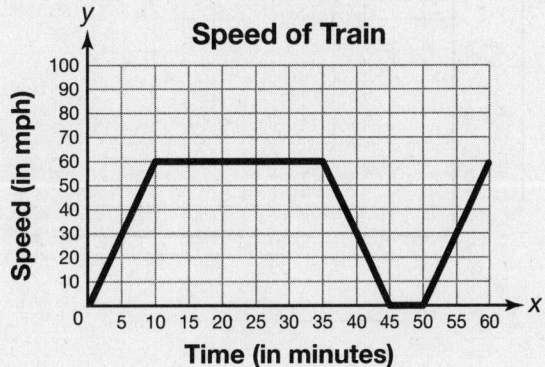

Speed of Train

Solution   The completed graph of the function is shown in Step 2.

Draw a graph of the function that represents the time and distance Felipe was away from home.

Felipe rode his bicycle 1 mile to get from his house to his friend's house. It took him 5 minutes to get there. He stayed at his friend's house for 15 minutes. Then Felipe rode to the library. It took 15 minutes to get to the library, which is 3 miles farther away from his home. He stayed at the library for 5 minutes before riding home. The ride home took 20 minutes.

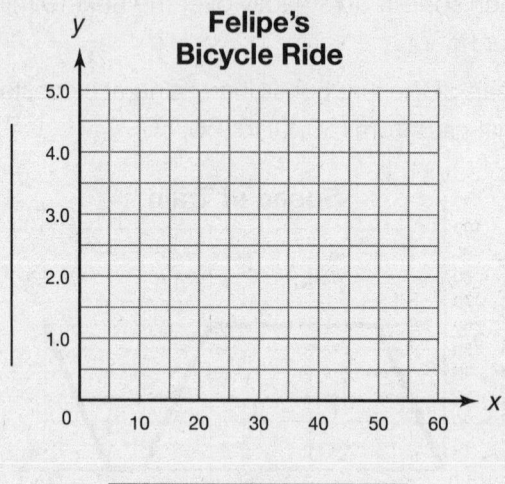

Set up the graph.

The x-coordinates represent _____ and

the y-coordinates represent _____.

The first part of Felipe's bicycle trip took _____ minutes. During this time, he rode to a point

that was _____ mile(s) from his home. Draw a line segment from (0, 0) to (_____, _____) to

represent this part of the trip. This part of the function is _____.

Felipe was at his friend's house for _____ minutes. Since he remained the same distance from

home during this time, draw a _____ line segment to represent this part of

the trip. The line segment ends at (_____, _____). This part of the function is _____.

The next part of Felipe's bicycle trip took _____ minutes. During this time, he rode

to a point that was _____ miles farther from his home. Draw a line segment from

(_____, _____) to (_____, _____) to represent this part of the trip. This part of the

function is _____.

Felipe was at the library for _____ minutes. Since he remained the same distance from home

during this time, draw a _____ line segment ending at (_____, _____) to

represent this part of the trip. This part of the function is _____.

The last part of Felipe's bicycle trip took _____ minutes. During this time, he rode all the way back

home. Draw a line segment from (_____, _____) to (_____, _____) to represent this part

of the trip. This part of the function is _____.

The completed graph of the function is shown above.

1 Select a graph that represents an increasing nonlinear function. Circle all that apply.

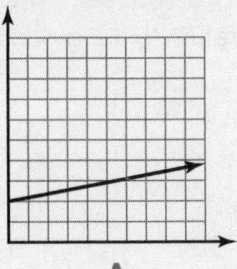

A.

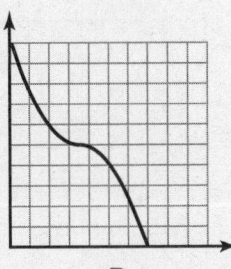

C.

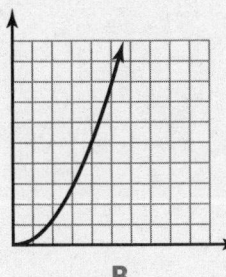

B.

D.

2 The graph shows the price of a mutual fund over a period of 10 days.

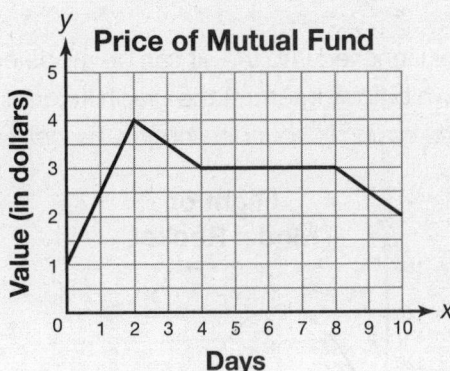

Price of Mutual Fund

Part A

Use words from the box to complete each sentence.

Between $x = 0$ and $x = 2$, the function is _____.

Between $x = 2$ and $x = 4$, the function is _____.

Between $x = 4$ and $x = 8$, the function is _____.

Between $x = 8$ and $x = 10$, the function is _____.

increasing

decreasing

constant

Part B

Is the function represented by the graph linear or nonlinear? Explain your reasoning.

_____

3 A hot air balloon rises steadily for 15 minutes until it is 2,000 feet above the ground. It then flies at this altitude for 30 minutes. Over the next 15 minutes, the balloon drops 500 feet. It flies at this new altitude for 30 minutes. Then the balloon takes 30 minutes to return to the ground.

Draw a graph of the function that represents the situation.

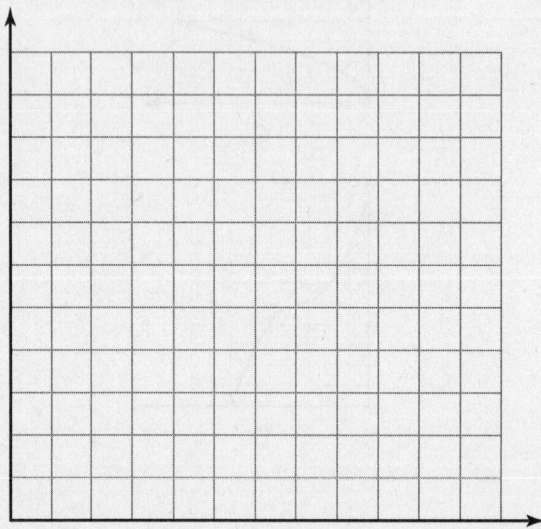

4 The height of a model rocket launched into the air can be modeled by a nonlinear function. A graph of the function is shown below. Interpret the graph in terms of the situation it models. Use the words *increasing* and *decreasing* in your description, as well as specific values from the graph.

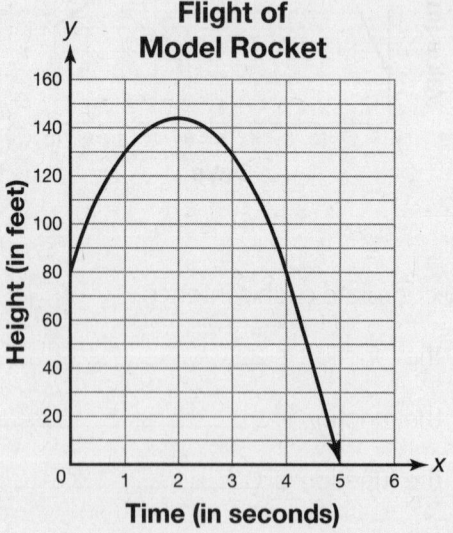

5 Tyrone created a graph to show how he spent the 3 hours between the time he left school and the time he had dinner. Complete the description of the sequence of events represented by the graph.

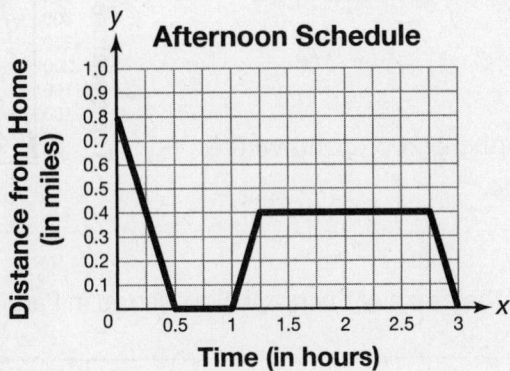

Tyrone left school and walked _____ mile home. He remained at home for _____ minutes. He then walked _____ mile to his friend Ben's house. He and Ben worked on their project for _____ hours, at which time Tyrone left and walked home. The walk home took _____ minutes.

6 Graph a function that has the following characteristics on the grid below:

- It is decreasing for all values of x between 0 and 4.
- It is constant for all values of x between 4 and 7.
- It is increasing for all values of x greater than 7.
- Its graph contains the points (3, 5) and (5, 3).
- A piece of the graph is a curve.

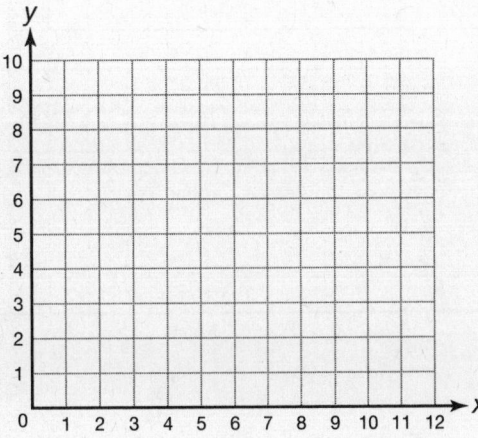

7 Katherine is roasting a large ham in her oven. Partway through the cooking process, she pulls the ham out of the oven to add a glaze. The graph shows the temperature of the oven during the roasting process.

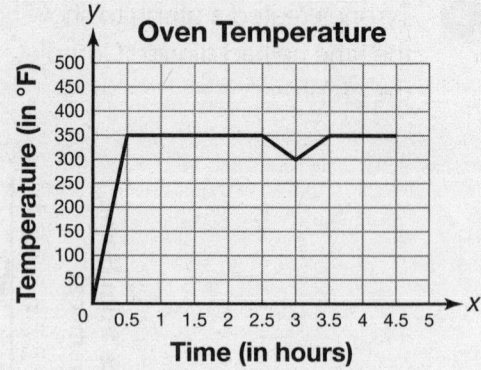

Part A

Circle the part of the graph that represents where the function is decreasing.

Part B

Interpret the meaning of the piece of the graph you circled in Part A.

8 Mrs. Kim plans to run three errands this morning. She leaves the house at 9:00 a.m., drives 4 miles to the post office, drives 5 miles farther to the drugstore, and returns home, stopping at the library along the way, which is only 1 mile from her house. She spends 10 minutes at each stop, and she is home by 10:00 a.m.

Draw the graph of a function that could represent the situation.

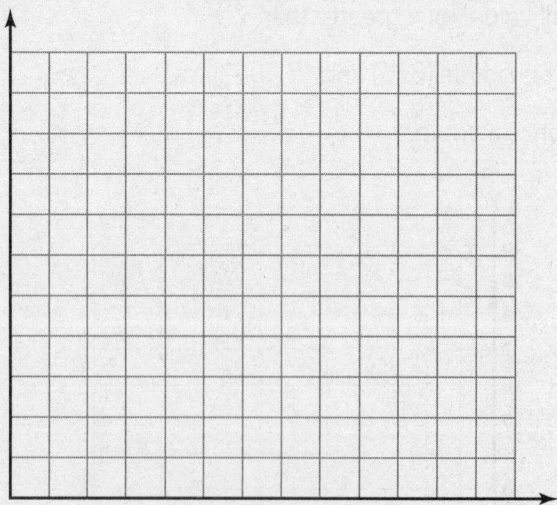

1. Richard and Aiden leave their homes at the same time and walk at a constant speed to a nearby park. Richard's speed is modeled by the equation $y = -0.07x + 1.47$, where y represents the remaining distance to the park and x represents the time in minutes since he left home. The table describes Aiden's speed.

Time Since Leaving Home (in minutes), x	0	9.5	22.5
Distance from the Park (in miles), y	1.35	0.78	0

Part A

Who is walking faster, Richard or Aiden? Explain.

Part B

Will Richard or Aiden arrive at the park first? Explain.

2. A linear function represents Caitlin's income. She earns $35 plus $8 for each item she sells. Determine whether each point is on the graph of her earnings, y, as a function of the number of items sold, x. Write each ordered pair in the correct box.

(7, 91)   (11, 121)   (9, 110)   (4, 67)   (5, 72)   (3, 59)

On the Graph	Not on the Graph

3 For each equation in the table, indicate with an "X" whether the equation is a linear function, nonlinear function, or not a function.

Equation	Linear Function	Nonlinear Function	Not a Function
$y = 2\sqrt{x} + 23$			
$3x + 4y - 18 = 0$			
$x^2 + y^2 = 25$			
$y = \frac{x - 9}{7}$			
$x = 25y - 9$			
$y = 25x$			
$y = 0.5x^2 + 10$			

4 Chan read her book each day after school this week.

- She read 30 pages in 45 minutes on Monday.
- On Tuesday, she read 62 pages in 96 minutes.
- It took her 84 minutes to read 52 pages on Wednesday.
- On Thursday, she read 48 pages in 72 minutes.
- She read 69 pages in 92 minutes on Friday.

Part A

Use the information above to complete the table of values. The inputs are the number of pages Chan read. The outputs are the number of minutes she read.

Chan's Reading

Number of Pages					
Time (in minutes)					

Part B

Is the relation shown in the table a function? Explain your answer.

5 Gavin cut grass for 8 weeks during the summer. He put the money he earned each week into his savings account. The table shows the amount in his savings account after each week.

Gavin's Savings

Week	1	2	3	4	5	6	7	8
Savings (dollars)	81	104	127	150	173	196	219	242

Part A

Gavin saved the same amount each week. Determine the rate at which Gavin saved. Show your work.

_____

Part B

How much money did he have in his savings account before he started adding to it? _____

Part C

Write an equation to model the relationship between the number of weeks Gavin saved and the amount of money in his savings account.

_____

6 Zoe and Nora each have a pail with a small amount of water in it. Each girl slowly begins to add water to her pail. The table describes the cups of water y in Zoe's pail as a linear function of the time x that she spends filling it. The graph describes the cups of water as a function of time that Nora spends filling her pail. Is Zoe or Nora filling her pail at a faster rate? Explain.

Zoe's Pail

x (in minutes)	2	3	4
y (in cups)	5.7	7.5	9.3

Nora's Pail

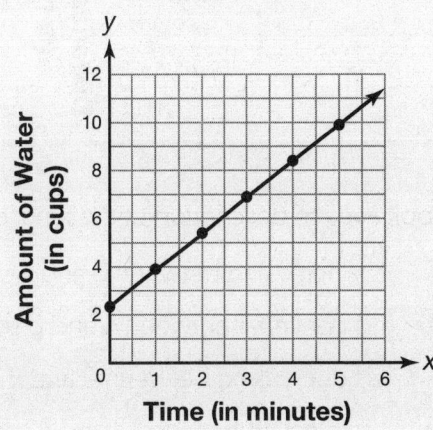

_____

7 The table shows the relationship between time (in minutes) and the number of people who have entered a water park just after it opens. Does the table represent a linear function or a nonlinear function? Explain how you know.

Time (in minutes)	Number of People
2	125
3	197
5	341
7	482
9	626

8 Micah walked at different speeds to a spot 8 meters away and then turned and started back. The graph models his motion.

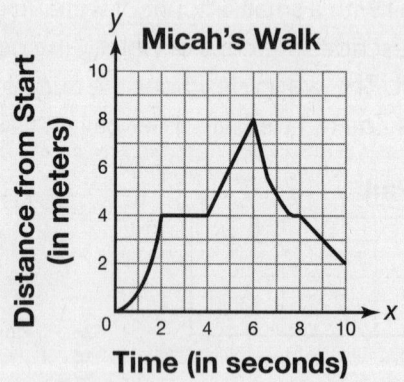

Look at each description of the function. Select True or False for each statement.

A. It is increasing between 0 and 4 seconds. ○ True ○ False

B. It is nonlinear between 4 and 6 seconds. ○ True ○ False

C. It is decreasing between 6 and 8 seconds. ○ True ○ False

D. It is constant between 2 and 4 seconds. ○ True ○ False

E. It is nonlinear between 0 and 2 seconds. ○ True ○ False

F. It is increasing between 8 and 10 seconds. ○ True ○ False

9 An amusement park charges a $15 entrance fee plus $3.25 for each ride.

Part A

Write an equation that represents the situation. Write your answer in slope-intercept form.

Part B

Identify the initial value and the rate of change for the function that represents the situation.

The initial value is _____.

The rate of change is _____.

Part C

How much would it cost to enter the amusement park and ride on seven rides? Show your work.

10 Tristan spends 20 minutes walking 1.2 miles from his home to the library. He stays there for 10 minutes, and then he spends 30 minutes walking 1.3 miles to the park. After watching the ducks there for 15 minutes, he leaves and walks 2.5 miles back to his home in 45 minutes.

Draw the graph of a function that could represent the situation.

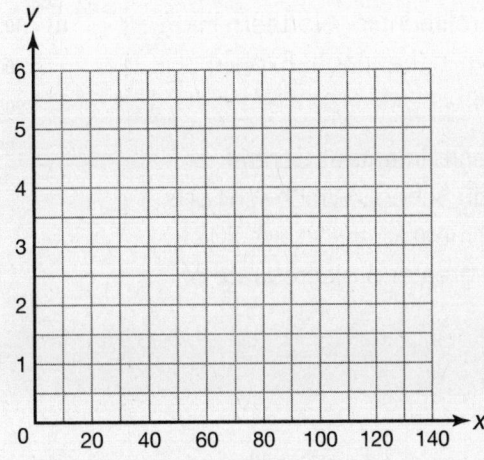

Student Enrollment

The school board will be meeting to analyze projected student enrollments at three high schools in the school district.

Part A The table below shows the projected number of students at Central High School, where $x = 0$ corresponds to the 2020–2021 school year. Determine if the relationship between the two quantities in the table represents a function and explain why or why not.

Projected Enrollment at Central High School

Year, x	0	1	2	3	4
Enrollment, y	880	924	968	1,012	1,056

Part B Find the rate of change in enrollment from each year to the next.

Determine if the relationship is better modeled by a linear function or by a nonlinear function.

Part C Determine if the function is increasing or decreasing over time. Justify your reasoning. Then write an equation, in slope-intercept form, that models the relationship between the two quantities in the table.

Part D The graph to the right shows the projected enrollment at Northern High School, another high school in the same school district as Central High School. On the graph, $x = 0$ corresponds to the 2020–2021 school year. Does the graph represent a linear function or a nonlinear function? Is that function increasing or decreasing?

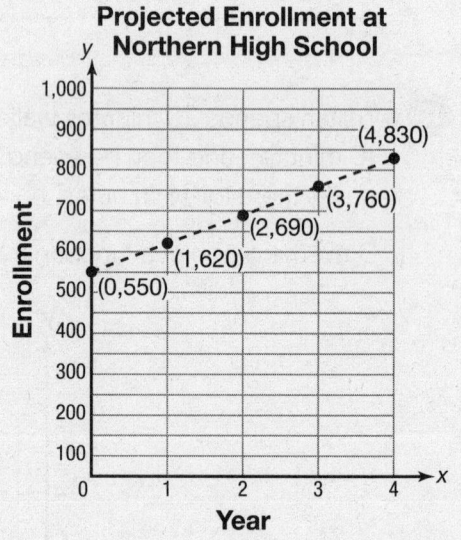

Projected Enrollment at Northern High School

Part E What does the y-intercept of the graph tell you about the number of students at Northern High School?

Estimate the rate of change in enrollment for Northern High School for the school years shown in the graph. Explain how you found your answer.

Part F Compare the projected enrollments at Central High School and at Northern High School. Which school is expected to have a greater enrollment for the 2020–2021 school year? Which school has a greater projected rate of change in enrollment?

DOMAIN 4

Geometry

Understanding Translations

1 GETTING THE IDEA

A **transformation** is a change in the position or size of a geometric figure. The original figure is called the **pre-image**. A figure can be named by a single letter or by the letters at each vertex. After the transformation, the figure is called the **image**. If a vertex of the pre-image is labeled with a letter, such as *A*, the corresponding vertex of the image is labeled with the same letter with a prime symbol, such as *A'*.

A **translation** is a type of transformation in which the pre-image slides to a different location without turning or changing it in any way. The image is **congruent** to the pre-image, which means the figure's size and shape do not change.

Example 1

Select a figure that shows a translation of △*T*. Circle all that apply.

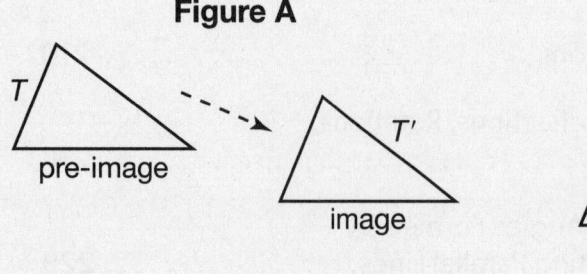

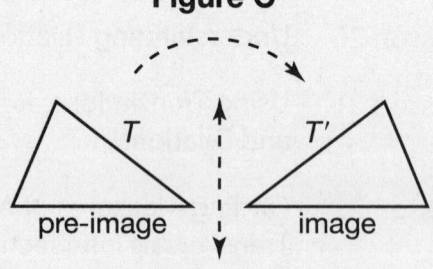

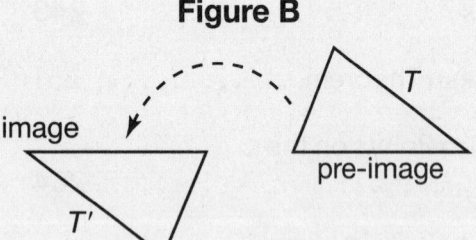

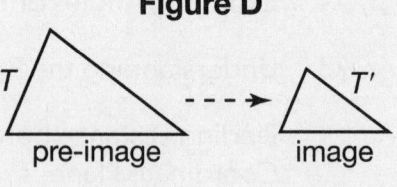

Strategy   Compare each image to the pre-image. Look for a slide to a different location.

Step 1   Compare each image to the pre-image.

In Figure A, a congruent image is formed by sliding triangle *T* to a different location.

In Figure B, a congruent image is formed by turning triangle *T* around a point.

In Figure C, a congruent image is formed by flipping triangle *T* horizontally across a line.

In Figure D, the image is formed by sliding triangle *T* to a different location and by reducing its size. The image is not congruent to the pre-image.

Step 2 Identify which of the four figures shows a translation of the pre-image.

Figure **A** shows a translation because the image slides without changing size or shape.

Solution The image in Figure A is a translation of △*T*.

Example 2

Verify that trapezoid *A'B'C'D'* is a translation of the pre-image *ABCD* by showing that (a) the sides of the image and pre-image are congruent, (b) the angles of the image and pre-image are congruent, and (c) the parallel sides of the pre-image are parallel in the image.

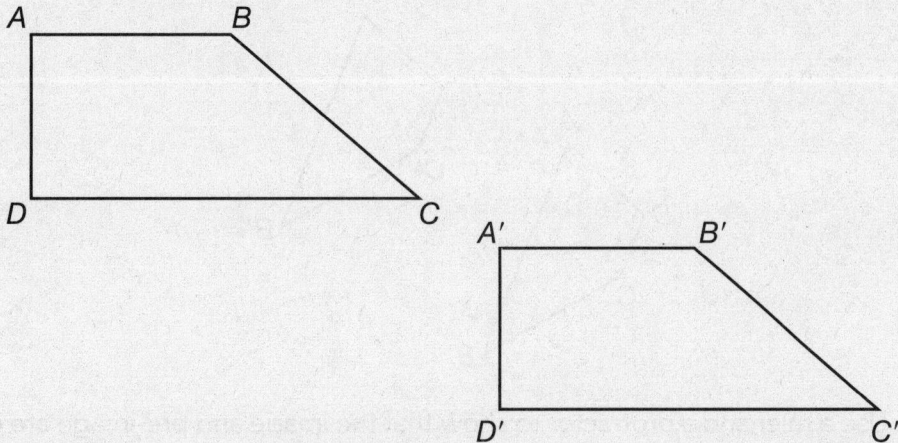

Strategy Use a ruler to show that corresponding sides are congruent. Use a protractor to show that corresponding angles are congruent. Compare corresponding parallel sides of the image and pre-image.

Step 1 Use a ruler to show that corresponding sides of the image and pre-image are congruent.

$AB = A'B' = 2.7$ cm, so $\overline{AB} \cong \overline{A'B'}$

$BC = B'C' = 3.4$ cm, so $\overline{BC} \cong \overline{B'C'}$

$CD = C'D' = 5.2$ cm, so $\overline{CD} \cong \overline{C'D'}$

$DA = D'A' = 2.2$ cm, so $\overline{DA} \cong \overline{D'A'}$

Step 2 Use a protractor to show that corresponding angles of the image and pre-image are congruent.

$m\angle A = m\angle A' = 90°$, so $\angle A \cong \angle A'$

$m\angle B = m\angle B' = 140°$, so $\angle B \cong \angle B'$

$m\angle C = m\angle C' = 40°$, so $\angle C \cong \angle C'$

$m\angle D = m\angle D' = 90°$, so $\angle D \cong \angle D'$

Step 3 Compare the corresponding parallel sides of the image and pre-image.

$\overline{AB}$ and $\overline{DC}$ are parallel. They both form right angles with $\overline{AD}$.

$\overline{A'B'}$ and $\overline{D'C'}$ both form right angles with side $\overline{A'D'}$.

$\overline{A'B'}$ and $\overline{D'C'}$ are parallel.

Solution When trapezoid *ABCD* is translated to form trapezoid *A'B'C'D'*, corresponding sides are congruent, corresponding angles are congruent, and corresponding pairs of parallel sides are parallel.

Example 3

Show that the quadrilateral *ABCD* and its image after a translation are congruent.

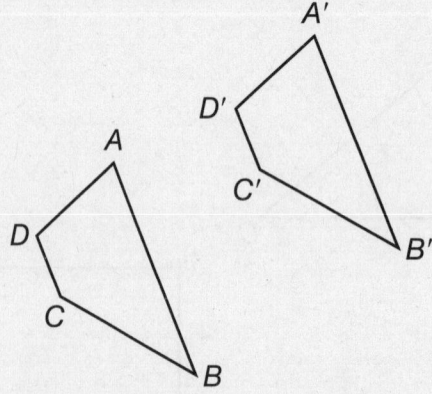

Strategy Use a ruler and a protractor to show that the image and pre-image are congruent after a translation.

Step 1 Use a ruler to show that corresponding sides of the image and pre-image are congruent.

$AB = A'B' = 3$ cm, so $\overline{AB} \cong \overline{A'B'}$

$BC = B'C' = 2.2$ cm, so $\overline{BC} \cong \overline{B'C'}$

$CD = C'D' = 0.9$ cm, so $\overline{CD} \cong \overline{C'D'}$

$DA = D'A' = 1.4$ cm, so $\overline{DA} \cong \overline{D'A'}$

Step 2 Use a protractor to show that corresponding angles of the image and pre-image are congruent.

$m\angle A = m\angle A' = 70°$, so $\angle A \cong \angle A'$

$m\angle B = m\angle B' = 40°$, so $\angle B \cong \angle B'$

$m\angle C = m\angle C' = 140°$, so $\angle C \cong \angle C'$

$m\angle D = m\angle D' = 110°$, so $\angle D \cong \angle D'$

Solution Corresponding sides and corresponding angles of quadrilateral *ABCD* and its image quadrilateral *A'B'C'D'* are congruent; therefore, quadrilaterals *ABCD* and *A'B'C'D'* are congruent.

Example 4

Translate quadrilateral *JKLM* 5 units to the right and 5 units up. Then verify that the pre-image is congruent to the image.

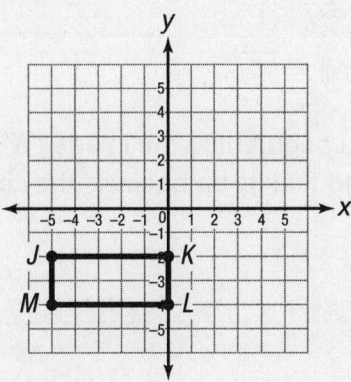

Strategy Record the ordered pairs of the pre-image and image. Use the ordered pairs to find the length of each side.

Step 1 Identify the coordinates of each vertex on the image.

$J(-5, -2)$ $K(0, -2)$ $L(0, -4)$ $M(-5, -4)$

Step 2 Translate the pre-image and record the coordinates of each vertex.

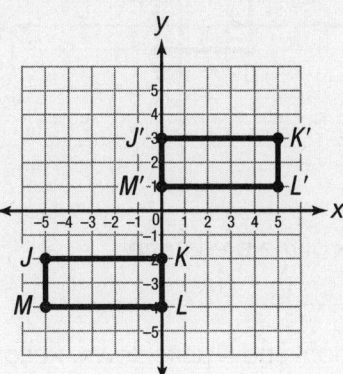

$J'(0, 3)$ $K'(5, 3)$ $L'(5, 1)$ $M'(0, 1)$

Compare the two sets of coordinates. Notice that adding 5 to the *x*- and *y*-coordinates of the pre-image results in the coordinates of the image. A translation of 5 to the right and 5 up means you add 5 to each coordinate.

Step 3 Record the length of each side of both the pre-image and the image.

$JK = J'K' = 5$ units

$KL = K'L' = 2$ units

$LM = L'M' = 5$ units

$MJ = M'J' = 2$ units

Step 4   Compare the corresponding sides.

Since $JK = J'K'$, $\overline{JK} \cong \overline{J'K'}$.

Since $KL = K'L'$, $\overline{KL} \cong \overline{K'L'}$.

Since $LM = L'M'$, $\overline{LM} \cong \overline{L'M'}$.

Since $MJ = M'J'$, $\overline{MJ} \cong \overline{M'J'}$.

Solution   Quadrilateral *JKLM* is *congruent* to the image *J′K′L′M′* formed by a translation 5 units to the right and 5 units up because the corresponding sides are congruent.

 COACHED EXAMPLE

Translate rectangle *WXYZ* 2 units to the right and 4 units down. Then verify that the image is congruent to the pre-image.

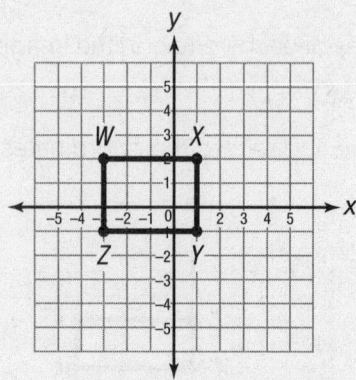

Record the coordinates of each vertex of the pre-image.

W(_____, _____)   X(_____, _____)   Y(_____, _____)   Z(_____, _____)

Translate the rectangle 2 units to the right and 4 units down. Record the coordinates of each vertex of the image.

W′(_____, _____)   X′(_____, _____)   Y′(_____, _____)   Z′(_____, _____)

Use the coordinates to calculate the length of each side of the pre-image and image.

WX = _____ = _____ units   YZ = _____ = _____ units

XY = _____ = _____ units   ZW = _____ = _____ units

Write a congruency statement for each pair of corresponding sides:

_____ ≅ _____   _____ ≅ _____

_____ ≅ _____   _____ ≅ _____

Since corresponding sides are congruent after a translation of _____ units to the right and _____ units down, _____ ≅ _____.

1 Chandra rearranged the furniture in a small room. The room has the shape of a square 8 feet wide and 8 feet long. The grid shows the old location of a table and the new location where Chandra moved it. Circle numbers and words to describe the translation of the table.

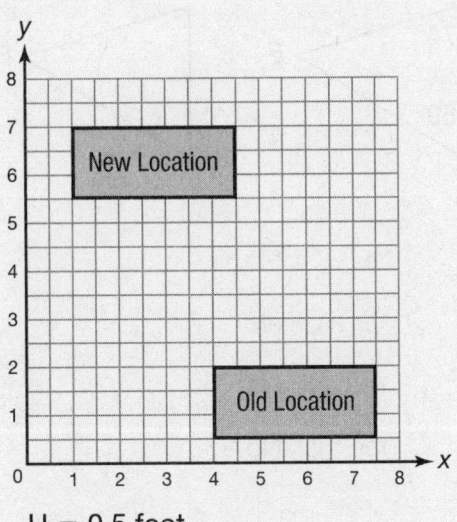

H = 0.5 foot

The table was translated

3
4.5
5
6
7
10

feet to the

right
left

and then

3
4.5
5
6
7
10

feet

down
up

.

2 The vertices of △WXY have the coordinates (2, −4), (9, 1), and (6, 5). Select the coordinates of the vertices of the image of △WXY by translating it 7 units left and 9 units down. Circle all that apply.

A. (−1, 5)   **D.** (16, 10)

B. (2, −8)   **E.** (−5, −13)

C. (9, −8)   **F.** (−1, −4)

3 The figure shows a translation of △*DEF* to △*D'E'F'*. Decide whether you can determine the following from the figure showing the translation. Select Yes or No.

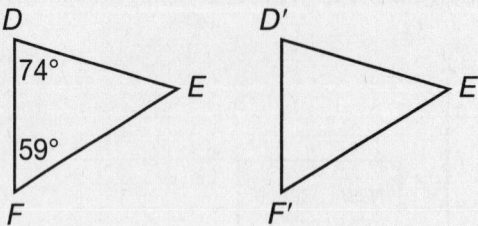

A. ∠*D'* = 180° − 74°   ○ Yes ○ No

B. $\overline{EF} \cong \overline{E'F'}$ ○ Yes ○ No

C. ∠*F'* = 59°   ○ Yes ○ No

D. $\overline{E'F'} \cong \overline{DF}$ ○ Yes ○ No

4 The figure below shows a logo that Jana is designing for an art project. First she drew a star on a grid. She then translated it to produce a shadow behind the original star. Describe the translation that Jana used for the shadow star.

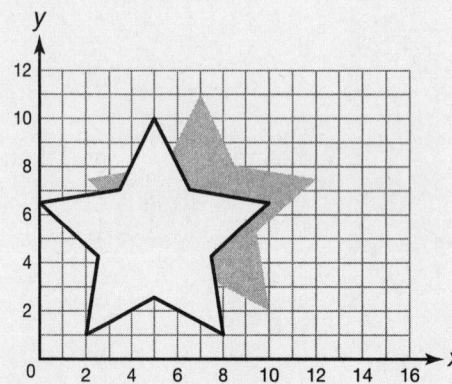

5 Students in a class were instructed to draw a triangle on a grid and then translate it to produce a congruent triangle. The figure shows the triangles and images that three students drew. Did each student draw a congruent translated image? Select Yes or No.

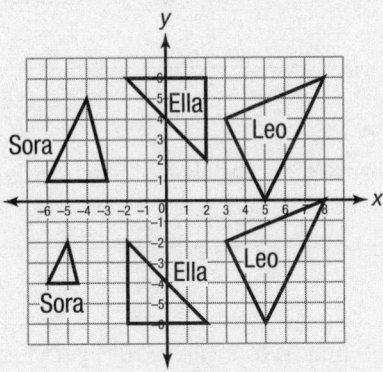

A. Sora   ○ Yes   ○ No

B. Ella   ○ Yes   ○ No

C. Leo   ○ Yes   ○ No

6 The diagram shows the layout and shape of various exhibits at a zoo.

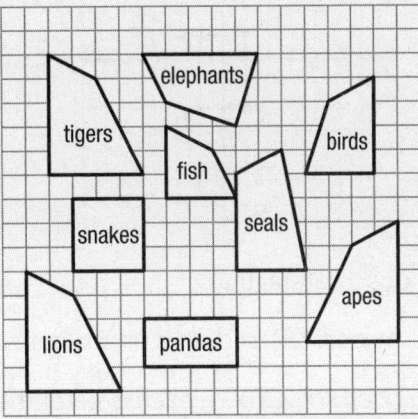

Part A

Which exhibit has a shape that is a translation of the lions' exhibit shape?

_____

Part B

Describe the translation.

_____

7 The coordinates of the vertices of a rectangle are W(3, 0), X(3, 7), Y(2,7), and Z(2, 0).

Part A

Describe the translation needed for the image of the rectangle to have W' at point (−5, 6).

_____

Part B

Write the coordinates for the remaining vertices of the translated rectangle.

_____

Part C

Verify that the translation for the image triangle would produce $\overline{WX} \cong \overline{W'X'}$.

_____

8 The figure shows quadrilateral *PQRS*.

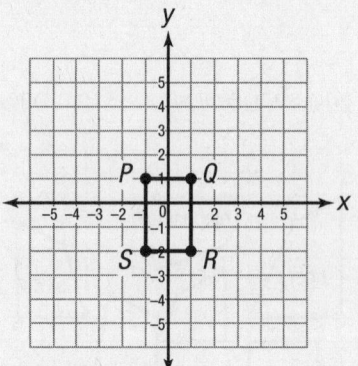

Describe a translation of this quadrilateral that:

• uses as few movements as possible and uses only whole numbers of units.

• results in an image with coordinates (x, y) each greater than 0.

Use words or numbers to justify your answer.

LESSON 18

8.G.1.a, 8.G.1.b, 8.G.1.c, 8.G.2, 8.G.3

Understanding Reflections

1 GETTING THE IDEA

A **reflection** is a type of transformation in which you flip a figure across a line called the **line of reflection**. The starting figure is called the **pre-image**, and the figure after the reflection is called the **image**. The names of the points in the images of a transformation are shown using a prime symbol (′).

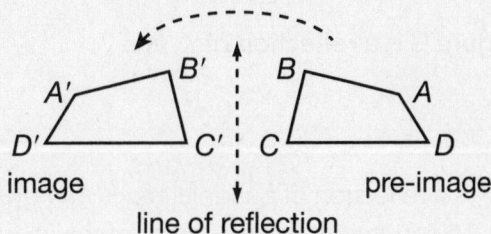

The image formed by a reflection is **congruent** to the pre-image because the figure's size and shape do not change. Unlike other types of transformations, a reflection forms a mirror image, so the figures are congruent and the same distance from the line of reflection.

Example 1

Which figure shows the reflected image of a triangle?

Figure A

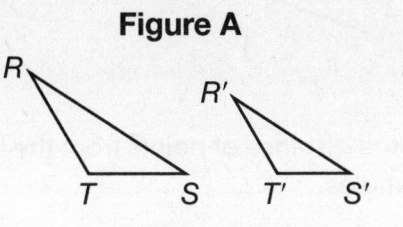

Figure C

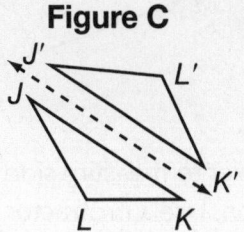

Figure B

Figure D

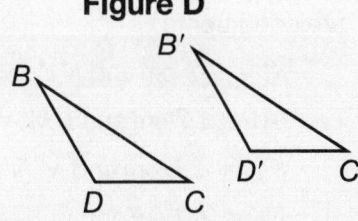

Strategy   Compare each image to the pre-image. Look for a mirror image.

Step 1   Compare each image to the pre-image.

In Figure A, the image is formed by sliding △RST to a different location and by reducing its size. The image is not congruent to the pre-image.

In Figure B, a congruent image is formed by turning △LMN around a point.

In Figure C, a congruent image is formed by flipping △JKL over a line.

In Figure D, the image is formed by sliding △BCD to a different location. The image is congruent to the pre-image.

Step 2   Identify which of the four figures shows a reflection of the pre-image.

Figure **C** shows a reflection because the pre-image flips across a line of reflection to form a congruent mirror image.

Solution   The image in Figure C is a reflection of △ JKL.

Example 2

Verify that quadrilateral K′L′M′N′ is a reflection of quadrilateral KLMN by showing that (a) the sides of the image and the pre-image are congruent, (b) the angles of the image and the pre-image are congruent, and (c) corresponding vertices are the same distance from the line of reflection.

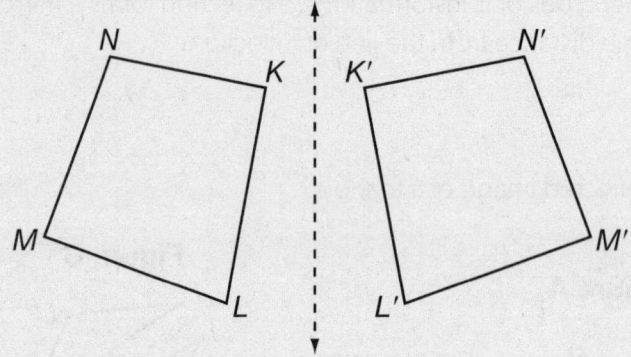

Strategy   **Use a ruler to measure side lengths and the distance of points from the line of reflection. Use a protractor to measure angles.**

Step 1   Use a ruler to show that corresponding sides of the image and the pre-image are congruent.

KL = 2.9 cm and $K'L'$ = 2.9 cm, so $\overline{KL} \cong \overline{K'L'}$

LM = 2.7 cm and $L'M'$ = 2.7 cm, so $\overline{LM} \cong \overline{L'M'}$

MN = 2.6 cm and $M'N'$ = 2.6 cm, so $\overline{MN} \cong \overline{M'N'}$

NK = 2.2 cm and $N'K'$ = 2.2 cm, so $\overline{NK} \cong \overline{N'K'}$

Step 2 Use a protractor to show that corresponding angles of the image and the pre-image are congruent.

$m\angle K = m\angle K' = 90°$, so $\angle K \cong \angle K'$

$m\angle L = m\angle L' = 82°$, so $\angle L \cong \angle L'$

$m\angle M = m\angle M' = 88°$, so $\angle M \cong \angle M'$

$m\angle N = m\angle N' = 100°$, so $\angle N \cong \angle N'$

Step 3 Use a ruler to show that corresponding vertices of the image and the pre-image are the same distance from the line of reflection.

Draw a line segment from each vertex of quadrilateral *KLMN* to the corresponding vertex of quadrilateral *K'L'M'N'*. Then measure the distance from each vertex to the line of reflection.

distance from point *K* to the line = distance from point *K'* to the line = 0.7 cm

distance from point *L* to the line = distance from point *L'* to the line = 1.2 cm

distance from point *M* to the line = distance from point *M'* to the line = 3.7 cm

distance from point *N* to the line = distance from point *N'* to the line = 2.8 cm

Since corresponding vertices of the image and the pre-image are the same distance from the line of reflection, the image and the pre-image are congruent.

Solution Since corresponding sides are congruent, corresponding angles are congruent, and corresponding vertices are the same distance from the line of reflection, quadrilateral *K'L'M'N'* is a reflection of quadrilateral *KLMN*.

Example 3

Show that quadrilateral *EFGH* and its image after a reflection, quadrilateral *E'F'G'H'*, are congruent.

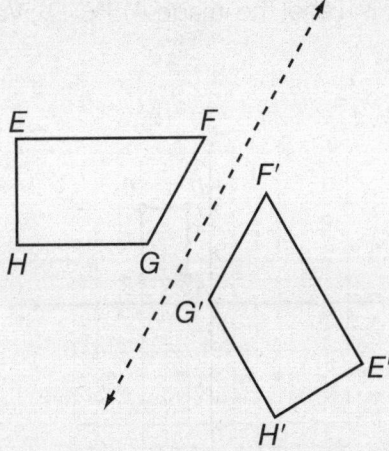

Strategy Use a ruler to measure side lengths and compare. Use a protractor to measure angles and compare.

Step 1 Use a ruler to show that corresponding sides of the image and the pre-image are congruent.

$EF = E'F' = 2.6$ cm, so $\overline{EF} \cong \overline{E'F'}$

$FG = F'G' = 1.6$ cm, so $\overline{FG} \cong \overline{F'G'}$

$GH = G'H' = 1.7$ cm, so $\overline{GH} \cong \overline{G'H'}$

$HE = H'E' = 1.4$ cm, so $\overline{HE} \cong \overline{H'E'}$

Step 2 Use a protractor to show that corresponding angles of the image and the pre-image are congruent.

$m\angle E = m\angle E' = 90°$, so $\angle E \cong \angle E'$

$m\angle F = m\angle F' = 60°$, so $\angle F \cong \angle F'$

$m\angle G = m\angle G' = 120°$, so $\angle G \cong \angle G'$

$m\angle H = m\angle H' = 90°$, so $\angle H \cong \angle H'$

Step 3 Use a ruler to show that corresponding vertices of the image and the pre-image are the same distance from the line of reflection.

distance from point E to the line = distance from point E' to the line = 2.8 cm

distance from point F to the line = distance from point F' to the line = 0.5 cm

distance from point G to the line = distance from point G' to the line = 0.6 cm

distance from point H to the line = distance from point H' to the line = 2.1 cm

Solution Quadrilateral *EFGH* and its image quadrilateral *E'F'G'H'* are congruent because their corresponding sides and angles are congruent and corresponding vertices are the same distance from the line of reflection.

Example 4

Reflect rectangle *ABCD* over the *y*-axis. Label the image *A'B'C'D'*. Verify that pre-image *ABCD* and image *A'B'C'D'* are congruent.

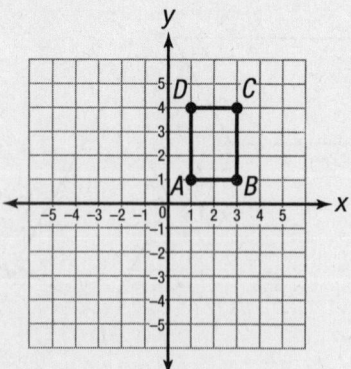

Strategy Find the ordered pairs for the vertices of *A'B'C'D'*. Then use the ordered pairs to find side lengths and compare.

Step 1   Determine the coordinates of each vertex on the pre-image.

         $A(1, 1)$ $B(3, 1)$ $C(3, 4)$ $D(1, 4)$

Step 2   Reflect *ABCD* over the *y*-axis, and record the coordinates of the image.

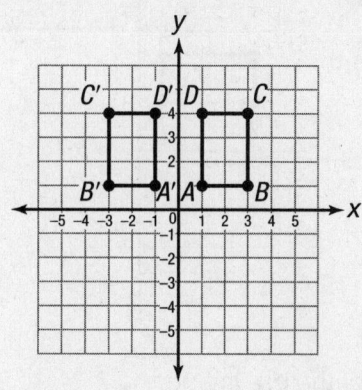

         $A'(-1, 1)$ $B'(-3, 1)$ $C'(-3, 4)$ $D'(-1, 4)$

Notice that the *y*-coordinates stayed the same. Only the sign on the *x*-coordinates changed.

Step 3   Find the lengths of each side and compare.

         $AB = A'B' = CD = C'D' = 2$ units

         $BC = B'C' = DA = D'A' = 3$ units

         Corresponding sides are congruent.

Step 4   Find the measure of each angle and compare.

         All of the angles in rectangles *ABCD* and *A'B'C'D'* are right angles. Corresponding angles are congruent.

Solution   The ordered pairs for the image *A'B'C'D'* are $A'(-1, 1)$, $B'(-3, 1)$, $C'(-3, 4)$, and $D'(-1, 4)$. Corresponding sides and angles are congruent, so the pre-image and image are congruent.

Reflect rectangle *JKLM* over the *x*-axis. Then verify that the image is congruent to the pre-image.

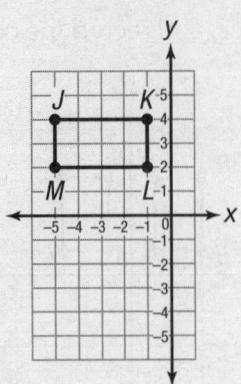

Write the coordinates of each vertex of the pre-image.

J(_____, _____)   K(_____, _____)   L(_____, _____)   M(_____, _____)

Reflect rectangle *JKLM* over the *x*-axis, and record the coordinates of each vertex of the image.

J'(_____, _____)   K'(_____, _____)   L'(_____, _____)   M'(_____, _____)

Find the lengths of each side, and compare.

JK = _____ = _____ units

KL = _____ = _____ units

LM = _____ = _____ units

MJ = _____ = _____ units

Corresponding sides are _____.

Compare the measures of corresponding angles.

All angles are _____ angles, so corresponding angles are _____.

The pre-image and image are congruent because _____.

1 The figure shows quadrilateral *ABCD* reflected over the dashed line to produce quadrilateral *A'B'C'D'*. Based on this reflection, complete each statement.

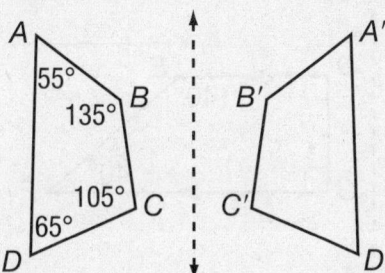

m∠*D'* = _____   m∠*B'* = _____

$\overline{AB}$ ≅ _____ $\overline{B'C'}$ ≅ _____

2 What are the coordinates of each vertex of the image *A'B'C'D'* if quadrilateral *ABCD* is reflected over the *x*-axis or the *y*-axis?

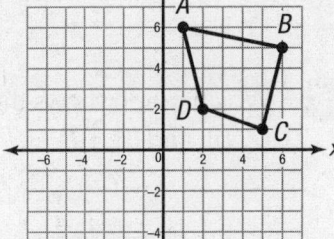

Reflected over the *x*-axis:

A': (_____, _____)

B': (_____, _____)

C': (_____, _____)

D': (_____, _____)

Reflected over the *y*-axis:

A': (_____, _____)

B': (_____, _____)

C': (_____, _____)

D': (_____, _____)

3 Renee created the following four figures to use as designs on wallpaper. Select the design(s) that shows a reflection over the dashed line. Circle all that apply.

A.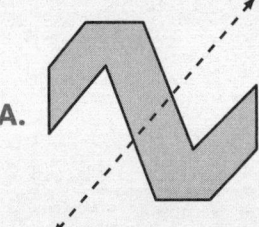

C.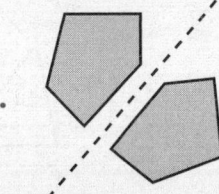

B.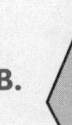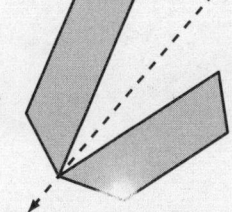

D.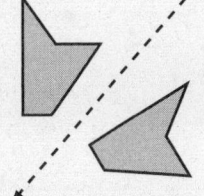

4 Which statements correctly describe the image formed if trapezoid *DEFG* is reflected over the dashed line shown? Circle all that apply.

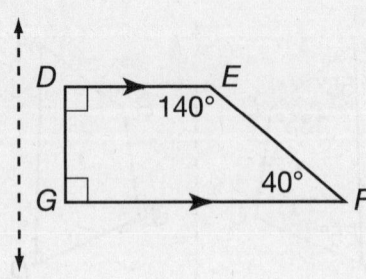

A. $\overline{D'E'} \cong \overline{F'G'}$

B. $\angle F'$ is a right angle.

C. $m\angle E' = 140°$

D. $\overline{E'F'}$ is parallel to $\overline{EF}$.

E. $\overline{F'G'}$ is parallel to $\overline{D'E'}$.

5 Which graph shows the reflection over the *y*-axis of a triangle with vertices at coordinates (1, 1), (2, 6), and (6, 1)?

A.
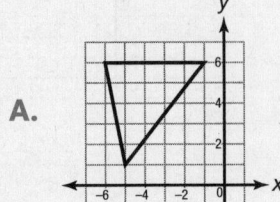

C.
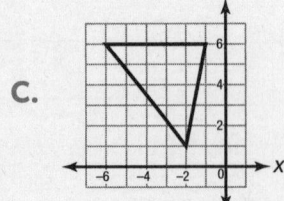

B.
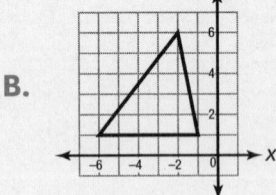

D.
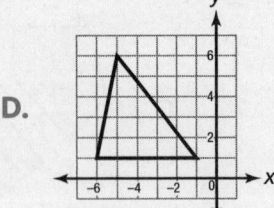

6 Each street sign shown below has a vertical line drawn on it. Select a sign in which the part of the figure on the left of the line is reflected over the line to form the part of the figure on the right of the line. Circle all that apply.

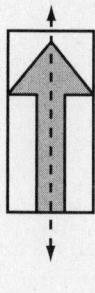 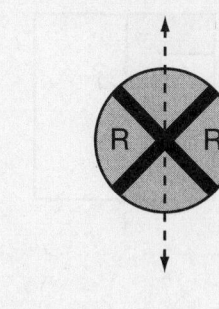  

   A.   **B.**   **C.**   **D.**

7 The vertices of a quadrilateral on a coordinate plane are: $A(3, -1)$, $B(5, -1)$, $C(5, -5)$, $D(3, -5)$.

Part A

What are the coordinates of each vertex of the image formed if the original quadrilateral is reflected over the *x*-axis? You may use the grid to help you.

$A'($_____, _____$)$ $B'($_____, _____$)$ $C'($_____, _____$)$ $D'($_____, _____$)$

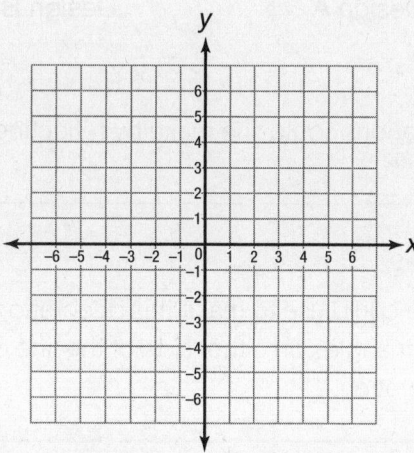

Part B

Verify that each side of the image is congruent to the corresponding side of the pre-image. Record the lengths of the corresponding sides.

8 Kim sews designs for a quilt by reflecting an image in different ways. The figures below show the pre-image and the line of reflection. Draw the image that Kim can produce by each reflection.

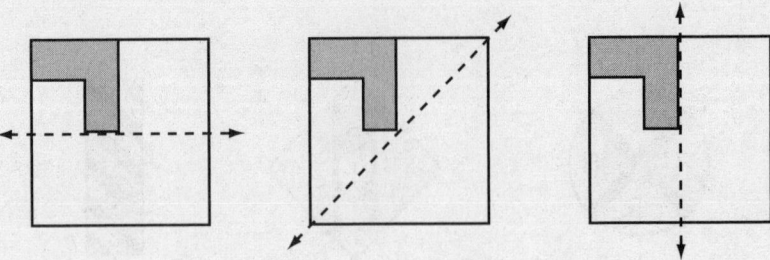

9 The figure shows two designs that Leila used in stained glass decorations. The shaded area shows the starting shape for each decoration.

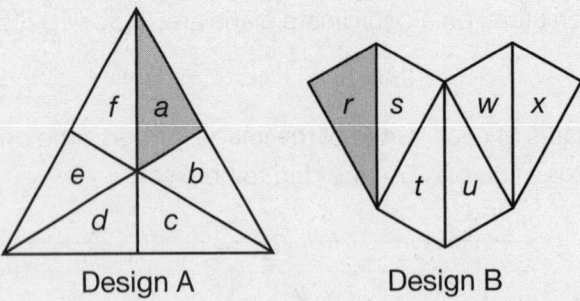

Design A   Design B

Part A

Which one of the two decorations could she make by reflecting the starting triangle five times?

_____

Part B

Describe five reflections Leila could use to make this decoration. In your answer, use the letters on the figure to indicate the triangles on either side of the line of reflection that the artist could use for each part of the decoration.

10 The figure shows quadrilateral *KLMN* on a coordinate grid. $\overline{KL}$ is parallel to $\overline{NM}$. Quadrilateral *KLMN* is reflected over the *y*-axis. Select True or False for each statement about the image formed by the reflection.

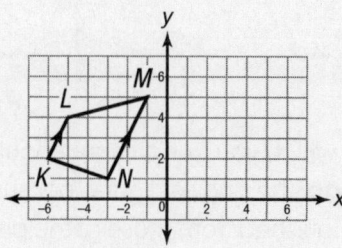

A. $\overline{K'L'}$ will be parallel to $\overline{N'M'}$. ○ True ○ False

B. $\angle K \cong \angle K'$ ○ True ○ False

C. Vertex *K* will be one unit from the *y*-axis. ○ True ○ False

D. $\angle M \cong \angle N'$ ○ True ○ False

E. $\overline{L'M'} \cong \overline{LM}$ ○ True ○ False

11 The figure shows △*ABC*.

Part A

Draw and label the image △*A'B'C'* by reflecting △*ABC* over the *y*-axis.

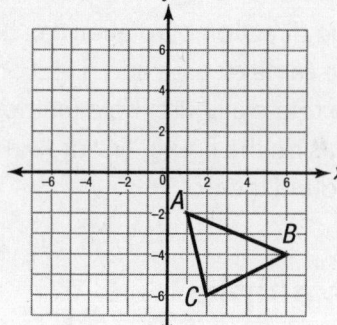

Part B

Draw and label the image △*A"B"C"* by reflecting △*A'B'C'* over the *x*-axis.

Part C

Compare the coordinates of the pre-image with the two images. Describe how the coordinates change when the pre-image is reflected over the *y*-axis. How do they change when the image is reflected over the *x*-axis?

8.G.1.a, 8.G.1.b, 8.G.1.c, 8.G.2, 8.G.3

Understanding Rotations

1 GETTING THE IDEA ─────────────────────────────────────

A **rotation** is a type of transformation in which you turn a figure about a fixed point. The **image** formed by a rotation is **congruent** to the **pre-image**, the original figure, because the figure's size and shape do not change. Each point of the image is distinguished from those of the pre-image by using a prime symbol (').

CLOCKWISE

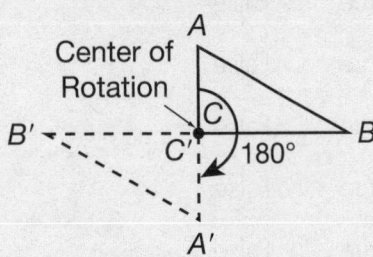

COUNTERCLOCKWISE

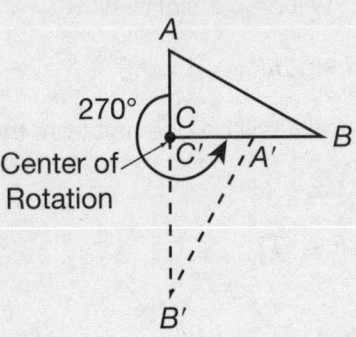

The direction of rotation can be **clockwise** or **counterclockwise**. Each point on the figure is rotated the same degree and direction around the center of rotation, indicated by a dot in the diagram above. To rotate a figure, hold the dot fixed while turning the rest of the figure. If the center of rotation is outside the figure, first draw a segment between any vertex and the dot, and then turn the segment around the dot.

Example 1

Which figure shows a rotation of △*KLM*?

Figure A   **Figure B**   **Figure C**   **Figure D**

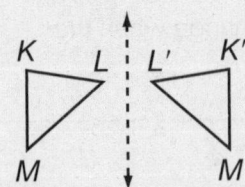   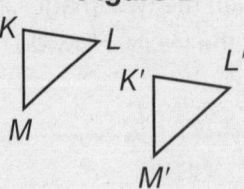   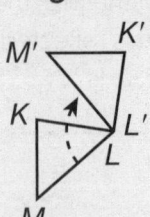   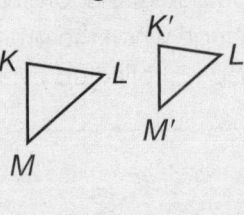

Strategy   Compare each image to the pre-image. Then decide which shows a rotation.

Step 1   Compare each image to the pre-image.

In Figure A, a congruent image is formed by flipping △KLM over a line.

In Figure B, a congruent image is formed by sliding △KLM to a different location.

In Figure C, a congruent image is formed by turning △KLM about a point.

In Figure D, the image is formed by sliding △KLM to a different location and by reducing its size. The shape is the same, but the image is not congruent to the pre-image.

Step 2   Identify which of the four figures shows a rotation of the pre-image.

Figure **C** shows a rotation because the pre-image is turned about a center of rotation at point *L* to form a congruent image.

Solution   The image in Figure C is a rotation of △*KLM*.

Example 2

△*D′E′F′* is formed by a counterclockwise 45° rotation of △*DEF* about the point indicated by a dot. Verify that the rotation produced a congruent image by showing that (a) the sides of the image and the pre-image are congruent and (b) the angles of the image and the pre-image are congruent.

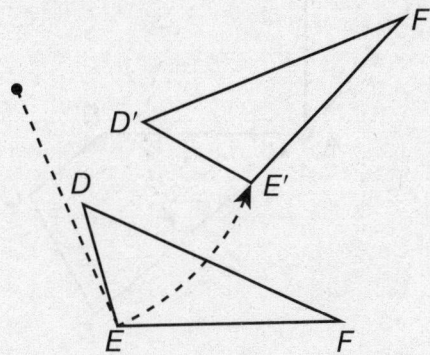

Strategy   Use a ruler to show that the sides are congruent. Use a protractor to show that the angles are congruent.

Step 1   Use a ruler to show that corresponding sides of the image and the pre-image are congruent.

$\overline{DE}$ = 1.7 cm and $\overline{D'E'}$ = 1.7 cm, so $\overline{DE} \cong \overline{D'E'}$

$\overline{EF}$ = 3.1 cm and $\overline{E'F'}$ = 3.1 cm, so $\overline{EF} \cong \overline{E'F'}$

$\overline{FD}$ = 3.8 cm and $\overline{F'D'}$ = 3.8 cm, so $\overline{FD} \cong \overline{F'D'}$

Corresponding sides of △*DEF* and △*D′E′F′* are congruent.

Step 2	Use a protractor to show that corresponding angles of the image and the pre-image are congruent.

$$m\angle D = 50° \text{ and } m\angle D' = 50°, \text{ so } \angle D \cong \angle D'$$

$$m\angle E = 105° \text{ and } m\angle E' = 105°, \text{ so } \angle E \cong \angle E'$$

$$m\angle F = 25° \text{ and } m\angle F' = 25°, \text{ so } \angle F \cong \angle F'$$

Corresponding angles of $\triangle DEF$ and $\triangle D'E'F'$ are congruent.

Solution	$\triangle DEF \cong \triangle D'E'F'$ because corresponding sides are congruent and corresponding angles are congruent.

Example 3

Show that trapezoid *ABCD* and its image after a clockwise 130° rotation about point *A*, trapezoid *A'B'C'D'*, are congruent.

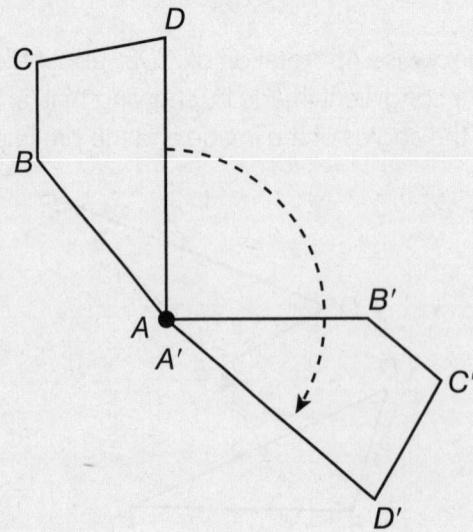

Strategy	**Use a ruler to measure side lengths and compare. Use a protractor to measure angles and compare.**
Step 1	Use a ruler to show that corresponding sides of the image and the pre-image are congruent.

$$\overline{AB} = 2.7 \text{ cm and } \overline{A'B'} = 2.7 \text{ cm, so } \overline{AB} \cong \overline{A'B'}$$

$$\overline{BC} = 1.3 \text{ cm and } \overline{B'C'} = 1.3 \text{ cm, so } \overline{BC} \cong \overline{B'C'}$$

$$\overline{CD} = 1.8 \text{ cm and } \overline{C'D'} = 1.8 \text{ cm, so } \overline{CD} \cong \overline{C'D'}$$

$$\overline{DA} = 3.7 \text{ cm and } \overline{D'A'} = 3.7 \text{ cm, so } \overline{DA} \cong \overline{D'A'}$$

Step 2 Use a protractor to show that corresponding angles of the image and the pre-image are congruent.

$$m\angle A = 40° \text{ and } m\angle A' = 40°, \text{ so } \angle A \cong \angle A'$$

$$m\angle B = 140° \text{ and } m\angle B' = 140°, \text{ so } \angle B \cong \angle B'$$

$$m\angle C = 100° \text{ and } m\angle C' = 100°, \text{ so } \angle C \cong \angle C'$$

$$m\angle D = 80° \text{ and } m\angle D' = 80°, \text{ so } \angle D \cong \angle D'$$

Solution Trapezoid *ABCD* and its image, trapezoid *A'B'C'D'*, are congruent because their corresponding sides and angles are congruent.

You can use coordinates to rotate a figure on the coordinate plane. The table below summarizes how to rotate a figure 90°, 180°, or 270° around the origin.

Rotation about the Origin	90°	180°	270°
Clockwise	$(x, y) \rightarrow (y, -x)$	$(x, y) \rightarrow (-x, -y)$	$(x, y) \rightarrow (-y, x)$
Counterclockwise	$(x, y) \rightarrow (-y, x)$	$(x, y) \rightarrow (-x, -y)$	$(x, y) \rightarrow (y, -x)$

Example 4

Rotate rectangle *QRST* 270° clockwise about the origin. Label the image *Q'R'S'T'*. Verify that the pre-image and the image are congruent.

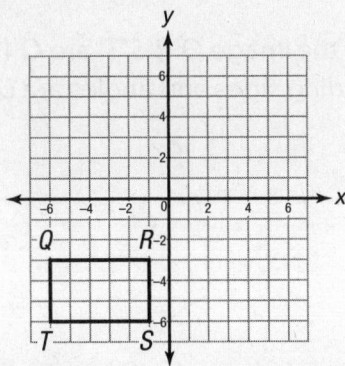

Strategy Determine the coordinates of the vertices of the pre-image and the image. Find the side lengths of the pre-image and the image and compare.

Step 1 Determine the coordinates of each vertex of the pre-image.

$$Q(-6, -3) \qquad R(-1, -3) \qquad S(-1, -6) \qquad T(-6, -6)$$

Step 2 Determine the coordinates of each vertex of the image using the table.

Rotating a figure 270° clockwise about the origin changes (x, y) to $(-y, x)$.

$$Q'(3, -6) \qquad R'(3, -1) \qquad S'(6, -1) \qquad T'(6, -6)$$

Step 3   Draw the rotated figure on the coordinate grid.

Step 4   Find the side lengths of the pre-image and the image and compare.

Notice that for each horizontal side of both rectangles, the *y*-coordinate of both vertices is the same, but the *x*-coordinate is different. For each vertical side, the *x*-coordinate of both vertices is the same, but the *y*-coordinate is different. In each case, the side length is the difference in the coordinates.

$$\overline{QR} = \overline{Q'R'} = 5 \text{ units}$$

$$\overline{RS} = \overline{R'S'} = 3 \text{ units}$$

$$\overline{ST} = \overline{S'T'} = 5 \text{ units}$$

$$\overline{TQ} = \overline{T'Q'} = 3 \text{ units}$$

Step 5   Find the measure of each angle and compare.

All of the angles in rectangles $QRST$ and $Q'R'S'T'$ are right angles. Corresponding angles are congruent.

Solution   The ordered pairs for the image $Q'R'S'T'$ are $Q'(3, -6)$, $R'(3, -1)$, $S'(6, -1)$, and $T'(6, -6)$. Corresponding sides and angles are congruent, so the pre-image and image are congruent.

Rotate rectangle *EFGH* 90° counterclockwise about the origin to form image *E'F'G'H'*.
Then verify that the image and the pre-image are congruent.

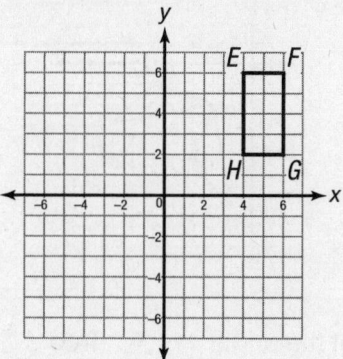

Write the coordinates of each vertex of the pre-image rectangle:

   E(_____, _____)   F(_____, _____)   G(_____, _____)   H(_____, _____)

Rotating a figure 90° counterclockwise about the origin changes (*x, y*) to (_____, _____).

Write the coordinates of each vertex of the rotated figure:

   E'(_____, _____)   F'(_____, _____)   G'(_____, _____)   H'(_____, _____)

Plot each of these four points on the coordinate grid above. Then draw line segments between the points to form the image rectangle.

Find the lengths of each side, and compare.

   $\overline{EF}$ = _____ = _____ units

   $\overline{FG}$ = _____ = _____ units

   $\overline{GH}$ = _____ = _____ units

   $\overline{HE}$ = _____ = _____ units

Compare the measures of corresponding angles.

   All of the angles are _____ angles, so corresponding angles are _____.

The pre-image and the image are congruent because _____

_____.

1 The figure shows △PQR rotated to produce △P′Q′R′. Select True or False for each statement.

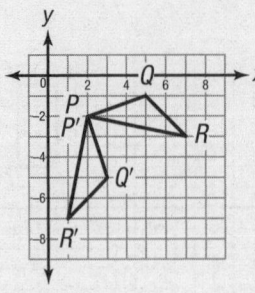

A. △PQR is rotated 45° about the origin. ○ True ○ False

B. ∠Q ≅ ∠Q′ ○ True ○ False

C. The center of rotation is at point P. ○ True ○ False

D. $\overline{PR} \cong \overline{P'R'}$ ○ True ○ False

2 Anton and Kiera both tried to rotate △TUV by 180°. They drew the triangles shown on the grid.

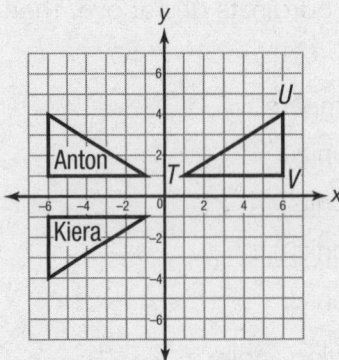

Part A

Who correctly rotated △TUV 180°?

_____

Part B

What are the coordinates of the center of rotation for the 180° rotation?

_____

3   The vertices of a triangle on the coordinate plane are (1, 1), (4, 4), and (3, 1). What are the coordinates of the image triangle produced by each of the following rotations?

Part A

a 90° clockwise rotation about the origin

(_____, _____), (_____, _____), (_____, _____)

Part B

a 270° clockwise rotation about the origin

(_____, _____), (_____, _____), (_____, _____)

Part C

a 180° counterclockwise rotation about the origin

(_____, _____), (_____, _____), (_____, _____)

4   The figure shows the rotation of quadrilateral *CDEF* to form quadrilateral *C'D'E'F'*.

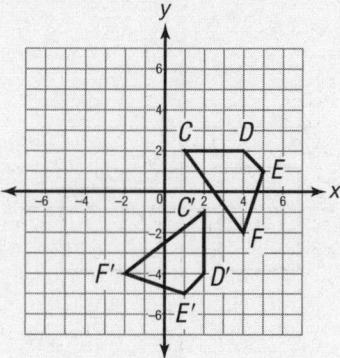

Describe two ways you could rotate quadrilateral *CDEF* to form quadrilateral *C'D'E'F'*.

5 Draw the image of △*JKL* by rotating it 90° clockwise about the origin. What are the coordinates of the image triangle?

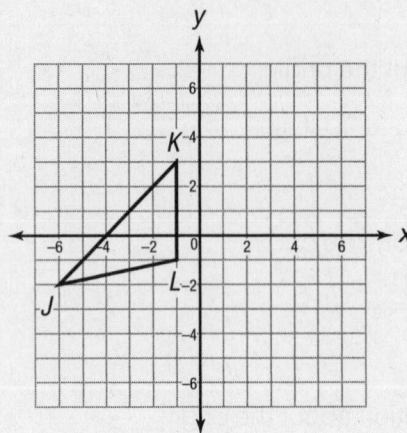

6 The figure shows rectangle *PQRS* and its image after a rotation, rectangle *P'Q'R'S'*.

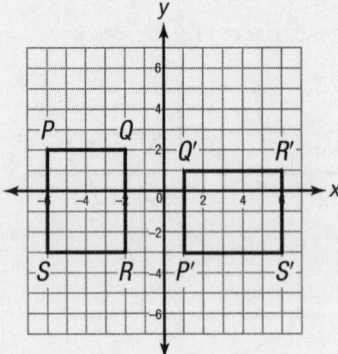

Verify that rectangle *PQRS* ≅ rectangle *P'Q'R'S'*.

7 Use a protractor and a ruler to draw the image formed by rotating △ABC in the figure below 90° clockwise about the center of rotation indicated by the dot.

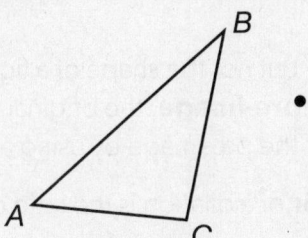

8 The figure shows trapezoid *WXYZ*.

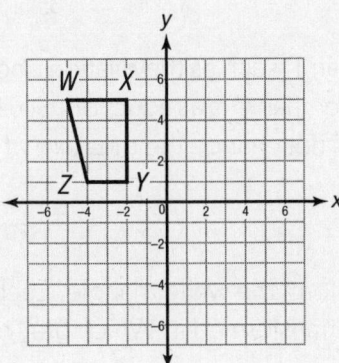

Part A

What are the coordinates of the image *W′X′Y′Z′* produced if *WXYZ* is rotated 90° clockwise about the origin?

W′(_____, _____)   X′(_____, _____)   Y′(_____, _____)   Z′(_____, _____)

Part B

What are the coordinates of a second image produced by rotating *W′X′Y′Z′* 180° clockwise about the origin?

W″(_____, _____)   X″(_____, _____)   Y″(_____, _____)   Z″(_____, _____)

8.G.3

Understanding Dilations

 GETTING THE IDEA

A **dilation** is a **transformation** that changes the size but not the shape of a figure. Therefore, the **image** created by the dilation is not congruent to the **pre-image**, the original figure; it is **similar**. Each point of the image is distinguished from those of the pre-image by using a prime symbol (').

A dilation is defined by a scale factor. The **scale factor** of a dilation is the ratio of a length in the image to the corresponding length in the pre-image. The scale factor of the dilation below is $\frac{3}{2}$, or 1.5.

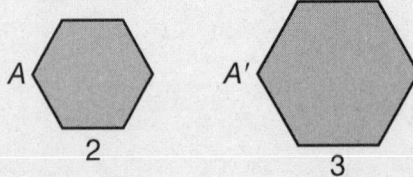

A dilation with a scale factor greater than 1, such as the dilation above, is an enlargement. A dilation with a scale factor less than 1 but greater than 0 is a reduction. So, in general, a dilation either enlarges or reduces the size of a figure but does not change the measure of the angles.

Example 1

Sasha used geometry software to transform the white triangle. Each numbered gray triangle is an image of the white triangle after Sasha transformed it. Which gray triangle is the image of the white triangle after Sasha dilated it?

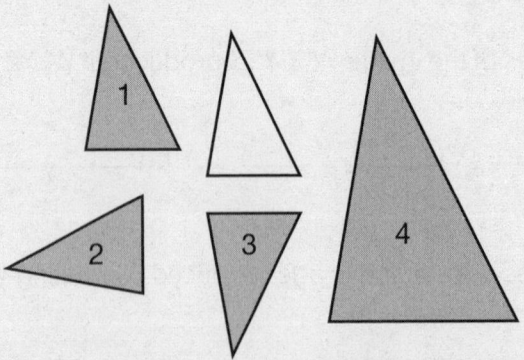

Strategy   Determine which gray triangle is similar to the white triangle.

Step 1   Compare each gray triangle to the white triangle.

Triangle 1 appears to be congruent to the white triangle. Its position has changed by a translation.

Triangle 2 appears to be congruent to the white triangle. Its position has changed by a rotation.

Triangle 3 appears to be congruent to the white triangle. Its position has changed by a reflection.

Triangle 4 appears to be similar not congruent to the white triangle because its size has changed by a dilation. Its position has changed by a translation.

Step 2   Identify which gray triangle is the image of the white triangle after a dilation.

Triangle 4 is larger than the white triangle, so they are similar. Triangle 4 is the image of the white triangle after a dilation.

Solution   **Triangle 4 is the image of the white triangle after a dilation.**

You can dilate a figure in the coordinate plane. To find the image of a figure after a dilation with the origin as the center of dilation, multiply the *x*- and *y*-coordinates of the pre-image by the scale factor.

Example 2

Triangle *ABC* has coordinates $A(2, 4)$, $B(5, 4)$, and $C(2, 8)$. Find the image of $\triangle ABC$ after a dilation with scale factor 2.

Strategy   **Multiply the coordinates of $\triangle ABC$ by the scale factor.**

Step 1   Multiply the coordinates of each vertex by 2.

$$A(2, 4) \rightarrow A'(2 \times 2, 4 \times 2) = A'(4, 8)$$
$$B(5, 4) \rightarrow B'(5 \times 2, 4 \times 2) = B'(10, 8)$$
$$C(2, 8) \rightarrow C'(2 \times 2, 8 \times 2) = C'(4, 16)$$

Step 2   Graph the pre-image and the image.

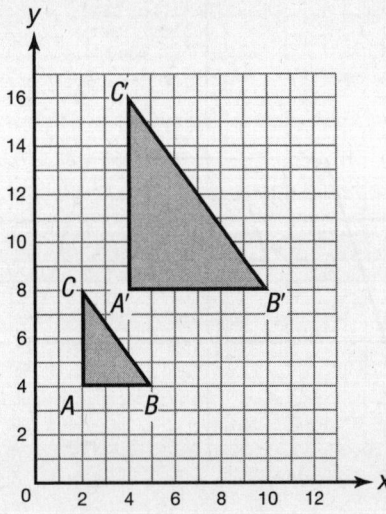

Solution   **The image is $\triangle A'B'C'$, with vertices $A'(4, 8)$, $B'(10, 8)$, and $C'(4, 16)$.**

Example 3

Trapezoid *WXYZ* shows the blueprint for the seats in an outdoor amphitheater. The architect dilates the trapezoid by the factor $\frac{1}{3}$ to show where the sound equipment should be located. Sketch the figure that represents where the sound equipment should be located.

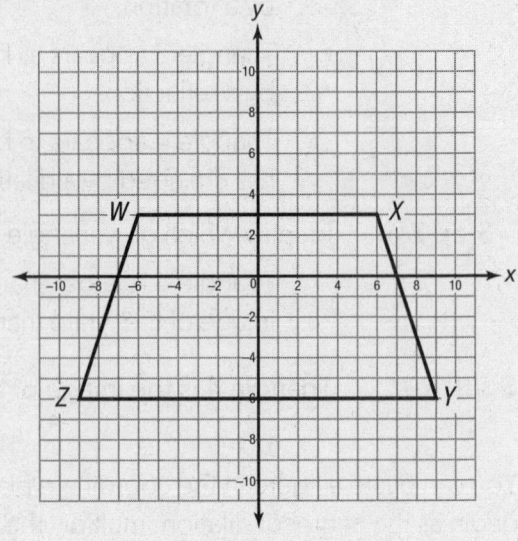

Strategy   Multiply the coordinates of trapezoid *WXYZ* by the scale factor and plot the new coordinates.

Step 1   Multiply the coordinates of each vertex by $\frac{1}{3}$.

$$W(-6, 3) \rightarrow W'\left(-6 \times \tfrac{1}{3}, 3 \times \tfrac{1}{3}\right) = W'(-2, 1)$$

$$X(6, 3) \rightarrow X'\left(6 \times \tfrac{1}{3}, 3 \times \tfrac{1}{3}\right) = X'(2, 1)$$

$$Y(9, -6) \rightarrow Y'\left(9 \times \tfrac{1}{3}, -6 \times \tfrac{1}{3}\right) = Y'(3, -2)$$

$$Z(-9, -6) \rightarrow Z'\left(-9 \times \tfrac{1}{3}, -6 \times \tfrac{1}{3}\right) = Z'(-3, -2)$$

Step 2   Graph the image.

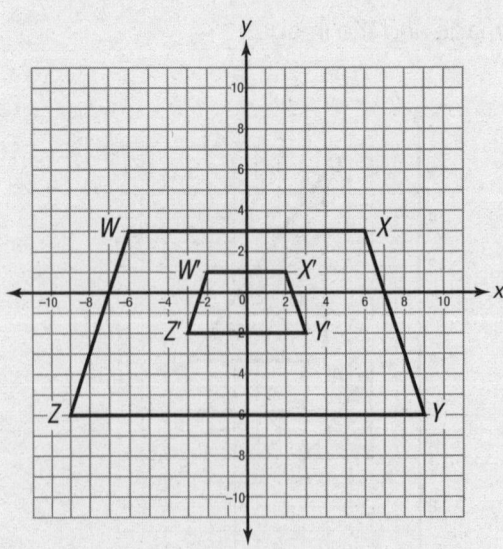

Solution   The sound equipment should be located within trapezoid *W'X'Y'Z'*, with vertices *W'*(−2, 1), *X'*(2, 1), *Y'*(3, −2), and *Z'*(−3, −2).

Find the image of quadrilateral *MNPQ* after dilation with a scale factor of $\frac{3}{2}$.

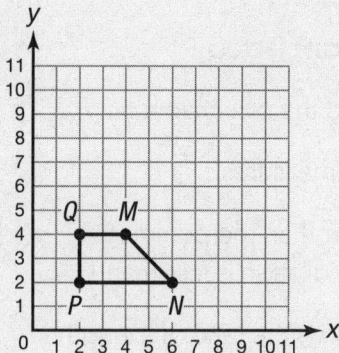

Multiply the coordinates of each vertex by _____.

$M(\underline{\hspace{0.7cm}}, \underline{\hspace{0.7cm}}) \rightarrow M'\left(\underline{\hspace{0.7cm}} \times \frac{3}{2}, \underline{\hspace{0.7cm}} \times \frac{3}{2}\right) = M'(\underline{\hspace{0.7cm}}, \underline{\hspace{0.7cm}})$

$N(\underline{\hspace{0.7cm}}, \underline{\hspace{0.7cm}}) \rightarrow N'\left(\underline{\hspace{0.7cm}} \times \frac{3}{2}, \underline{\hspace{0.7cm}} \times \frac{3}{2}\right) = N'(\underline{\hspace{0.7cm}}, \underline{\hspace{0.7cm}})$

$P(\underline{\hspace{0.7cm}}, \underline{\hspace{0.7cm}}) \rightarrow P'\left(\underline{\hspace{0.7cm}} \times \frac{3}{2}, \underline{\hspace{0.7cm}} \times \frac{3}{2}\right) = P'(\underline{\hspace{0.7cm}}, \underline{\hspace{0.7cm}})$

$Q(\underline{\hspace{0.7cm}}, \underline{\hspace{0.7cm}}) \rightarrow Q'\left(\underline{\hspace{0.7cm}} \times \frac{3}{2}, \underline{\hspace{0.7cm}} \times \frac{3}{2}\right) = Q'(\underline{\hspace{0.7cm}}, \underline{\hspace{0.7cm}})$

Graph the image on the grid above.

The image is _____, **with vertices** _____, _____, _____, **and** _____.

1 Select True or False for each statement.

A. A dilation is defined by a scale factor. ○ True ○ False

B. A dilated image is similar to the pre-image. ○ True ○ False

C. A dilation preserves angle measures. ○ True ○ False

D. If the dilated image is larger than the pre-image, then the scale factor of the dilation is less than 1. ○ True ○ False

E. The scale factor of a dilation is the ratio of a length of a side of the image to the corresponding side length of the pre-image. ○ True ○ False

F. If a dilation reduces the size of a figure, then the scale factor of the dilation must be less than 0. ○ True ○ False

2 Suppose you dilate a figure by the given scale factor. Will the image be a reduction? Select Yes or No.

A. 2 ○ Yes ○ No

B. $\frac{5}{4}$ ○ Yes ○ No

C. $\frac{2}{3}$ ○ Yes ○ No

D. $\frac{3}{4}$ ○ Yes ○ No

E. 1 ○ Yes ○ No

F. $\frac{7}{5}$ ○ Yes ○ No

3 Choose the scale factor or coordinates that make each statement true.

$$T(-3, 7) \times \boxed{\begin{array}{c} \frac{7}{8} \\ \frac{49}{24} \\ \frac{63}{8} \end{array}} \to T'\left(-\frac{21}{8}, \frac{49}{8}\right)$$

$$\boxed{\begin{array}{c} V(8, 9.6) \\ V(10.8, 12.8) \\ V(12.5, 15) \end{array}} \times 0.8 \to V'(10, 12)$$

4 Consider each transformation described below. Is the image after the transformation a reduction of, congruent to, or an enlargement of the pre-image? Write the transformation in the correct box.

Reflection over a horizontal line	Dilation with scale factor 3.5	Rotation 90° about the origin	Translation 4 units up	Dilation with scale factor 1	Dilation with scale factor $\frac{7}{8}$

Reduction of Pre-image	Congruent to Pre-image	Enlargement of Pre-image

5 Point H is a vertex of a rectangle. You are dilating the rectangle by a scale factor of $\frac{3}{5}$. Select numbers from the box so that the following statement is true.

$$H(\underline{\hspace{1cm}}, -5) \rightarrow H'(-3, \underline{\hspace{1cm}})$$

−5
−3
3
5

Consider quadrilateral *EFGH* with vertices $E(-10, 8)$, $F(8, 8)$, $G(10, -6)$, and $H(-6, -10)$.

Part A

Find the coordinates of the image of *EFGH* after a dilation with scale factor $\frac{3}{4}$.

Part B

Graph *EFGH* and its image after a dilation with scale factor $\frac{3}{4}$.

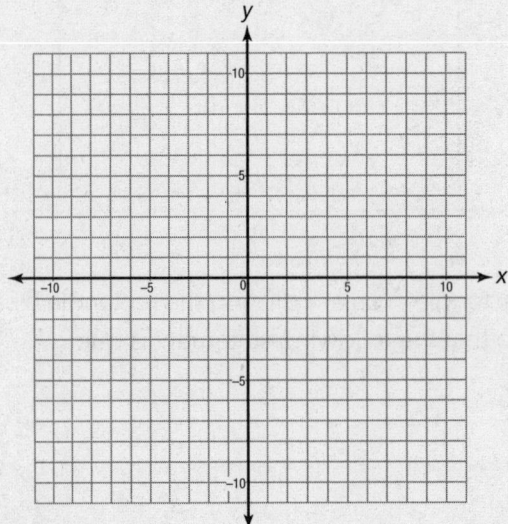

7 A digital photo on the screen of a smartphone is 5 cm wide and 6.5 cm high. After you "pinch" the screen to reduce the size of the photo, the photo is reduced to 3 cm wide by 3.9 cm high. What is the scale factor of the dilation? Explain your reasoning.

8 Your digital sketch of the Math Club's new logo is $1\frac{1}{4}$ inches wide. You need an enlarged copy of the logo for the yearbook. The copy must fit in a space that is $6\frac{1}{2}$ inches wide. What scale factor should you use on the printer to adjust the size of your sketch of the logo if you want it to be as large as possible and still fit on the page? Justify your answer with words and numbers.

9 Consider $\triangle STU$ with vertices $S(0, 0)$, $T(0, 6)$, and $U(8, 0)$.

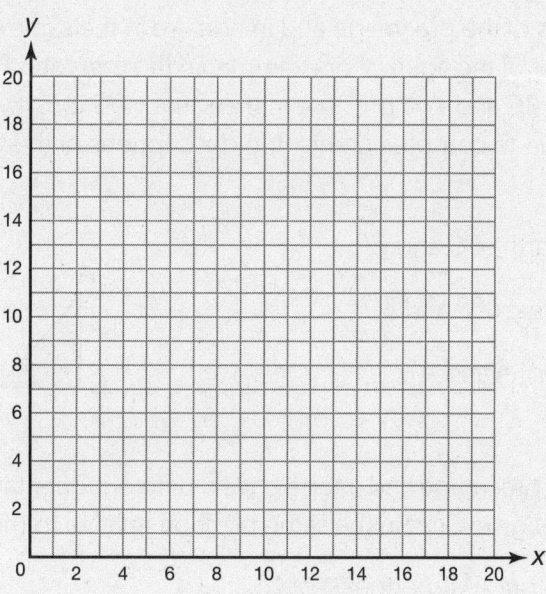

Part A

Graph $\triangle STU$. Draw the image of $\triangle STU$ after a dilation with scale factor 2.5. Label the image $\triangle S'T'U'$.

Part B

What is the relationship between the area of $\triangle STU$ and the area of $\triangle S'T'U'$? Use words and numbers to justify your answer.

8.G.2, 8.G.3, 8.G.4

Using Translations, Reflections, Rotations, and Dilations

A **rigid motion**, such as a translation, reflection, or rotation, changes only the position of a figure. In other words, a rigid motion maps a pre-image to a **congruent** image.

After a translation, the pre-image and the image have the same orientation. Two figures have the same orientation if the vertices of the pre-image and image are in the same position compared to one another or to the center of the figure. For example, in the translation shown below, the corresponding vertices of $\triangle ABC$ and $\triangle A'B'C'$ are in the same position. If you were to describe the positions of the vertices relative to compass points, the descriptions of the vertices for the two figures would be the same.

- A and A' are directly north of C and C'.

- C and C' are directly west of B and B'.

- B and B' are southeast of A and A'.

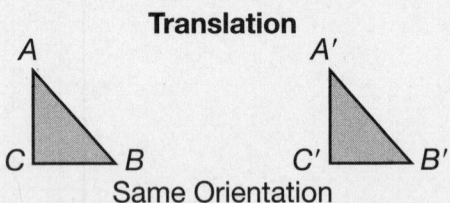

Translation

Same Orientation

When you rotate a figure, the pre-image and image have a different orientation. After a 45° clockwise rotation, the vertices of the image are not in the same position relative to the pre-image.

- A is directly north of C, but A' is northeast of C'.

- C is directly west of B, but C' is northwest of B'.

- B is southeast of A, but B' is slightly southwest of A'.

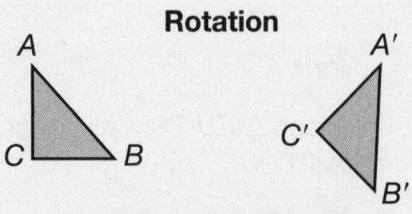

Rotation

Different Orientation

After a reflection, the pre-image and the image have opposite orientations. Two figures have opposite orientations if one or more vertices are in opposite positions in relation to each other.

- *A* is directly north of *C*, but *A'* is directly south of *C'*.

- Both *C* and *C'* are directly west of *B* and *B'*.

- *B* is southeast of *A*, but *B'* is northeast of *A'*.

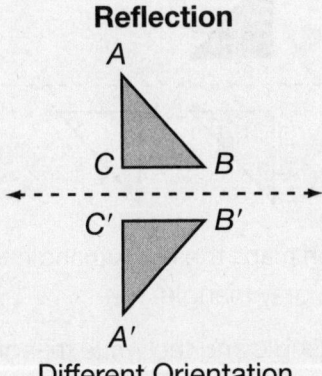

A combination or two or more rigid motions, one performed after the other, is called a sequence of rigid motions. A sequence of rigid motions maps a pre-image to a congruent image. Conversely, if two figures are congruent, then there is a sequence of one or more rigid motions that will map one figure to the other figure.

Example 1

What sequence of rigid motions can be used to show that the black triangle is congruent to the white triangle?

Strategy   Look for a combination of translations, reflections, and/or rotations that maps the black triangle to the white triangle.

Step 1   Determine if the black triangle and the white triangle have the same orientation.

> The black triangle and the white triangle have opposite orientations. Specifically, the white triangle appears to be a mirror image of the black triangle.
>
> So a reflection over a horizontal line is one of the rigid motions that map the black triangle to the white triangle.

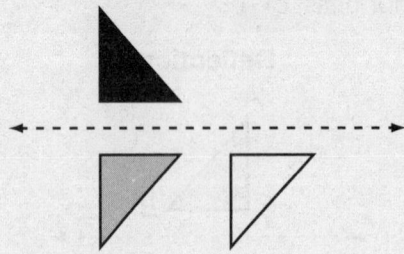

> Because a reflection maps the black triangle to the gray triangle, the black triangle is congruent to the gray triangle.

Step 2   Determine if the gray triangle and the white triangle have the same orientation.

> The gray triangle and the white triangle have the same orientation. So, a translation will map the gray triangle to the white triangle.
>
> The white triangle is to the right of the gray triangle. A horizontal translation to the right will map the gray triangle onto the white triangle.

Step 3   Describe the sequence of rigid motions that can be used to show that the black triangle is congruent to the white triangle.

> A reflection over the horizontal line, followed by a horizontal translation to the right, maps the black triangle to the white triangle. Therefore, the black triangle is congruent to the white triangle.

Solution   **A reflection over a horizontal line, followed by a horizontal translation to the right, can be used to show that the black triangle is congruent to the white triangle.**

Dilating an image causes the image to enlarge or shrink. A dilation is called a nonrigid motion because it changes the size of a figure. Rigid motions only change the position of a figure and always produce a congruent figure.

A sequence of transformations that contains a dilation, maps a pre-image to a **similar** image. Similar figures have the same shape but not necessarily the same size. Two figures are similar if you can use a sequence of rotations, reflections, translations, and dilations to obtain one from the other.

Example 2

What sequence of transformations can be used to show that the black trapezoid is similar to the white trapezoid?

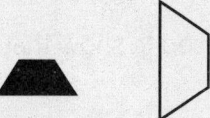

Strategy   **Look for a combination of translations, reflections, rotations, and dilations that maps the black trapezoid to the white trapezoid.**

Step 1   Find a transformation that will map the black trapezoid to a trapezoid that has the same orientation as the white trapezoid.

Notice that the two bases of the black trapezoid are horizontal line segments. The two bases of the white trapezoid are vertical line segments. A 90° clockwise rotation will position the bases of the pre-image so they are vertical and create an image with the same orientation as the white trapezoid. The gray trapezoid is congruent to the black trapezoid.

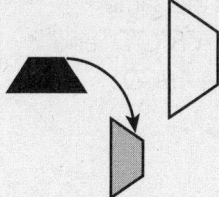

Step 2   Find a transformation that maps the gray trapezoid to the white trapezoid.

The white trapezoid is an enlargement of the gray trapezoid. A dilation maps the gray trapezoid to the white trapezoid.

Solution   **A 90° clockwise rotation, followed by a dilation, can be used to show that the black trapezoid is similar to the white trapezoid.**

You can use the properties of transformations to show that two figures in the coordinate plane are congruent.

Example 3

What sequence of transformations can be used to show that rectangle *ABCD* is congruent to rectangle *A″B″C″D″*?

Strategy **Look for a combination of translations, reflections, and/or rotations that maps rectangle *ABCD* to rectangle *A″B″C″D″*.**

Step 1 Find a transformation that will map rectangle *ABCD* to a rectangle that has the same orientation as rectangle *A″B″C″D″*.

Notice that $\overline{AB}$ is a horizontal line segment, but $\overline{A″B″}$ is a vertical line segment. A rotation of 90° about the origin counterclockwise maps rectangle *ABCD* to rectangle *A′B′C′D′*. Rectangle *A′B′C′D′* has the same orientation as rectangle *A″B″C″D″* and is congruent to rectangle *ABCD*.

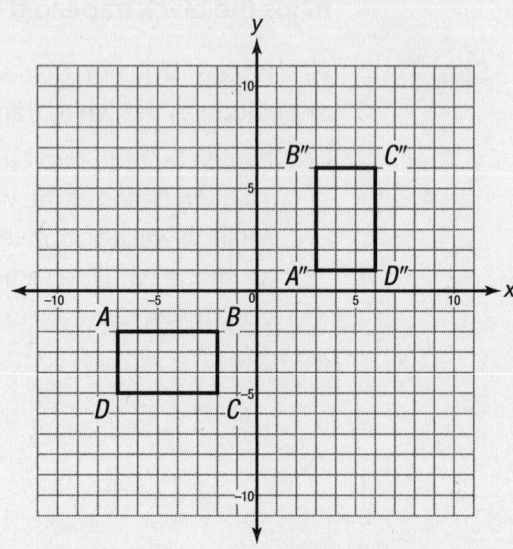

Step 2 Find a transformation that maps rectangle *A′B′C′D′* to rectangle *A″B″C″D″*.

A translation 1 unit right and 8 units up maps rectangle *A′B′C′D′* to rectangle *A″B″C″D″*. So, rectangle *A′B′C′D′* is congruent to rectangle *A″B″C″D″*.

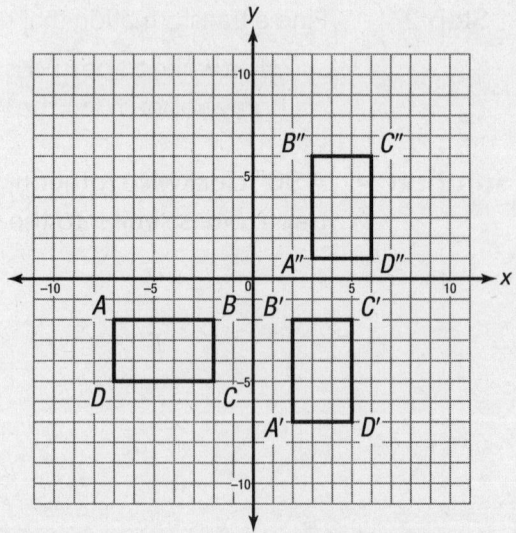

Solution A 90° rotation about the origin counterclockwise, followed by a translation 1 unit right and 8 units up, can be used to show that rectangle *ABCD* is congruent to rectangle *A″B″C″D″*.

You can use the properties of transformations to show that two figures in the coordinate plane are similar.

Example 4

What sequence of transformations can be used to show that $\triangle P''Q''R''$ is similar to $\triangle PQR$?

Strategy   Look for a combination of translations, reflections, rotations, and dilations that maps $\triangle PQR$ to $\triangle P''Q''R''$.

Step 1   Find a transformation that maps $\triangle PQR$ to a triangle that has the same orientation as $\triangle P''Q''R''$.

A reflection across the line $y = 3$ maps $\triangle PQR$ to $\triangle P'Q'R'$, which has the same orientation as $\triangle P''Q''R''$. $\triangle P'Q'R'$ is congruent to $\triangle PQR$.

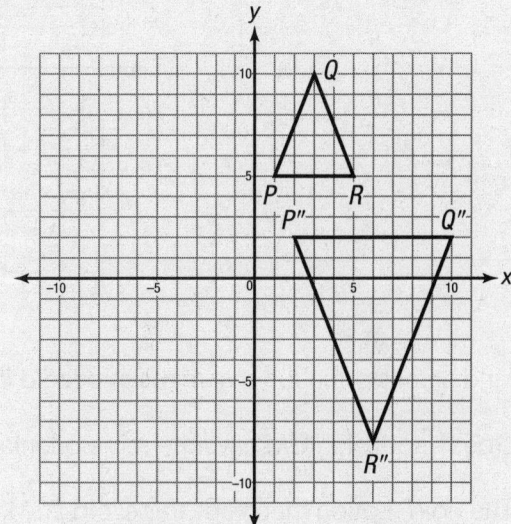

Step 2   Find a transformation that maps $\triangle P'Q'R'$ to $\triangle P''Q''R''$.

$\triangle P''Q''R''$ is an enlargement of $\triangle P'Q'R'$. The transformation needed is a dilation.

Step 3   Find a scale factor that relates a pair of corresponding sides of the triangles.

$\overline{P'R'} = 4$ units and $\overline{P''R''} = 8$ units

$\frac{8}{4} = 2$, so the scale factor is 2.

A dilation with a scale factor of 2 maps $\triangle P'Q'R'$ to $\triangle P''Q''R''$. So, $\triangle PQR$ is similar to $\triangle P''Q''R''$.

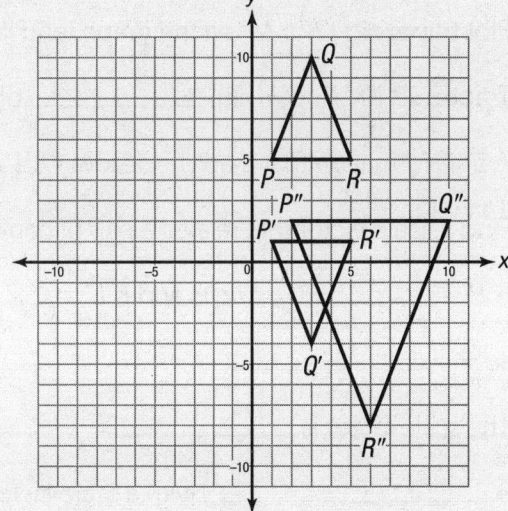

Solution   A reflection across the line $y = 3$, followed by a dilation with a scale factor of 2, can be used to show that $\triangle PQR$ is similar to $\triangle P''Q''R''$.

What sequence of transformations can be used to show that trapezoid *JKLM* is similar to trapezoid *J"K"L"M"*?

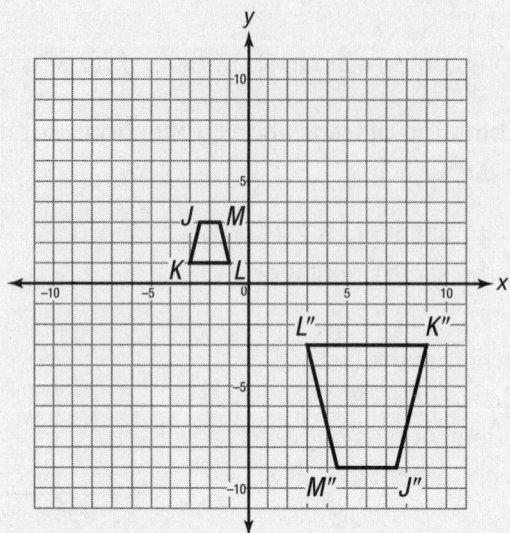

Find a transformation that maps trapezoid *JKLM* to trapezoid *J"K"L"M"*.

Does trapezoid *JKLM* have the same orientation as trapezoid *J"K"L"M"*? _____

The rigid motion that maps trapezoid *JKLM* to a trapezoid with the same orientation as trapezoid *J"K"L"M"* is a _____ around the origin.

Plot trapezoid *J'K'L'M'* on the graph, and label the vertices.

Trapezoid *J"K"L"M"* is a(n) _____ of trapezoid *J'K'L'M'*.

A transformation that maps trapezoid *J'K'L'M'* to trapezoid *J"K"L"M"* is a(n) _____.

Find a scale factor that relates a pair of corresponding sides of the trapezoids.

$\overline{K'L'}$ = _____ units and $\overline{K"L"}$ = _____ units,

so $\frac{6}{2}$ = _____

The scale factor is _____.

A _____ with a scale factor of _____ maps trapezoid *J'K'L'M'* to *J"K"L"M"*, so trapezoid *JKLM* is similar to trapezoid *J"K"L"M"*.

A _____, followed by a
_____, can be used to show

that trapezoid *JKLM* is similar to trapezoid *J"K"L"M"*.

1 Select True or False for each statement.

A. A rotation followed by a dilation maps a pre-image to a congruent image.
○ True ○ False

B. A translation followed by a reflection maps a pre-image to a congruent image.
○ True ○ False

C. A dilation followed by a translation maps a pre-image to a similar image.
○ True ○ False

D. A rotation followed by a dilation maps a pre-image to a similar image.
○ True ○ False

E. If two figures are congruent, then there is a sequence of transformations that maps one figure to the other.
○ True ○ False

F. If two figures are similar, the sequence of transformations that maps one figure to the other must include a translation.
○ True ○ False

2 Use the transformations described below to create a sequence of motions in which the pre-image and image are congruent. Then create another sequence of motions in which the pre-image and image are similar but not congruent. Write each sequence of motions in the correct box.

| dilation with scale factor $\frac{1}{4}$ | reflection over a vertical line | rotation 180° about the origin | translation 3 units left and 5 units down |

Pre-image and Image Are Congruent	Pre-image and Image Are Similar but Not Congruent
A _____ followed by a _____.	A _____ followed by a _____.

3 You perform a sequence of motions on a figure with point A. First, you reflect the figure over the line $y = 2$ to get A'. Then you dilate the figure by the scale factor $\frac{1}{2}$ to get A''. Use numbers from the box to complete the statement.

$$A(-3, \underline{\quad}) \rightarrow A'(\underline{\quad}, 5) \rightarrow A''\left(-1\frac{1}{2}, \underline{\quad}\right)$$

-6
-3
-1
$-\frac{1}{2}$
1
$2\frac{1}{2}$
5
10

4 You use a sequence of motions to transform a figure with point K. First you dilate the figure to get K'. Then you reflect the figure to get K''. Circle the scale factor and the line of reflection that make the mappings true.

$$K(4, -2) \times \begin{array}{c} \frac{1}{4} \\ \frac{1}{2} \\ 4 \end{array} \rightarrow K'\left(1, -\frac{1}{2}\right) \text{ reflection in } \begin{array}{c} x\text{-axis} \\ y\text{-axis} \\ \text{the line } y = x \end{array} \rightarrow K''\left(-\frac{1}{2}, 1\right)$$

5 Look at △PQR, △STV, and △WXY.

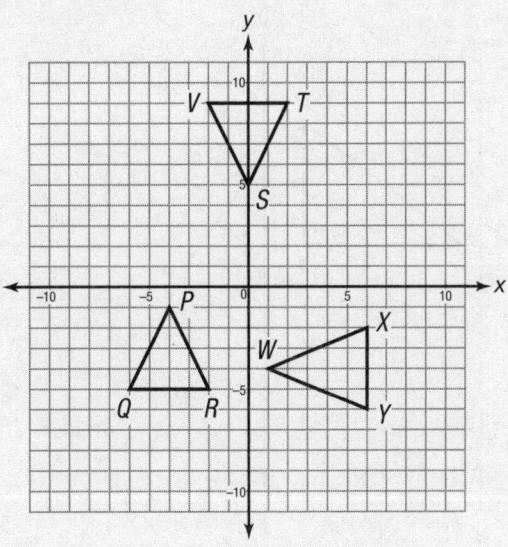

Part A

Identify a pair of congruent triangles.

Part B

Use transformations from the box to create two different sequences of transformations that verify that the two triangles are congruent.

A _____ followed

by a _____

verifies that the two triangles are congruent.

A _____ followed

by a _____

verifies that the two triangles are congruent.

dilation with a scale factor of 2
translation 4 units right
reflection over $x = y$
reflection over line $y = 2$
dilation with a scale factor of $\frac{1}{2}$
translation 4 units left and 4 units up
rotation 180° clockwise

6 A sequence of transformations occurred to produce the image △*GHI* from △*ABC*.

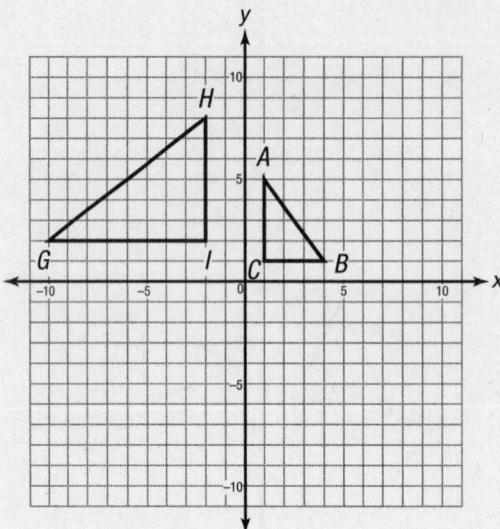

Part A

Is △*GHI* similar or congruent to △*ABC*?

_____

Part B

Describe one sequence of transformations to justify your answer to Part A.

_____

7 The point *C*(*x*, *y*) is in Quadrant I. It is the vertex of a triangle. You reflect the triangle over the *x*-axis, then you dilate the triangle by the scale factor 2. Select an ordered pair that could be the coordinates of *C*″ after the sequence of motions described. Circle all that apply.

A. (3, 2)   **E.** (−5, −4)

B. (5, 8)   **F.** (−2, −1)

C. (−3, 10)   **G.** (8, −7)

D. (−9, 1)   **H.** (1, −1)

Finding Measures of Angles Formed by Transversals Intersecting Parallel Lines

1 GETTING THE IDEA

The figure below shows two **parallel lines**, *j* and *k*. The parallel lines, ll, are intersected by a **transversal** *t* (a line that intersects two or more lines). Special pairs of angles are formed when a transversal intersects two lines.

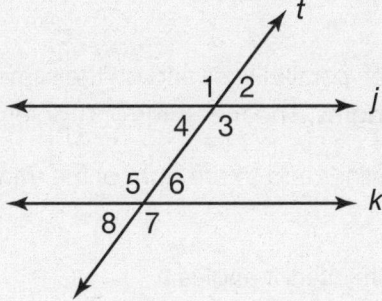

Corresponding Angles

Corresponding angles are on the same side of the transversal and on the same side of the parallel lines. Corresponding angles have the same measure.

- ∠1 is in the upper left section of the intersection of lines *j* and *t*. ∠5 is also in the upper left section of the intersection of lines *k* and *t*, so ∠1 and ∠5 are corresponding angles.

- ∠2 and ∠6, ∠3 and ∠7, and ∠4 and ∠8 are also pairs of corresponding angles.

Alternate Exterior Angles

Alternate exterior angles are outside the parallel lines and on opposite sides of the transversal. Alternate exterior angles have the same measure.

- ∠2 is above line *j* and ∠8 is below line *k*. They are on opposite sides of the transversal, so ∠2 and ∠8 are alternate exterior angles.

- ∠1 and ∠7 are also alternate exterior angles.

Alternate Interior Angles

Alternate interior angles are on the inside of the parallel lines and are on opposite sides of the transversal. Alternate interior angles have the same measure.

- $\angle 3$ is below line j and $\angle 5$ is above line k. The angles are on opposite sides of the transversal, so $\angle 3$ and $\angle 5$ are alternate interior angles.

- $\angle 4$ and $\angle 6$ are also alternate interior angles.

Vertical Angles

Vertical angles are opposite angles formed by two intersecting lines. Vertical angles have the same measure.

- $\angle 2$ and $\angle 4$ are both formed by the intersection of line j and line t. The angles are opposite of each other, so $\angle 2$ and $\angle 4$ are vertical angles.

- $\angle 1$ and $\angle 3$, $\angle 6$ and $\angle 8$, and $\angle 5$ and $\angle 7$ are also vertical angles.

Same-Side Interior Angles

Same-side interior angles are between parallel lines and on the same side of the transversal. Same-side interior angles are **supplementary angles.** The measures of supplementary angles add to 180°.

- $\angle 3$ and $\angle 6$ are between the lines and to the right of the transversal, so $\angle 3$ and $\angle 6$ are same-side interior angles.

- $\angle 4$ and $\angle 5$ are also same-side interior angles.

Example 1

Line *m* ‖ *n*, and intersected by transversal *l*. Identify all pairs of corresponding angles, alternate exterior angles, vertical angles, alternate interior angles, and same-side interior angles in the figure below.

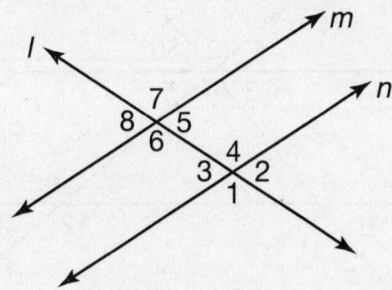

Strategy   Use the definitions to find all of the pairs of angles.

Step 1 Find all of the pairs of corresponding angles.

∠8 and ∠3, ∠7 and ∠4, ∠6 and ∠1, and ∠5 and ∠2 are corresponding angles.

Step 2 Find all of the pairs of alternate exterior angles.

∠8, ∠7, ∠2, and ∠1 are outside the two lines.

∠7 and ∠1 are on opposite sides of the transversal.

∠8 and ∠2 are on opposite sides of the transversal.

Step 3 Find all of the pairs of vertical angles.

∠1, ∠2, ∠3, and ∠4 are formed by the intersection of lines *n* and *l*.

∠1 and ∠4, and ∠2 and ∠3 are vertical angles.

∠5, ∠6, ∠7, and ∠8 are formed by the intersection of lines *m* and *l*.

∠6 and ∠7, and ∠5 and ∠8 are vertical angles.

Step 4 Find all of the pairs of alternate interior angles.

∠3, ∠4, ∠5, and ∠6 are between the lines.

∠4 and ∠6 are on opposite sides of the transversal.

∠3 and ∠5 are on opposite sides of the transversal.

Step 5 Find all of the pairs of same-side interior angles.

∠3, ∠4, ∠5, and ∠6 are between the lines.

∠3 and ∠6 are on the same side of the transversal.

∠4 and ∠5 are on the same side of the transversal.

Solution   The pairs of angles can be identified as follows:

Corresponding angles: ∠2 and ∠5; ∠1 and ∠6; ∠4 and ∠7; ∠3 and ∠8

Alternate exterior angles: ∠1 and ∠7; ∠2 and ∠8

Vertical angles: ∠1 and ∠4; ∠2 and ∠3; ∠6 and ∠7; ∠5 and ∠8

Alternate interior angles: ∠4 and ∠6; ∠3 and ∠5

Same-side interior angles: ∠3 and ∠6; ∠4 and ∠5

Example 2

In the figure below, *a* ∥ *b*, and both lines are cut by transversals *c* and *d*. What are the missing angle measures in the figure?

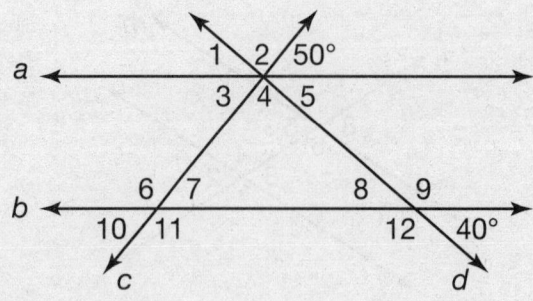

Strategy   Break the figure into sections based upon transversals.

Step 1   Focus on the angles formed by parallel lines *a* and *b* that are cut by transversal line *c*.

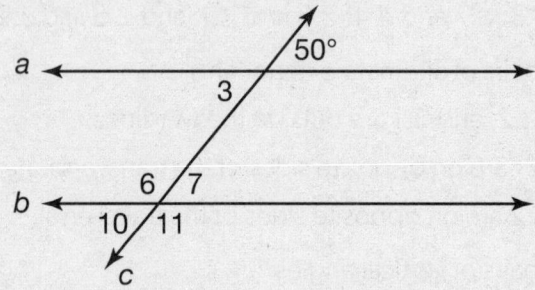

Create a table to help organize your work.

Angle Pair	Classification	How Are the Measures Related When Lines Are Parallel?	What Can I Figure Out?
∠3 and the angle marked 50°	vertical angles	equal measure	m∠3 = 50°
∠3 and ∠7	alternate interior angles	equal measure	m∠7 = 50°
∠3 and ∠10	corresponding angles	equal measure	m∠10 = 50°
∠3 and ∠6	same-side interior angles	sum of 180°	m∠3 + m∠6 = 180° 50° + m∠6 = 180° m∠6 = 130°
∠6 and ∠11	vertical angles	equal measure	m∠11 = 130°

Step 2   Focus on the angles formed by parallel lines *a* and *b*, cut by transversal line *d*.

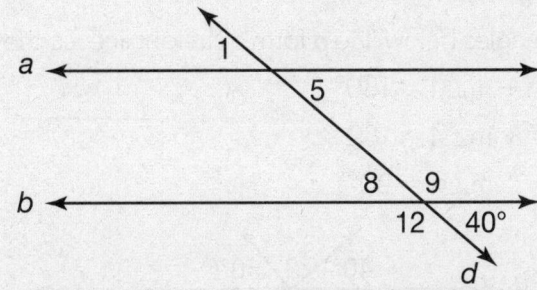

Angle Pair	Classification	How Are the Measures Related When Lines Are Parallel?	What Can I Figure Out?
∠8 and the angle marked 40°	vertical angles	equal measure	m∠8 = 40°
∠5 and ∠8	alternate interior angles	equal measure	m∠5 = 40°
∠1 and ∠8	corresponding angles	equal measure	m∠1 = 40°
∠9 and the angle marked 40°	supplementary angles	sum of 180°	m∠9 + 40° = 180° m∠9 = 140°
∠9 and ∠12	vertical angles	equal measure	m∠12 = 140°

Step 3   Fill in the known angle measures in the figure. Use this information to find the measures of the remaining angles.

The three angles below line *a* form a straight line, so they have a sum of 180°.

$$50° + 40° + m\angle 4 = 180°$$
$$90° + m\angle 4 = 180°$$
$$m\angle 4 = 90°$$

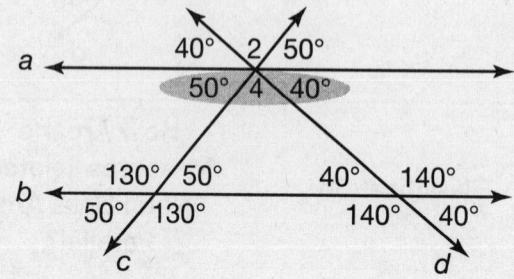

$\angle 2$ and $\angle 4$ are vertical angles, so $m\angle 2 = 90°$.

Solution
$$m\angle 1 = m\angle 5 = m\angle 8 = 40°$$
$$m\angle 2 = m\angle 4 = 90°$$
$$m\angle 3 = m\angle 7 = m\angle 10 = 50°$$
$$m\angle 6 = m\angle 11 = 130°$$
$$m\angle 9 = m\angle 12 = 140°$$

In the figure below, lines *g* and *h* are parallel and cut by transversal *m*. What is the measure of ∠2?

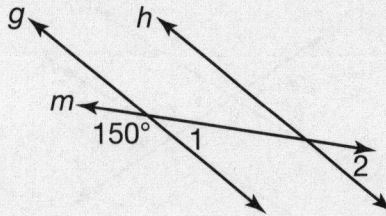

The angle marked 150° and m∠1 have a sum of _____ since they form a

_____.

Therefore, 150° + m∠1 = _____ , so m∠1 = _____.

Since line *g* and line *h* are _____ , ∠1 and ∠2 are _____

angles and the measures of ∠1 and ∠2 are _____ ,

m∠2 = _____

Use the figure below for questions 1 and 2. Lines *m* and *n* are parallel and are cut by transversal *l*.

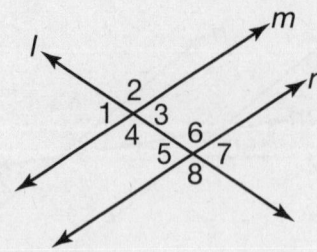

1 List four different pairs of vertical angles.

2 Look at each pair of angles. Do the angles have the same measure? Select Yes or No.

A. ∠3 and ∠2 ○ Yes ○ No

B. ∠5 and ∠1 ○ Yes ○ No

C. ∠4 and ∠6 ○ Yes ○ No

D. ∠4 and ∠8 ○ Yes ○ No

E. ∠3 and ∠6 ○ Yes ○ No

3 Draw a pair of parallel lines intersected by a transversal so at least one angle is a 45° angle. Label all of the angle measures in your drawing.

Use the figure below for questions 4 and 5.

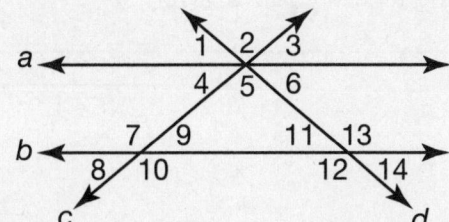

④ Classify each pair of angles. Write the angle pair in the correct box.

| ∠8 and ∠9 | ∠4 and ∠9 | ∠14 and ∠1 |

| ∠12 and ∠13 | ∠6 and ∠11 | ∠8 and ∠4 |

Vertical Angles	Corresponding Angles	Alternate Interior Angles	Alternate Exterior Angles

⑤ Aarav measured ∠9 using a protractor and found it to be 39°. He said that ∠13 must also be 39° since ∠9 and ∠13 are corresponding angles. Do you agree with Aarav? Explain.

6 Can a pair of angles be both vertical angles and corresponding angles at the same time? Use words, numbers, or a drawing to justify your answer.

7 In the figure below, *j* ‖ *k*, and both lines are cut by transversal *t*. Suppose line *t* was moved so that ∠2 had a greater measure.

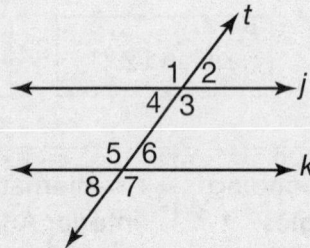

How will the other angle measures change? Select True or False for each statement.

A. The measure of ∠1 will stay the same.   ○ True   ○ False

B. The measure of ∠6 will increase.   ○ True   ○ False

C. The measure of ∠7 will decrease.   ○ True   ○ False

D. The measure of ∠4 will decrease.   ○ True   ○ False

E. The measure of ∠5 will decrease.   ○ True   ○ False

8 Santiago notices that when a pair of parallel lines is cut by a transversal and one angle is a right angle, all of the other angles are also right angles. Use words, numbers, or drawings to explain why Santiago's observation is true.

9 In the figure below, $\overleftrightarrow{AC} \parallel \overleftrightarrow{ED}$ and $\angle ABC$ and $\angle ECD$ are right angles.

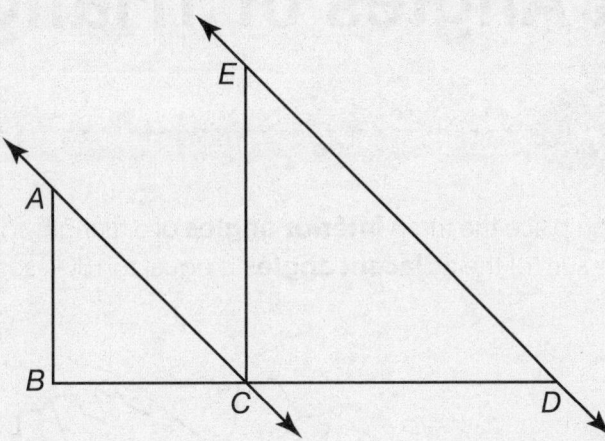

Part A

Find a pair of corresponding angles, a pair of alternate interior angles, and a pair of vertical angles in the figure.

Corresponding angles: _____ and _____

Alternate interior angles: _____ and _____

Vertical angles: _____ and _____

Part B

Find two pairs of angles from $\triangle ABC$ and $\triangle ECD$ that have the same measure. Explain how you found your answer.

8.G.5

Exploring Angles of Triangles

1 GETTING THE IDEA

The drawing shows that if you place the three **interior angles** of a triangle adjacent to each other, they form a straight line. The sum of the **adjacent angles** is equal to 180°, so the sum of the interior angles of a triangle is 180°.

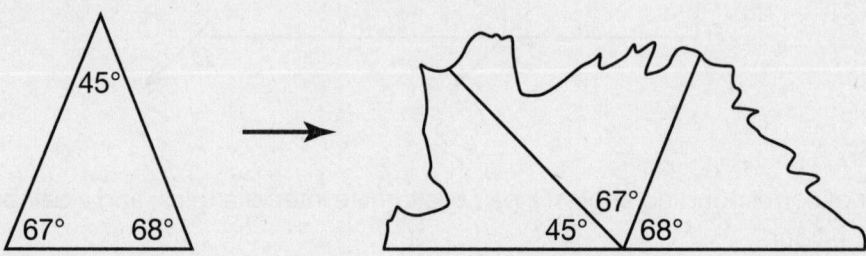

Example 1

$\triangle RST$ is a right triangle. Find m∠R.

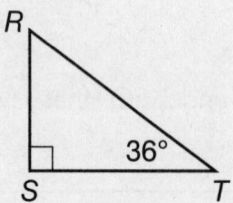

Strategy	**Write and solve an equation.**

Step 1 Identify the measures of the given angles.

∠S is a right angle, so m∠S = 90°

m∠T = 36°

Step 2 Write an equation. Substitute the measures of the given angles.

m∠R + m∠S + m∠T = 180°

m∠R + 90° + 36° = 180°

Step 3 Solve the equation for m∠R.

m∠R + **90°** + **36°** = 180°   Add like terms.

m∠R + 126° − **126°** = 180° − **126°**   Subtract 126° from both sides.

m∠R = 54°

Solution The measure of ∠R is 54°.

Recall that **similar** triangles are two triangles that have the same shape but may not have the same size. In similar triangles, **corresponding angles** are congruent, and the ratios of the lengths of **corresponding sides** are equal. The symbol ~ means similar.

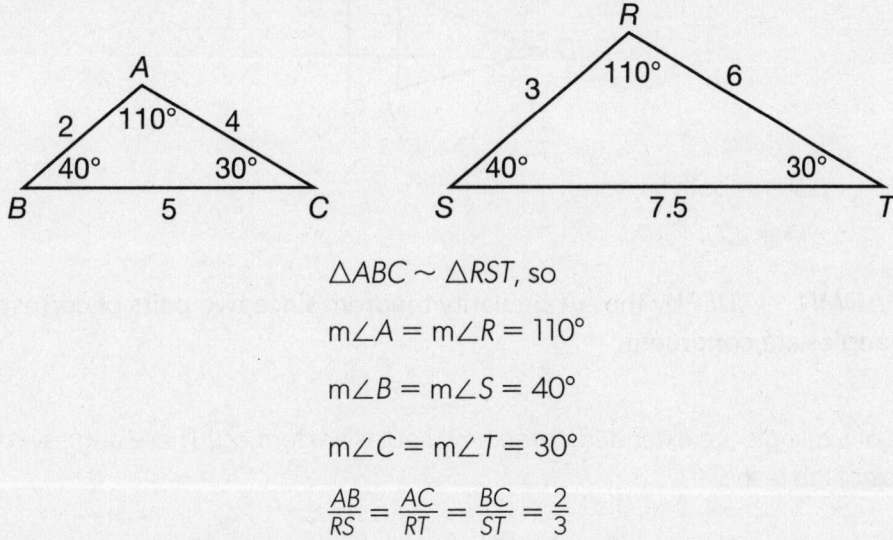

$\triangle ABC \sim \triangle RST$, so

$$m\angle A = m\angle R = 110°$$

$$m\angle B = m\angle S = 40°$$

$$m\angle C = m\angle T = 30°$$

$$\frac{AB}{RS} = \frac{AC}{RT} = \frac{BC}{ST} = \frac{2}{3}$$

The **angle-angle similarity theorem** states that when two pairs of corresponding angles of two triangles are congruent, the triangles are similar. If two pairs of corresponding angles are congruent, then the third pair of corresponding angles must also be congruent.

Example 2

In the figure below, $\overline{MN} \parallel \overline{EF}$. Explain how you can tell that $\triangle DMN \sim \triangle DEF$.

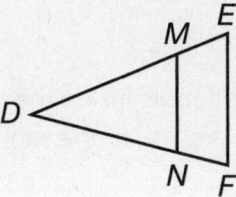

Strategy   Use the AA similarity theorem.

> **Step 1**   Find one pair of angles that are congruent.

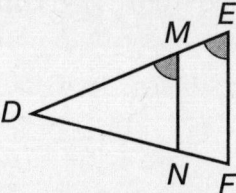

$\angle DMN$ and $\angle DEF$ are corresponding angles formed by parallel lines.

Corresponding angles are congruent; therefore, $\angle DMN \cong \angle DEF$.

Step 2　　Find a second pair of angles that are congruent.

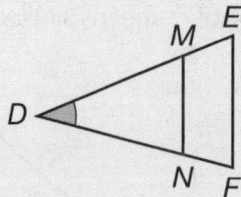

∠D is in both triangles.

∠D ≅ ∠D

Solution　　△DMN ~ △DEF by the AA similarity theorem since two pairs of corresponding angles are congruent.

When the sides of a triangle are extended, three new angles are formed. These angles are called **exterior angles** of the triangle.

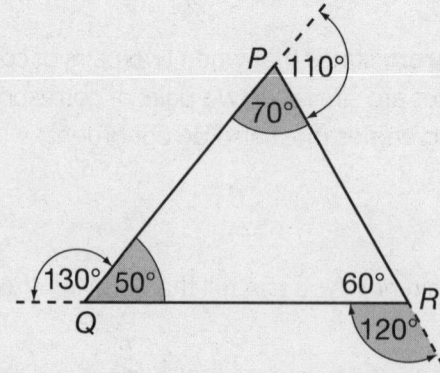

The two angles that are opposite an exterior angle inside the triangle are called **remote interior angles**. The measure of the exterior angle is equal to the sum of the measures of the remote interior angles.

The exterior angle and its adjacent interior angle form a 180° angle. When a pair of angles form a straight line, they are called **supplementary angles**. The sum of the measures of supplementary angles is 180°.

Similarly, a pair of angles that form a right angle are called **complementary angles**. The sum of the measures of complementary angles is 90°.

Example 3

Find the measure of the ∠MLN.

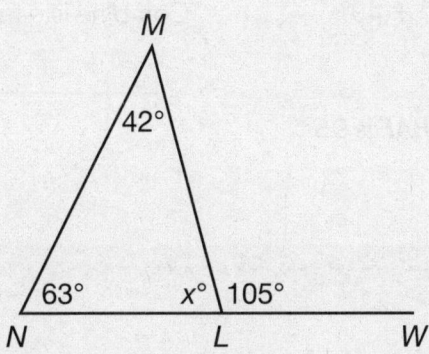

Strategy Use the supplementary interior angle and exterior angle of the triangle to write an equation. Then solve.

Step 1 Use supplementary angles to write an equation.

∠MLN and ∠MLW are adjacent angles that are supplementary.

m∠MLN + m∠MLW = 180°

Step 2 Solve for x.

$$x° + 105° = 180°$$
$$x° + 105° - \mathbf{105°} = 180° - \mathbf{105°} \qquad \text{Subtract 105° from both sides.}$$
$$x° = 75°$$

Solution The measure of ∠MLN is 75°.

Example 4

Find the measure of ∠BAE.

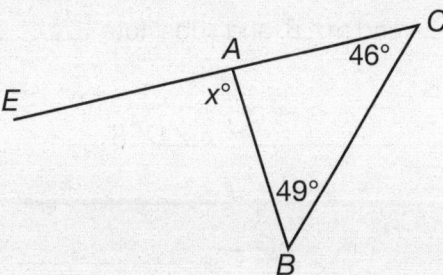

Strategy Write and solve an equation.

Step 1 Use the exterior angle and its remote interior angles to write an equation.

∠BAE is an exterior angle of △CAB.

∠C and ∠B are its remote interior angles.

m∠BAE = m∠C + m∠B

Step 2   Solve the equation.

$$m\angle BAE = m\angle C + m\angle B \qquad \text{Substitute.}$$
$$m\angle BAE = 46° + 49° \qquad \text{Combine like terms.}$$
$$m\angle BAE = 95°$$

Solution   The measure of $\angle BAE$ is 95°.

---

② COACHED EXAMPLE

$\triangle ABC$ is an isosceles triangle with $m\angle A = m\angle B$. Find $m\angle A$.

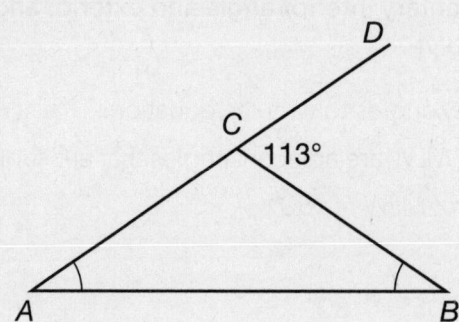

$\angle A$ and $\angle B$ are _____ _____ angles of $\angle DCB$.

The _____ of the measures of $\angle A$ and $\angle B$ is _____ to the measure of $\angle DCB$.

Write an equation.

$m\angle$ _____ $+ \, m\angle$ _____ $= m\angle DCB$

Since $m\angle A = m\angle B$, they can both be assigned the variable x.

Substitute _____ for $m\angle A$ and $m\angle B$, and substitute _____ for $m\angle DCB$.

Solve for x.

$m\angle$ _____ $+ \, m\angle$ _____ $= m\angle DCB$

$$x° + x° = \text{_____}$$
$$2x° = \text{_____}$$
$$x° = \text{_____}$$

$m\angle A = $ _____

1 Use angles from the box to complete the sentences.

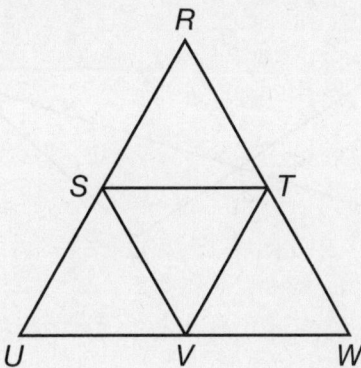

Angle _____ and angle _____ are remote interior angles of ∠SVW.

Angle _____ and angle SVW are supplementary angles.

Angle _____ and angle _____ are exterior angles of △TVW.

| U |
| VTR |
| SVU |
| TVU |
| USV |

2 Draw a right isosceles triangle. What are the measures of the interior angles of the triangle?

Use the triangles below for questions 3 and 4.

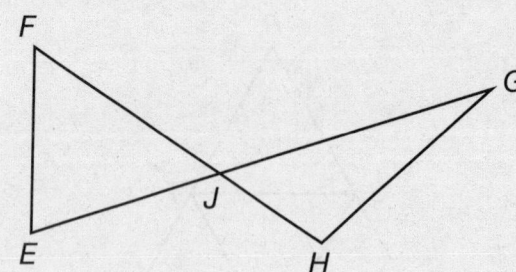

3 Select True or False for each equation.

A. $m\angle F + m\angle E + m\angle FJE = 180°$ ○ True   ○ False

B. $m\angle EJH = m\angle E + m\angle F$ ○ True   ○ False

C. $m\angle G + m\angle H + m\angle FJE = 180°$ ○ True   ○ False

D. $m\angle H = m\angle F + m\angle E$ ○ True   ○ False

E. $m\angle FJG = m\angle H + m\angle G$ ○ True   ○ False

4 Suppose $m\angle E = 72°$ and $m\angle F = 58°$. What is the measure of $\angle FJG$? Use words or numbers to justify your answer.

5 Given m∠*KNP* = 120° and m∠*K* = 40°, classify each angle by its measure. Write the angle in the correct box.

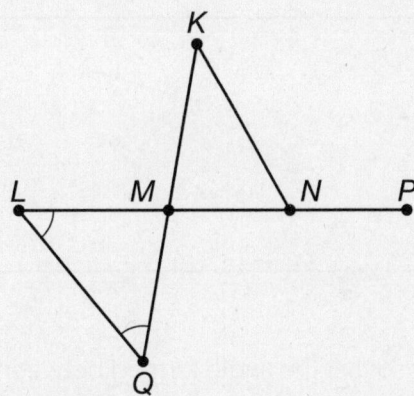

| ∠L | ∠Q | ∠LMQ | ∠KMN | ∠KNM |

Measure Equal to 50°	Measure Equal to 60°	Measure Equal to 80°

6 Given △*RST* ~ △*ABC*, find the value of *x*.

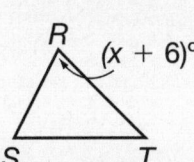 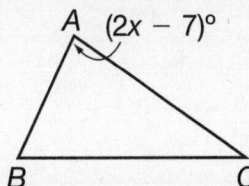

7 A triangle has angle measures in the ratio of 1:2:3. What is the measure of each angle of the triangle? Show your work.

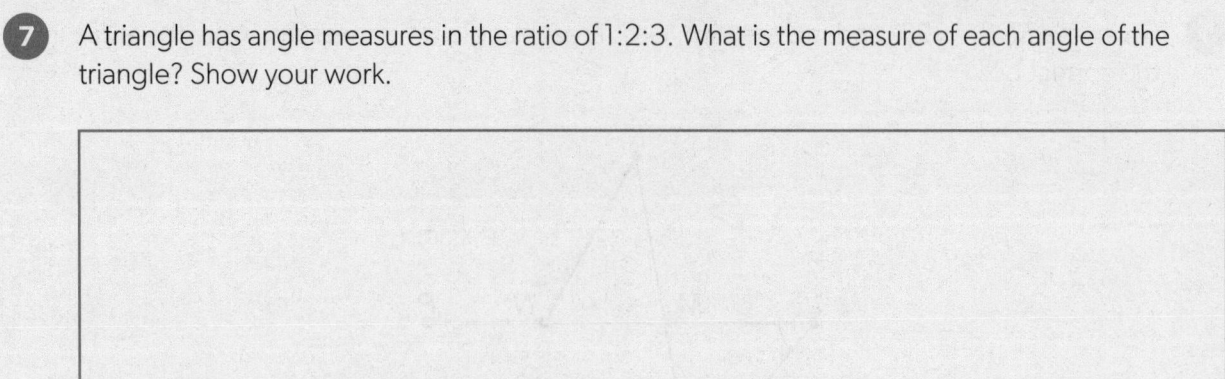

8 Luis set up an A-frame ladder so that the angle formed between each side of the ladder and the ground is 125°.

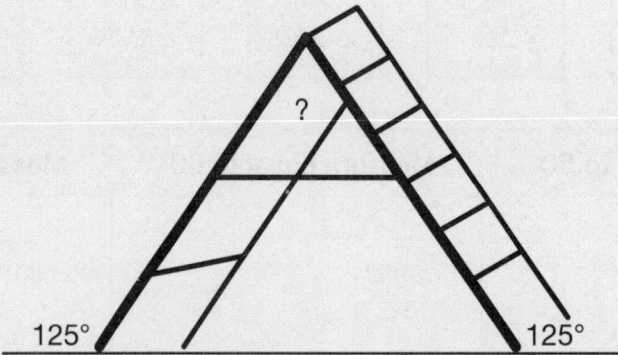

What is the measure of the angle at the top of the ladder? Explain how you found your answer.

9 In the figure below, ∠R is congruent to ∠U.

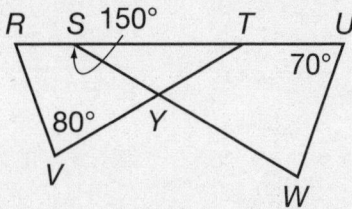

Is △RTV ~ △USW? Explain how you know.

[ ]

10 A tree and its shadow form △CBA as shown in the figure below. The tree forms a 62° angle with the ground, and the line from the top of the tree to the top of the shadow forms a 36° angle with the ground. Find the measure of ∠ABC. Explain how you found your answer.

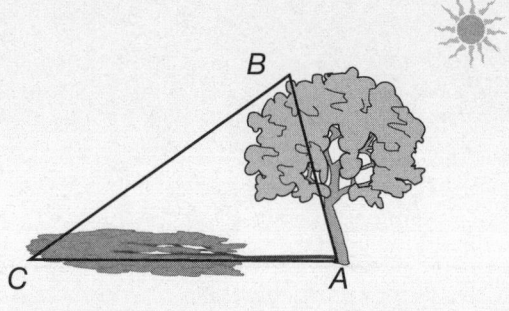

[ ]

11 In △ABC, m∠A = 55°, and m∠B = 72°. Select the measure of an exterior angle of the triangle. Circle all that apply.

A. 17°

B. 53°

C. 108°

D. 125°

E. 127°

12 **Part A**

Write and solve an equation to find the value of *x*. Show your work.

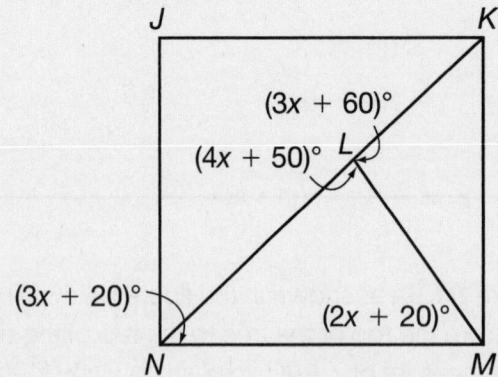

Part B

Use the value of *x* to find the measure of each angle of △MNL.

LESSON 24

Understanding the Pythagorean Theorem

8.G.6, 8.G.7

1 GETTING THE IDEA

A **right triangle** is a triangle that contains one right angle. The side opposite the right angle is called the **hypotenuse**. The other sides of the triangle, called the **legs**, form a right angle.

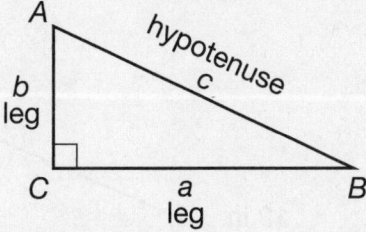

The Greek mathematician Pythagoras discovered a unique relationship that exists among the lengths of the sides of a right triangle. This relationship is known as the **Pythagorean theorem**.

Pythagorean Theorem

If a triangle is a right triangle with legs of length a and b and hypotenuse of length c, then $a^2 + b^2 = c^2$.

You can use the model below to verify the Pythagorean theorem. The number of square units on each side of the triangle represents the square of the length of that side of the triangle. Count the squares to verify that the sum of the unit squares on the legs is equal to the number of unit squares on the hypotenuse.

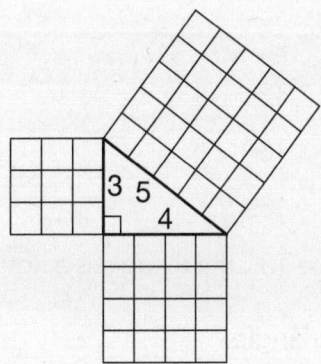

When you reverse the parts of an if-then statement, the new statement is called the **converse** of the original statement. Here is the converse of the Pythagorean theorem.

> ### Converse of the Pythagorean Theorem
>
> If a triangle has sides of length a and b with longest side of length c and
>
> $$a^2 + b^2 = c^2,$$
>
> then the triangle is a right triangle.

The converse of the Pythagorean theorem is true. You can use the converse of the Pythagorean theorem to determine whether a triangle is a right triangle.

Example 1

Verify that the triangle is a right triangle.

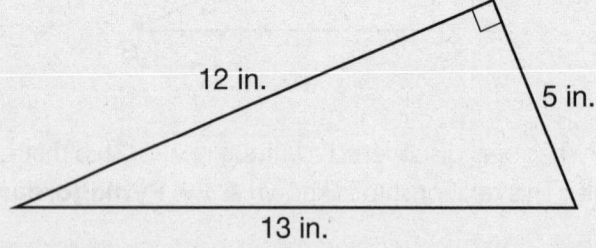

Strategy	Use the converse of the Pythagorean theorem.
Step 1	Identify a, b, and c.
	The hypotenuse is the side across from the right angle. It is also the longest side of the triangle.
	The length of the hypotenuse is 13 inches. So, $c = 13$.
	The lengths of the legs are 5 inches and 12 inches.
	So, $a = 5$ and $b = 12$.
Step 2	Check to see if $a^2 + b^2 = c^2$.

$$a^2 + b^2 = c^2$$

$$5^2 + 12^2 \stackrel{?}{=} 13^2$$

$$25 + 144 \stackrel{?}{=} 169$$

$$169 = 169 \checkmark$$

Since $5^2 + 12^2 = 13^2$, the triangle is a right triangle.

Solution	**The triangle is a right triangle.**

Example 2

Determine whether the triangle is a right triangle.

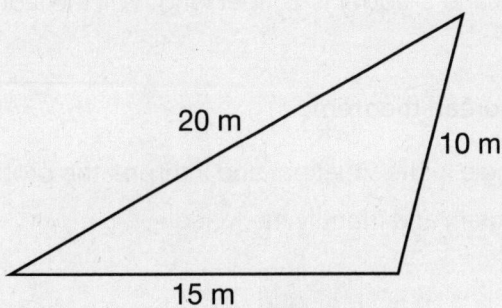

Strategy   Use the converse of the Pythagorean theorem.

Step 1   Identify a, b, and c.

The length of the longest side is 20 m. So, $c = 20$.

The lengths of the other sides are 10 m and 15 m. So, $a = 10$ and $b = 15$.

Step 2   Check to see if $a^2 + b^2 = c^2$.

$$a^2 + b^2 = c^2$$

$$10^2 + 15^2 \stackrel{?}{=} 20^2$$

$$100 + 225 \stackrel{?}{=} 400$$

$$325 \neq 400$$

Since $10^2 + 15^2 \neq 20^2$, the triangle is not a right triangle.

Solution   **The triangle is not a right triangle.**

Example 3

Mariano needs to repair a window that is 24 feet above the ground. He wants to place his ladder 7 feet from the base of the house. Mariano's ladder is 25 feet long. Will the ladder reach the bottom of the window? Explain.

Strategy   **Use the Pythagorean theorem.**

Step 1   Identify the triangle in the situation, and interpret the problem.

Draw a diagram and identify the triangle.

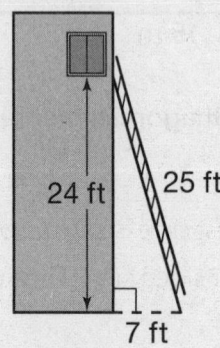

There is a right angle where the house meets the ground, so the triangle formed by the house, ground, and ladder is a right triangle.

Determine whether a triangle with legs that measure 7 feet and 24 feet has a hypotenuse that measures 25 feet.

Step 2   Substitute values for a and b, and solve for c.

The lengths of the legs are 7 feet and 24 feet. So, $a = 7$ and $b = 24$.

$$a^2 + b^2 = c^2$$
$$7^2 + 24^2 = c^2$$
$$49 + 576 = 625$$
$$\sqrt{625} = 25$$
$$c = 25$$

Since $7^2 + 24^2 = 25^2$, the ladder will reach the bottom of the window.

Solution   **The ladder will reach the bottom of the window.**

Example 4

Taylor is building a door for a cabinet. The corners of the door must be right angles for the door to fit the cabinet. The door is 7 feet tall and 2.5 feet wide. The diagonal of the door measures 7.5 feet. Is the door the correct shape? Explain.

Strategy   Use the converse of the Pythagorean theorem.

Step 1   Draw a picture to model the situation, and interpret the problem.

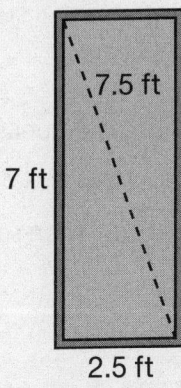

7.5 ft

7 ft

2.5 ft

If the door is the correct shape, then it has four right angles, and the triangle shown above is a right triangle. Determine whether a triangle with sides 2.5 feet, 7 feet, and 7.5 feet is a right triangle.

Step 2   Identify a, b, and c.

The length of the longest side is 7.5 feet. So, $c = 7.5$.

The lengths of the other sides are 2.5 feet and 7 feet. So, $a = 2.5$ and $b = 7$.

Step 3   Check to see if $a^2 + b^2 = c^2$.

$$a^2 + b^2 = c^2$$
$$2.5^2 + 7^2 \overset{?}{=} 7.5^2$$
$$6.25 + 49 \overset{?}{=} 56.25$$
$$55.25 \neq 56.25$$

Since $2.5^2 + 7^2 \neq 7.5^2$, the triangle is a not a right triangle.

Solution   **The door is not the correct shape because the triangle formed by two sides of the door is not a right triangle.**

You can use the Pythagorean theorem to find the length of a side of a right triangle when you know the lengths of the other two sides.

Example 5

Find the value of x.

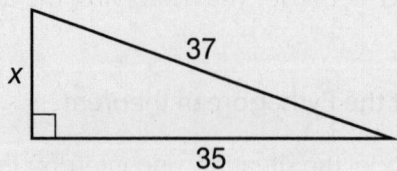

Strategy   **Use the Pythagorean theorem.**

Step 1   Identify a, b, and c.

The length of the hypotenuse is 37 units. So, $c = 37$.

The lengths of the legs are x units and 35 units. Let $a = x$ and $b = 35$.

Step 2   Substitute b and c into $a^2 + b^2 = c^2$. Then solve for x.

$$a^2 + b^2 = c^2$$
$$x^2 + 35^2 = 37^2$$
$$x^2 + 1{,}225 = 1{,}369$$
$$x^2 = 144$$
$$\sqrt{x^2} = \sqrt{144}$$
$$x = 12$$

Solution   The value of x is 12.

Example 6

A baseball diamond is a square with sides measuring 90 feet. What is the straight-line distance across the diamond from first base to third base?

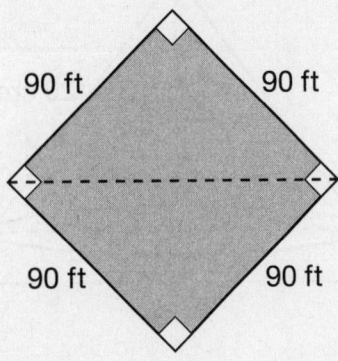

90 ft   90 ft

90 ft   90 ft

Strategy   **Use the Pythagorean theorem.**

Step 1   Identify a, b, and c.

The dashed line divides the square into two right triangles.

The legs of the triangles are 90 feet long. The dashed line represents the hypotenuse.

Let x represent the length of the hypotenuse. So, $c = x$.

Since the length of each leg is 90 feet, let $a = 90$ and $b = 90$.

Step 2   Substitute a and b into $a^2 + b^2 = c^2$. Then solve for x.

$$a^2 + b^2 = c^2$$
$$90^2 + 90^2 = x^2$$
$$8{,}100 + 8{,}100 = x^2$$
$$16{,}200 = x^2$$
$$\sqrt{16{,}200} = \sqrt{x^2}$$
$$127.3 \approx x$$

Solution   The straight-line distance across the baseball diamond from first base to third base is approximately 127.3 feet.

Example 7

Jeremiah constructed a paper cone with the measurements shown.

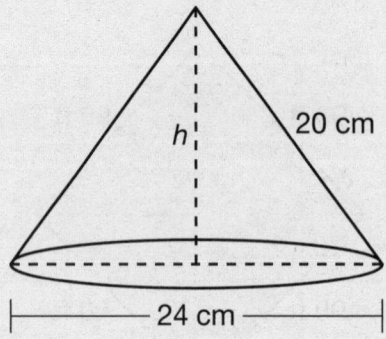

What is the height of the cone?

Strategy   **Use the Pythagorean theorem.**

Step 1   Identify the triangle in the situation.

The height of the cone and the radius of the base of the cone represent the legs of a right triangle, with a hypotenuse that measures 20 cm. Since the diameter of the base is 24 cm, the radius of the base is 12 cm.

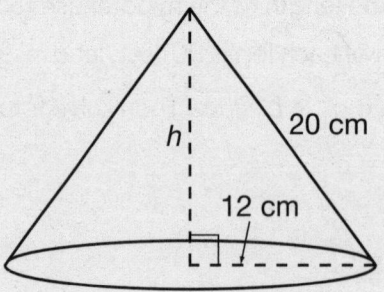

Step 2   Identify a, b, and c.

The hypotenuse of the triangle is the slant height of the cone, so $c = 20$.

Let $a = h$. The remaining leg is b, so $b = 12$.

Step 3   Substitute b and c into $a^2 + b^2 = c^2$. Then solve for h.

$$a^2 + b^2 = c^2$$
$$h^2 + 12^2 = 20^2$$
$$h^2 + 144 = 400$$
$$h^2 = 256$$
$$\sqrt{h^2} = \sqrt{256}$$
$$h = 16$$

Solution   **The height of the cone is 16 cm.**

A company has cylindrical mailing tubes to ship some of its products. The dimensions of the mailing tube are shown below.

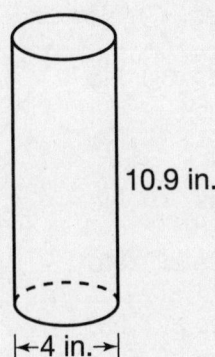

10.9 in.

|←4 in.→|

What is the approximate length of the longest glow stick that will fit in the mailing tube to the nearest tenth of an inch?

Add to the diagram a sketch of the longest glow stick that will fit in the mailing tube.

The glow stick represents the _____ of a right triangle, with _____ that measure _____ inches and _____ inches.

In the equation $a^2 + b^2 = c^2$, the variable _____ represents the length of the glow stick.

Use the measurements from the diagram to substitute into $a^2 + b^2 = c^2$. Then solve for the missing measurement.

The length of the longest glow stick that will fit in the mailing tube is approximately _____ inches.

1. Are the given measurements the lengths of the sides of a right triangle? Select Yes or No.

   A.   8 ft, 15 ft, 17 ft   ○ Yes   ○ No

   B.   4 m, 5 m, 6 m   ○ Yes   ○ No

   C.   9 in., 40 in., 41 in.   ○ Yes   ○ No

   D.   1 yd, 2.4 yd, 2.6 yd   ○ Yes   ○ No

   E.   14 cm, 50 cm, 48 cm   ○ Yes   ○ No

   F.   8.5 m, 1.3 m, 8.2 m   ○ Yes   ○ No

2. How does the diagram below illustrate the Pythagorean theorem?

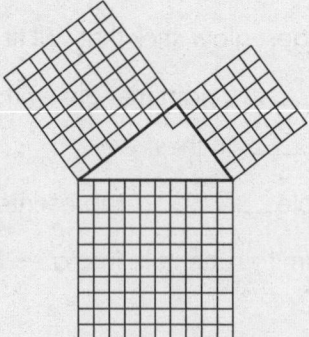

3. Nicolas places his 30-foot ladder against a house he is painting. If the foot of the ladder is 8 feet from the base of the house, how high above the ground is the top of the ladder touching the house? Give your answer to the nearest tenth of a foot. Show your work.

4 The two shorter sides of an obtuse triangle measure 15 inches and 3 feet. Describe the length of the longest side. Explain your reasoning.

5 Daniela needs to cut a rectangular hole in a wall where a new window will be installed. The window will be 4 feet high and 3 feet wide. She draws the outline for the window on the wall. If the only measurement tool that she has is a measuring tape, how can she be sure the shape she drew is a rectangle?

6 A support wire is attached to a utility pole at a point 4 feet below the top of the pole. The wire is anchored to a stake 10 feet from the base of the pole. If the wire is 26 feet long, how tall is the utility pole? Show your work.

7 Two sides of a right triangle measure 11 inches and 15 inches.

Part A

Use decimals rounded to the nearest tenth to complete the following statement.

The length of the third side of the triangle could be _____ inches or _____ inches.

Part B

Write two equations that justify your answers to Part A.

8 What is the height, h, of the isosceles trapezoid? Use words, numbers, or a drawing to justify your answer.

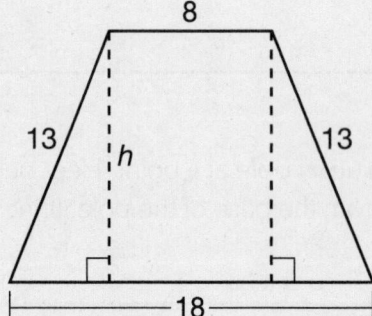

9 A tent has a square floor that measures 9.6 feet on each side. There is a 10-foot zipper in the center of the front panel of the tent that runs from the top of the tent to the floor. The tent has a center pole for support. Find the length of the center pole to the nearest tenth of a foot. Show your work.

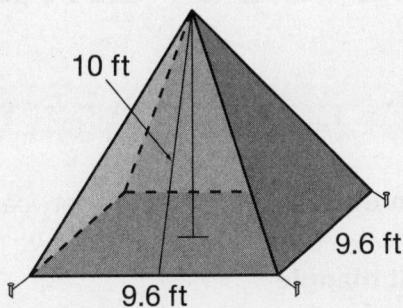

10 Suppose a spider was able to create one thread that would extend from the top-right back corner of a room to the bottom-left front corner. Approximately how long would that thread need to be for the room below to the nearest tenth of a foot? The path of the spider's thread is shown with a dotted line. (Hint: You will use the Pythagorean theorem twice.)

Finding Distance between Two Points on the Coordinate Plane

1 GETTING THE IDEA

You can use the **Pythagorean theorem** to find the distance between two points in the coordinate plane. The diagram below shows how the distance, d, between two points can be represented by the length of the **hypotenuse** of a **right triangle**.

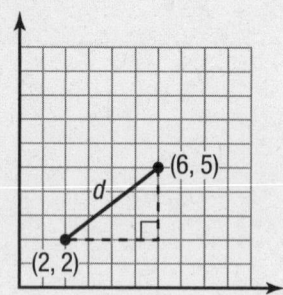

Find the horizontal and vertical distances that are the lengths of the **legs** of the right triangle. Then substitute into the formula $a^2 + b^2 = c^2$ to find the distance, d.

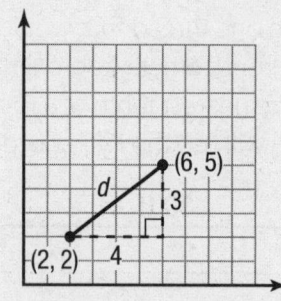

horizontal distance from (2, 2) to (6, 5) = $|2 - 6| = |-4| = 4$

vertical distance from (2, 2) to (6, 5) = $|2 - 5| = |-3| = 3$

$$a^2 + b^2 = c^2$$

$$4^2 + 3^2 = c^2$$

$$16 + 9 = c^2$$

$$25 = c^2$$

$$5 = c$$

The distance between the points is 5 units.

Example 1

Find the distance between the points (1, 6) and (7, 2). Round your answer to the nearest tenth.

Strategy   **Use the Pythagorean theorem.**

Step 1   Plot the points, and connect them with a segment. Then draw a right triangle that has the segment as its hypotenuse.

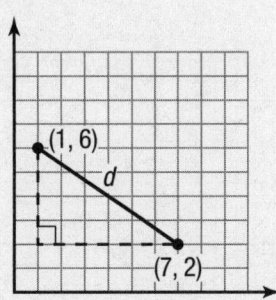

Step 2   Identify a, b, and c.

The length of the hypotenuse is d, so let $c = d$.

Use absolute value to find the horizontal and vertical distances that are the lengths of the legs.

horizontal distance from (1, 6) to (7, 2) $= |1 - 7| = |-6| = 6$

vertical distance from (1, 6) to (7, 2) $= |6 - 2| = 4$

The lengths of the legs are 4 units and 6 units. So, $a = 4$ and $b = 6$.

Step 3   Substitute into $a^2 + b^2 = c^2$. Then solve the equation for d.

$$a^2 + b^2 = c^2$$
$$4^2 + 6^2 = d^2$$
$$16 + 36 = d^2$$
$$52 = d^2$$
$$\sqrt{52} = d$$
$$7.2 \approx d$$

Solution   **The distance between the points (1, 6) and (7, 2) is approximately 7.2 units.**

Example 2

Find the distance between the points $(-4, -5)$ and $(3, 0)$. Round your answer to the nearest tenth.

Strategy   **Use the Pythagorean theorem.**

Step 1   Plot the points, and connect them with a segment. Then draw a right triangle that has the segment as its hypotenuse.

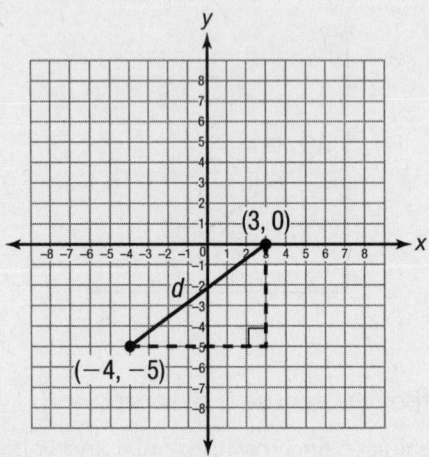

Step 2   Identify a, b, and c.

The length of the hypotenuse is d, so let $c = d$.

Use absolute value to find the horizontal and vertical distances that are the lengths of the legs.

horizontal distance from $(-4, -5)$ to $(3, 0) = |-4 - 3| = |-7| = 7$

vertical distance from $(-4, -5)$ to $(3, 0) = |-5 - 0| = 5$

The lengths of the legs are 7 units and 5 units. So, $a = 7$ and $b = 5$.

Step 3   Substitute into $a^2 + b^2 = c^2$. Then solve the equation for d.

$$a^2 + b^2 = c^2$$
$$7^2 + 5^2 = d^2$$
$$49 + 25 = d^2$$
$$74 = d^2$$
$$\sqrt{74} = d$$
$$8.6 \approx d$$

Solution   **The distance between the points $(-4, -5)$ and $(3, 0)$ is approximately 8.6 units.**

Example 3

Cali drew the map below showing her house and the houses of two of her friends. On the map, each unit square represents 1 square mile. What is the distance between Jenna's house and Mira's house to the nearest tenth of a mile?

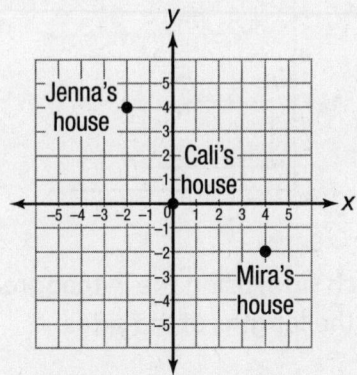

Strategy   Use the Pythagorean theorem.

Step 1   Connect the points representing Jenna's house and Mira's house with a segment. Then draw a right triangle that has the segment as its hypotenuse.

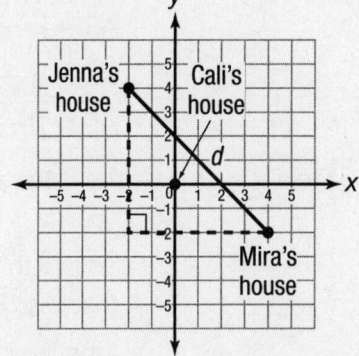

Step 2   Identify a, b, and c.

The length of the hypotenuse is d, so let $c = d$.

Use absolute value to find the horizontal and vertical distances that are the lengths of the legs.

horizontal distance from $(-2, 4)$ to $(4, -2) =$ $|-2 - 4| = |-6| = 6$

vertical distance from $(-2, 4)$ to $(4, -2) = |4 - (-2)| = |4 + 2| = 6$

The legs are both 6 units long. So, $a = 6$ and $b = 6$.

Step 3   Substitute into $a^2 + b^2 = c^2$. Then solve the equation for d.

$$a^2 + b^2 = c^2$$
$$6^2 + 6^2 = d^2$$
$$36 + 36 = d^2$$
$$72 = d^2$$
$$\sqrt{72} = d$$
$$8.5 \approx d$$

Solution   The distance between Jenna's house and Mira's house is approximately 8.5 miles.

Example 4

Find the perimeter of the trapezoid.

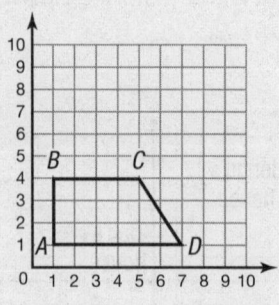

Strategy   Find the length of each side, using the Pythagorean theorem where necessary. Then find the sum of the lengths of the sides.

Step 1   Find the lengths of the horizontal and vertical sides.

Use absolute value to find the horizontal and vertical distances that are the lengths of sides $\overline{AB}$, $\overline{BC}$, and $\overline{AD}$.

$AB = |1 - 4| = |-3| = 3$ units

$BC = |1 - 5| = |-4| = 4$ units

$AD = |1 - 7| = |-6| = 6$ units

Step 2   Use the Pythagorean theorem to find the length of the slanted side.

To find the length of side $\overline{CD}$, draw a right triangle that has $\overline{CD}$ as its hypotenuse.

Identify a, b, and c.

The length of the hypotenuse is x, so let $c = x$.

The vertical distance is equal to AB, so is 3 units.

Use absolute value to find the horizontal distance.

horizontal distance from $(5, 1)$ to $(7, 1) = |5 - 7| = |-2| = 2$

The lengths of the legs are 3 units and 2 units. So, $a = 3$ and $b = 2$.

$$a^2 + b^2 = c^2$$

$$3^2 + 2^2 = x^2$$

$$9 + 4 = x^2$$

$$13 = x^2$$

$$\sqrt{13} = x$$

$$3.6 \approx x$$

So, the length of side $\overline{CD}$ is approximately 3.6 units.

Step 3   Find the sum of the lengths of the sides.

$$3 + 4 + 6 + 3.6 = 16.6$$

Solution   The perimeter is approximately 16.6 units.

② COACHED EXAMPLE

Find the approximate length of the longer diagonal of the kite *ABCD* **to the nearest tenth of a unit.**

Draw the diagonals of the kite, $\overline{AC}$ and $\overline{BD}$. Which is the longer diagonal? _____

Draw a right triangle using the longer diagonal as its hypotenuse. Label the diagonal "*x*".

Look at the right triangle you drew. Identify the lengths of *a*, *b*, and *c*.

    $a = $ _____ units

    $b = $ _____ units

    $c = $ _____ units

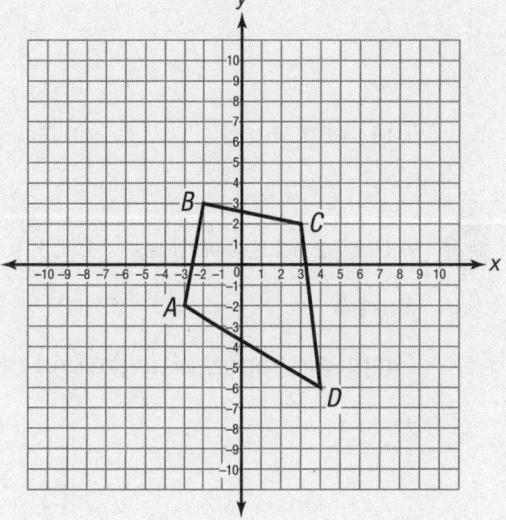

Write and solve an equation to find the value of *x*. **Round your answer to the nearest tenth.**

$$a^2 + b^2 = c^2$$

$$\underline{\hspace{2em}}^2 + \underline{\hspace{2em}}^2 = x^2$$

$$\underline{\hspace{1.5em}} + \underline{\hspace{1.5em}} = x^2$$

$$\underline{\hspace{2em}} = x^2$$

$$\sqrt{\underline{\hspace{2em}}} = x$$

$$\underline{\hspace{2em}} \approx x$$

The length of the longer diagonal is approximately _____ **units.**

1 Find the perimeter of rhombus *ABCD* below.

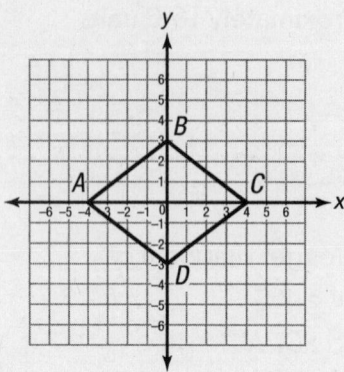

The perimeter is _____ units.

2 A trapezoid has vertices (−6, 2), (6, 7), (6, −4), and (−6, −4).

Part A

Graph the trapezoid on the grid below.

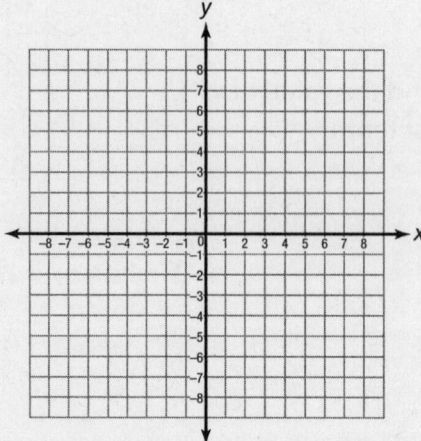

Part B

What is the perimeter of the trapezoid? Show your work.

3 The map below shows Tyler's house and the houses of two of his friends, Pedro and Jake. On the map, each unit square represents 1 square mile. Select True or False for each statement.

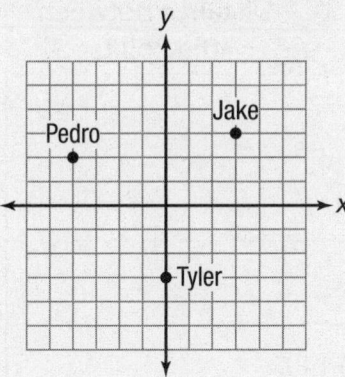

A. Tyler lives closer to Jake than to Pedro. ○ True ○ False

B. Pedro lives closer to Jake than to Tyler. ○ True ○ False

C. Jake lives about 0.4 mile closer to Tyler than to Pedro. ○ True ○ False

D. The sum of the distances between the boys' houses is less than 18 miles. ○ True ○ False

E. The sum of the distances between the boys' houses is greater than 20 miles. ○ True ○ False

4 A kite has vertices $(-6, -3)$, $(-5, 2)$, $(6, 5)$, and $(-1, -4)$. What is the difference between the lengths of the two diagonals of the kite? Round your answer to the nearest hundredth of a unit. Show your work.

5 Use expressions from the box to complete the table.

Points	Distance between the Points
$(-3, 5)$ and $(6, -1)$	
$(2, -3)$ and $(-2, -6)$	
$(7, -2)$ and $(3, -1)$	
$(-2, -4)$ and $(4, -1)$	

$\sqrt{9^2 + 4^2}$

$\sqrt{8^2 + 7^2}$

$\sqrt{4^2 + 3^2}$

$\sqrt{4^2 + 1^2}$

$\sqrt{9^2 + 6^2}$

$\sqrt{6^2 + 3^2}$

6 A coordinate grid is superimposed on a map of the county park. The grid shows a rectangular playground with vertices $(1, 4)$, $(5.5, 7)$, $(3, 1)$, and $(7.5, 4)$. Each unit on the grid represents 10 feet.

Part A

Graph the rectangle that represents the playground on the grid below.

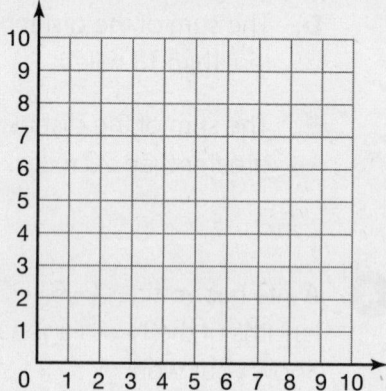

Part B

What is the area of the playground? Round your answer to the nearest square foot. Show your work.

7 Circle the numbers that make the sentence true

−6		−8
−4		−3
3		−1
5		5

The distance between the points (4, ____) and (____ , −7) is 13 units.

8 A plan for a mosaic made from tiles calls for triangles of different sizes and shapes. Adrianna is drawing patterns for the different shapes on grid paper. The figure below shows one side of what will be a tile in the shape of an equilateral triangle.

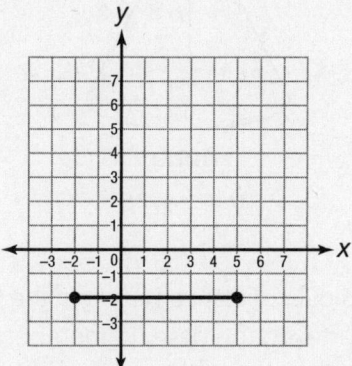

If the third vertex of the triangle is located in the first quadrant, what are the coordinates of the vertex? Round the coordinates to the nearest hundredth. Use words, numbers, and diagrams to justify your answer.

Understanding Volume of Cylinders, Cones, and Spheres

1 GETTING THE IDEA

The **volume** of a solid figure is the measure of the amount of space it occupies. For solid figures like the ones shown below, you can use formulas to find each volume. The volume formulas for these solid figures are all closely related to the formula for the area of a circle, $A = \pi r^2$.

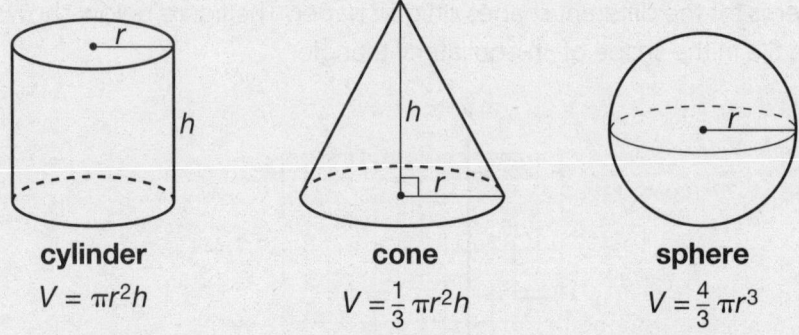

cylinder
$V = \pi r^2 h$

cone
$V = \frac{1}{3}\pi r^2 h$

sphere
$V = \frac{4}{3}\pi r^3$

The height of a cylinder is the perpendicular distance between the two bases. The height of a cone is the perpendicular distance from the vertex to the base. Remember, the **radius** of a circle is a line segment that can be drawn from any point on a circle to the center of the circle.

Example 1

The disk shown below is a cylinder. The volume is 450 cm^3. Find the approximate height of the disk.

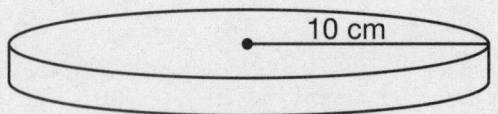

10 cm

Strategy Choose the formula, substitute the given information, and solve for the height. Use 3.14 for π.

Step 1 Choose the formula you need.

For a cylinder, the volume formula is $V = \pi r^2 h$.

Step 2 Substitute the given information in the formula, and simplify.

$450 = \pi(10^2)h$

$450 \approx (3.14)(100)h$

$450 \approx 314h$

Step 3   Solve for h.

$$450 \approx 314h$$

$$\frac{450}{314} \approx \frac{314h}{314}$$

$$1.43 \approx h$$

Solution   The height of the cylinder is about 1.43 cm.

When you use 3.14 in place of π, the result is always an approximate value. To record an exact value, do not substitute a value for π. For example, the volume can be shown in the form 143π cubic units.

Example 2

Find an exact value for the volume of the cone shown below.

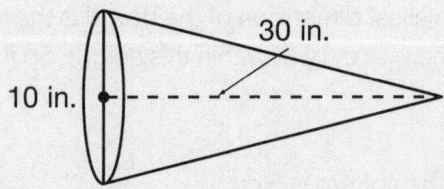

Strategy   Choose the formula you need, and substitute the given information. Leave π in the answer so it will be exact.

Step 1   Choose the formula you need.

For a cone, the volume formula is $V = \frac{1}{3}\pi r^2 h$.

Step 2   Find the radius.

The diameter, d, is 10 inches, so:

$r = \frac{10}{2} = 5$ inches

Step 3   Substitute the given information in the formula, and solve.

$$V = \frac{1}{3}\pi(5^2)(30)$$

$$= \frac{1}{3}(5^2)(30)\pi$$

$$= \frac{1}{3}(25)(30)\pi$$

$$= 250\pi$$

Solution   The exact volume of the cone is 250π in.^{3}

Example 3

Find the approximate volume of the largest sphere that can fit inside the box shown below.

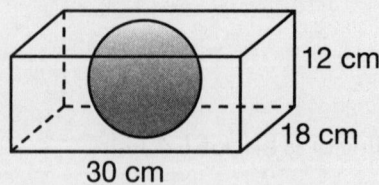

12 cm
18 cm
30 cm

Strategy   **Choose the formula you need, and substitute the given information. Use 3.14 for π to find an approximate volume.**

Step 1   Choose the formula you need.

For a sphere, the volume formula is $V = \frac{4}{3}\pi r^3$.

Step 2   Find the radius of the sphere.

Choose the smallest dimension of the box. It is the height, 12 cm. The largest sphere that will fit in the box must fit within this height. So its diameter must be 12 cm.

$$r = \frac{12}{2} = 6$$

The radius of the sphere is 6 cm.

Step 3   Substitute the given information in the formula, and solve.

$$V = \frac{4}{3}\pi(6^3)$$

$$V \approx \frac{4}{3}(3.14)(216)$$

$$V \approx 904.32$$

Solution   **The volume of the largest sphere is about 904.32 cm³.**

Example 4

A cylinder with a radius of 4 centimeters is partially filled with water. If you drop a solid glass ball into the cylinder, you raise the water level by 1 centimeter. Find the approximate volume of the water displaced by the glass ball. (The volume of the displaced water equals the volume of the glass ball.)

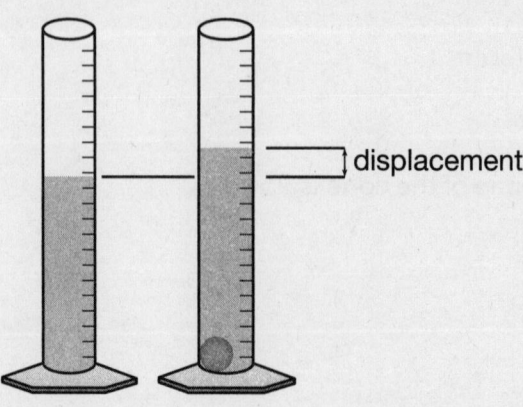

displacement

Strategy   Choose the formula you need, and substitute the given information. Use 3.14 for π to find an approximate volume.

> **Step 1**   Choose the formula you need.
>
> For a cylinder, the volume formula is $V = \pi r^2 h$.

> **Step 2**   Substitute the given information in the formula, and solve.
>
> The glass ball displaces the water by 1 centimeter, so use 1 centimeter as the height.
>
> $V = \pi(4^2)(1)$
>
> $V \approx (3.14)(16)(1)$
>
> $V \approx 50.24$

Solution   The water displaced by the glass ball has a volume of about 50.24 cm^3.

Example 5

A manufacturer makes a plastic cone puzzle. The dark gray pieces are half the volume of the cone. Find the approximate amount of plastic needed to make the dark gray puzzle pieces. Round your answer to the nearest hundredth of a cubic inch.

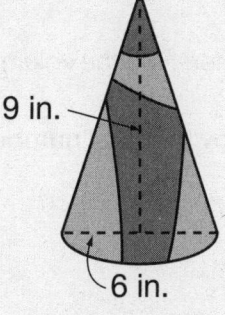

9 in.

6 in.

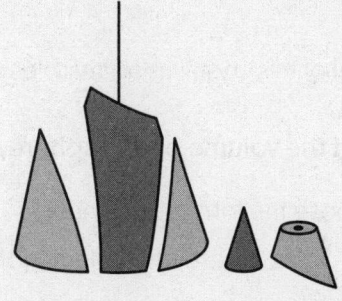

Strategy   Choose the formula you need, and substitute the given information. Divide by 2 to find half of the volume.

> **Step 1**   Choose the formula you need.
>
> For a cone, the volume formula is $V = \frac{1}{3}\pi r^2 h$.

> **Step 2**   Find the radius.
>
> $r = \frac{6}{2} = 3$ in.

> **Step 3**   Substitute the given information in the formula, and simplify.
>
> V of cone $= \frac{1}{3}\pi(3^2)(9)$
>
> $V \approx \frac{1}{3}(3.14)(9)(9)$
>
> $V \approx 84.78$

Step 4   Find the volume of the dark gray puzzle pieces.

V of half the cone $\approx 84.78 \div 2$

$V \approx 42.39$

Solution   The amount of plastic needed to make the dark gray puzzle pieces is about 42.39 in.^{3}

Example 6

When a solid crystallizes, the particles that form, shaped like spheres, pack together as tightly as possible. The arrangement below displays one layer of a zinc crystal.

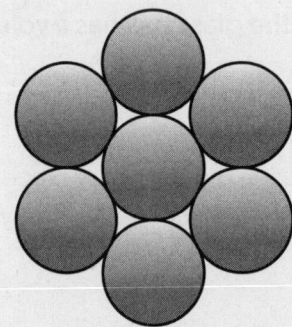

Maria made a model of this crystal using marbles with a 2-cm diameter. Find the volume of Maria's model.

Strategy   **Find the volume of one sphere, then multiply it by the total number of spheres.**

Step 1   Choose the formula you need.

For a sphere, the volume formula is $V = \frac{4}{3}\pi r^3$.

Step 2   Find the radius of one sphere.

$2 \div 2 = 1$

$r = 1$ cm

Step 3   Substitute the given information in the formula to find the volume of one sphere.

$V = \frac{4}{3}\pi(1^3)$

$V = \frac{4}{3}\pi$

Step 4   Find the volume of 7 spheres.

$7 \cdot \frac{4}{3}\pi = \frac{28}{3}\pi$

Solution   The volume of the model is $\frac{28}{3}\pi$ cm^3.

A sphere fits exactly inside a cylinder as shown below. The sphere takes up $\frac{2}{3}$ the volume of the cylinder. Find the volume of the cylinder if the radius of the sphere is 15 cm.

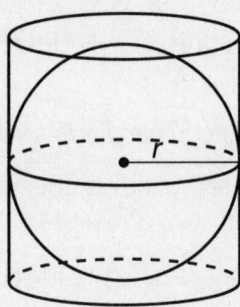

Find the volume of the sphere.

The formula for the volume of a sphere is _____.

So, the volume of the sphere is _____ π.

Write an equation to find the volume of the cylinder.

_____ $= \frac{2}{3} \cdot x$

$x =$ _____

The volume of the cylinder is _____ π cm^3, or approximately _____.

1 Select True or False for each statement.

    A. If you know the diameter of a sphere, you can find its radius.   ○ True   ○ False

    B. A volume formula for a sphere, cone, or cylinder must   ○ True   ○ False
include the irrational number π.

    C. If you know the radius of a cone, you can find its volume.   ○ True   ○ False

    D. If a cone and a sphere have the same radius, the volume   ○ True   ○ False
of the sphere must be greater.

    E. To find an exact volume for a sphere, use the fraction $\frac{22}{7}$ for π.   ○ True   ○ False

2 Four students wrote expressions to describe the volume of a cone. The cone has a height of
15 cm and a diameter of 8 cm. Each student made a different mistake. What mistake did each
student make?

Dan used $V = \pi(4^2)(15)$.   Jason used $V = \frac{1}{3}\pi(4)(15)$.

Lucia used $V = \frac{1}{3}\pi(8^2)(15)$.   Yolanda used $\frac{1}{3}\pi(15^2)(4)$.

3 A cylinder has a diameter that is twice its height. Another cylinder has a height that is twice
its diameter. Which cylinder has the greater volume? Use words and numbers to justify
your answer.

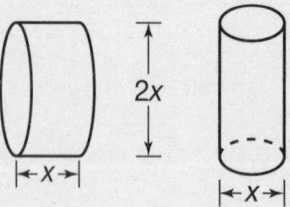

4 A large water fountain has a hemispherical bowl with a diameter of 16 feet. (A hemisphere is half of a sphere.)

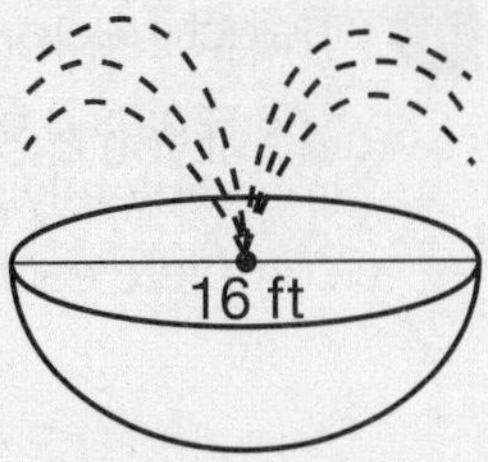

Part A

How many cubic feet of water are needed to fill the bowl? Round your answer to the nearest hundredth of a cubic foot.

Part B

One cubic foot holds about 7.5 gallons. How many gallons, to the nearest whole gallon, are needed to fill the bowl of the fountain?

5 The diagram shows a watering trough for farm animals.

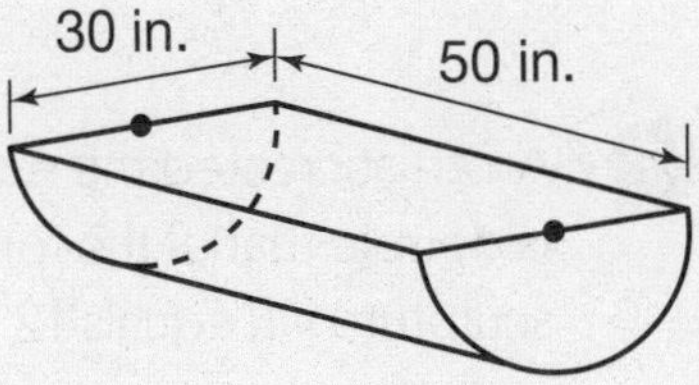

Part A

Find the volume of water the trough will hold to the nearest cubic inch.

Part B

One gallon of water takes up approximately 231 cubic inches. Find the capacity of the trough to the nearest gallon.

6 The frozen yogurt cone shown is made from a cone and a hemisphere. The radius is 6 cm. The total height of the figure is 24 cm. Suppose the cone is completely packed with frozen yogurt. Use numbers from the box to complete each statement.

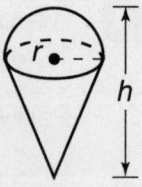

3
6
12
18
24
144
216
288
648

The height of the cone is _____ cm.

The height of the hemisphere is _____ cm.

The exact volume of the cone is _____ π cm^3.

The exact volume of the hemisphere is _____ π cm^3.

7 An artist created the sculpture shown with concrete. The radius of the bottom hemisphere is double that of the top hemisphere. Find the *exact* total volume of concrete used for the sculpture if R equals 12 feet.

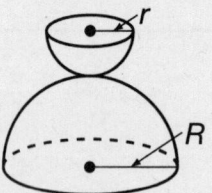

8 Compare the volume of each solid figure to 1,000 cubic units. Write the letter for each figure in the correct box.

Figure A: cone with radius of 12 and height of 5	**Figure B:** sphere with radius of 12	**Figure C:** cylinder with radius of 12 and height of 5
Figure D: cone with diameter of 12 and height of 20	**Figure E:** sphere with diameter of 12	**Figure F:** cylinder with diameter of 12 and height of 10

Less Than 1,000 Cubic Units	Greater Than 1,000 Cubic Units

9 A gigantic balloon used for a parade is shaped like an ice cream cone. The radius of the cone and the hemisphere is 12 feet. The height of the cone is 60 feet. If the balloon is filled with helium at the rate of 70 cubic feet per minute, about how many minutes will it take to fill the balloon? Round each volume to the nearest tenth of a cubic foot. Round the time to the nearest minute.

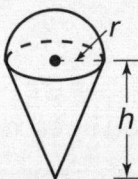

Volume of hemisphere: _____

Volume of cone: _____

Total volume: _____

Time to fill the balloon: _____

1 Jada makes the drawing shown below of her living room.

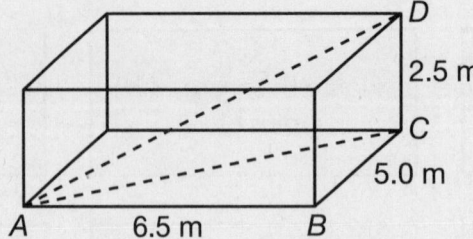

Part A

Find the length of $\overline{AC}$ to the nearest tenth of a meter. Show your work.

Part B

Find the length of $\overline{AD}$ to the nearest tenth of a meter. Show your work.

2 The vertices of a triangle on a coordinate plane are $(-4, 4)$, $(-2, 4)$, and $(-1, 6)$. What are the coordinates of the image triangle produced by each of the following rotations?

a 90° counterclockwise rotation about the origin

(_____, _____), (_____, _____), (_____, _____)

a 270° counterclockwise rotation about the origin

(_____, _____), (_____, _____), (_____, _____)

a 180° clockwise rotation about the origin

(_____, _____), (_____, _____), (_____, _____)

3 A builder uses the design below to create one wall of a room. All of the vertical beams of the wall are parallel. Identify the measure of each labeled angle in the design.

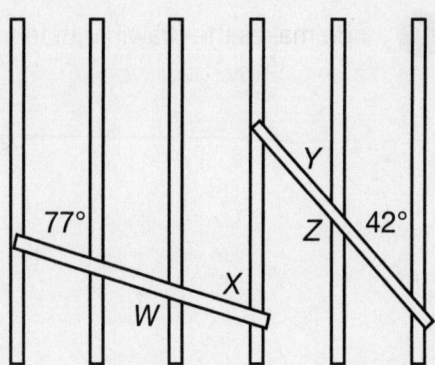

$m\angle W =$ _____

$m\angle Y =$ _____

$m\angle X =$ _____

$m\angle Z =$ _____

4 How does the diagram illustrate the Pythagorean theorem?

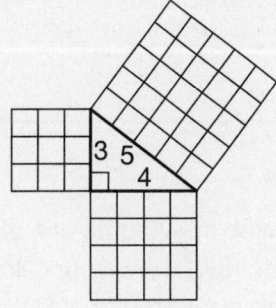

5 The figure shows quadrilateral *JKLM* on a coordinate grid. The figure is reflected over the *x*-axis to form quadrilateral *J'K'L'M'*. Select True or False for each statement.

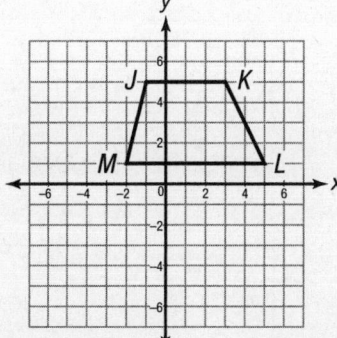

A. $\angle K \cong \angle J'$ ○ True   ○ False

B. $\overline{J'M'} \cong \overline{JM}$ ○ True   ○ False

C. $\angle L \cong \angle L'$ ○ True   ○ False

D. Vertex *K'* will be 5 units   ○ True   ○ False
from the *y*-axis.

E. $\overline{J'K'}$ will be parallel to $\overline{L'M'}$.   ○ True   ○ False

F. $\angle M \cong \angle K'$ ○ True   ○ False

6 Find the perimeter of right triangle *PQR* shown below. Round your answer to the nearest tenth of a unit. Show your work.

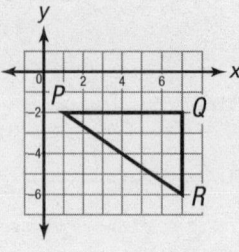

7 The diagram shows a way to determine the volume of a plastic cup by extending the sides to form a cone. For the questions that follow, show your calculations, use 3.14 for π, and round your answers to the nearest tenth of a cubic centimeter.

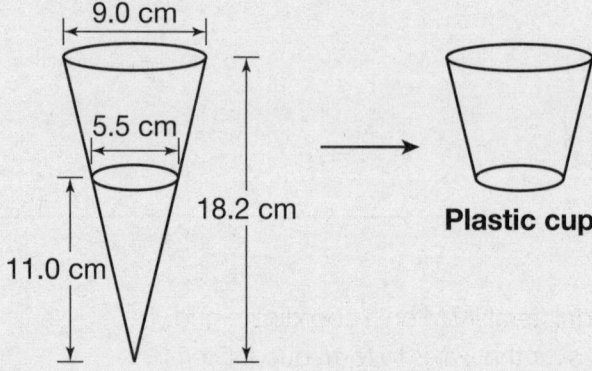

Part A

What is the approximate volume of the large cone?

Part B

What is the approximate volume of the small cone?

Part C

Use your previous measurements to determine the volume of the plastic cup.

8 Describe a sequence of three transformations of △*ABC* that will produce the image △*A'B'C'*.

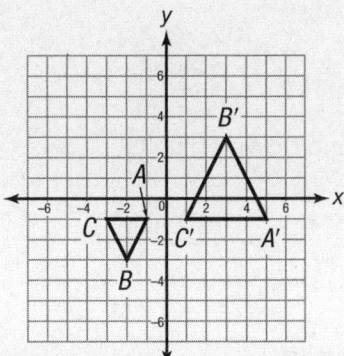

9 Circle the number or measure that makes each statement true.

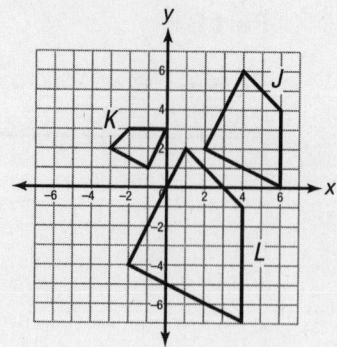

Image K is produced by dilating figure J by the scale factor [3/2 | 1/2 | 2] and

then rotating it [45° | 90° | 180°] counterclockwise around the origin.

Image L is produced by dilating figure J by the scale factor [2 | 3 | 3/2] and

then translating it left [2 units | 4 units | 5 units] and down [5 units | 6 units | 7 units] .

10 Lines a and b in the figure are parallel.
Use angles from the figure to complete the statements about each type of angle.

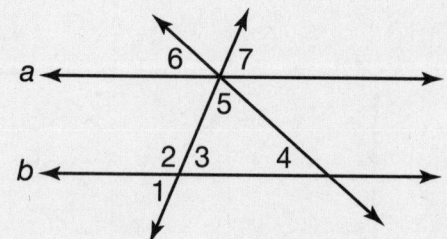

Vertical angles: ∠3 ≅ _____

Corresponding angles: ∠4 ≅ _____

Exterior angle of a triangle: m∠5 + m∠4 = m_____

Summer Camp Games

Every year at Lake Pythagoras Summer Camp, the campers divide into three teams: the Red Team, the Blue Team, and the Green Team. These three teams compete in several games. Camp counselors Ali, Cameron, and Jake are planning the games.

Part A The map below shows the campgrounds. The first game requires each team to find their team cup hidden by Ali, Cameron, and Jake in the surrounding woods. Each team starts at the fishing pier. Ali plans to hide the Red Team's cup 60 yards west and 80 yards north of the pier. How far will the cup be from the starting point?

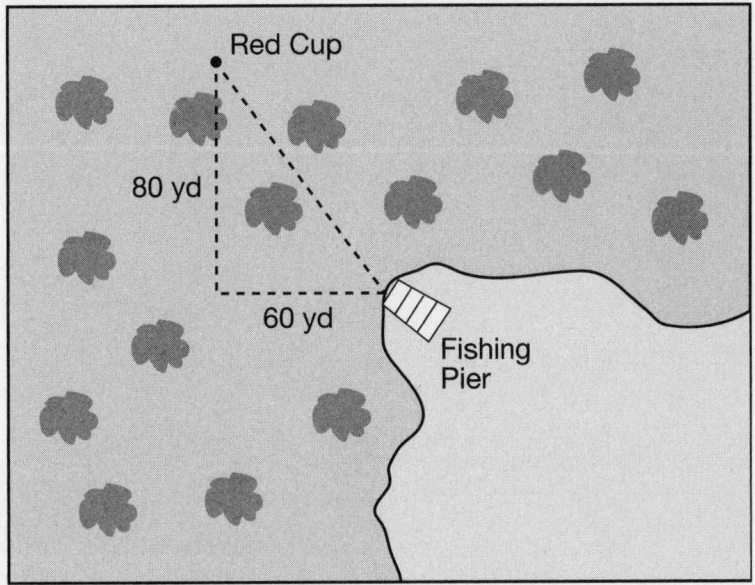

Part B Notice that the dashed lines to the Red Team's cup form a triangle. Cameron decides to find a location to hide the Green Team's cup by rotating this triangle 90° counterclockwise around the pier. Will the Green cup be the same distance from the pier as the Red cup? How do you know?

Part C Jake wants to hide the Blue Team's cup the same distance from the pier as the other two cups. Describe a transformation or a series of transformations that he can apply to the dashed-line triangle to find a good hiding place for the Blue Team's cup.

Part D Ali, Cameron, and Jake decide to try to trick the teams by placing a decoy cup 50 yards from the pier. Describe a transformation or a series of transformations that they can apply to the dashed-line triangle to find a location for the decoy.

DOMAIN 5

Statistics and Probability

8.SP.1, 8.SP.2

Understanding Scatter Plots

1 GETTING THE IDEA

A **scatter plot** is a graph that shows the relationship between two variables in a data set. Each point on the scatter plot represents an ordered pair of data. This table and the graph show the same bivariate data. **Bivariate data** involve two variables. The patterns shown from the plotted points provide a representation of how the data are related.

Car Age (in years)	Value (in thousands of dollars)
9.5	3.2
5	6.8
5.5	6.2
8.75	3.6
1	7.2
1.5	7.5
2	7.3
3.25	6.5
6	5.3
4.25	7.1
4.75	5.8
0.25	8.5
1	8.9
6	9.2
7.25	4.2
3	7.3
8	4.6

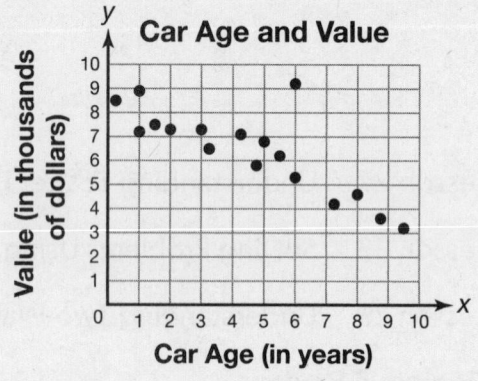

When comparing the table and the scatter plot, notice that the scatter plot shows that older cars have less value than newer cars in most cases. This relationship is much more obvious in the scatter plot than it is in the table.

An **outlier** is a value that is much greater or lesser than most of the other values in the data set. You can easily identify an outlier on this graph. The point at (6, 9.2) is an outlier, showing that one of the 6-year-old cars has a value considerably greater than most of the other cars that are about the same age.

Data can cluster around a line or around a point. A **cluster** is a set of closely grouped data. The data points on this graph appear to cluster around a line. Because of this, you can say the data set has a **linear association**. If the points do not cluster around a line, the data have a **nonlinear association**.

A linear association can be positive or negative. Because the line on this graph has a negative slope, the data have a **negative association**. As the age increases, the value decreases. If both data sets increase together, the data have a **positive association**.

The association between two data sets can also be described as strong or weak. The association shown on this scatter plot is strong since the data are very closely clustered in the shape of a line.

Example 1

Describe the association, if any, of the data shown on the scatter plot.

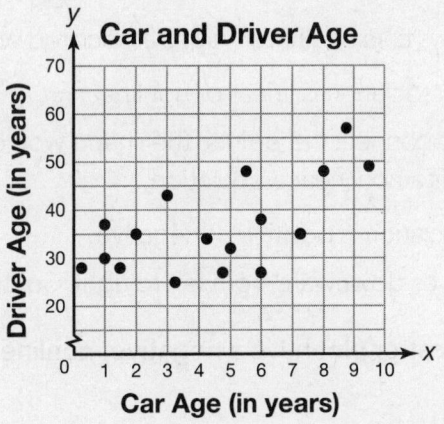

Strategy   Use the labels on the graph, and identify the association of the data as positive, negative, or no association.

> **Step 1**   Identify the variables.
>
> The horizontal scale shows the independent variable, the age of the car. The dependent variable, the age of the driver, is on the vertical scale.

> **Step 2**   Determine if the association is linear or nonlinear.
>
> The points on the graph are not randomly scattered. They generally move from the bottom left corner to the top right. The association is linear.

> **Step 3**   Identify attributes of the slope of the linear association.
>
> The data slope upward from left to right. So, the association is positive. For this group of car owners, older cars tend to have older drivers.

Solution   The data of this scatter plot have a positive, linear association.

Example 2

Describe the association of the data, if any, on this scatter plot.

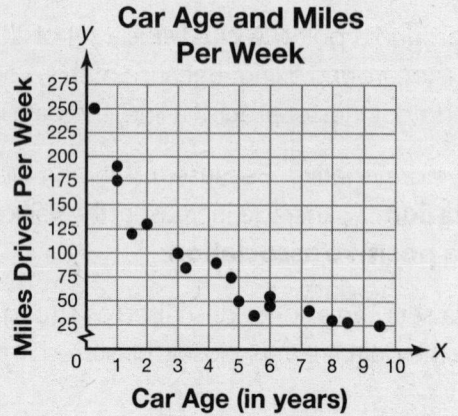

Car Age and Miles Per Week

Strategy	Identify the association of points on the graph.
Step 1	Identify the variables.
	The plot shows cars of different ages associated with miles driven per week.
Step 2	Determine if the association is linear or nonlinear.
	If you were to connect the points, the shape would look more like a curve than a line. So, this is a nonlinear association.
Step 3	Identify if the association is positive or negative.
	The data moves downward from left to right. So, the association is negative.
Solution	**The data of this scatter plot have a negative, nonlinear association.**

Example 3

The data set shows grades for individual students in two of their classes. Each pair of scores are the scores earned by one student. Construct a scatter plot for these data.

History Grade	93	82	93	92	75	68	87	85	73	85	75	78	70	96	88	88	98
English Grade	82	80	95	74	78	75	95	86	68	68	98	90	95	89	78	72	75

Strategy   Look at the range of the data set to create the scale for each axis.

Step 1   Choose the variables for the axes.

In this set of data, one set is not dependent on the other. So it does not matter which axis is used for either data set. Since the history grades are on top, you can use the horizontal axis for those grades. Then the English grades will be on the vertical axis.

Step 2   Identify the ranges for the scales.

The lowest grade is 68 for both sets of data. The highest grade is 98 for both sets of data. Labeling each axis by 5s from 65 to 100 will show all the data for both sets.

Step 3   Plot one point for each ordered pair.

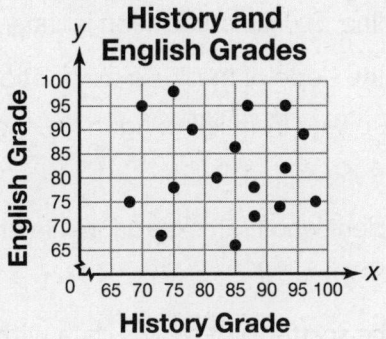

Solution   The scatter plot of students' grades in history and English is shown in Step 3.

Example 4

Interpret this scatter plot.

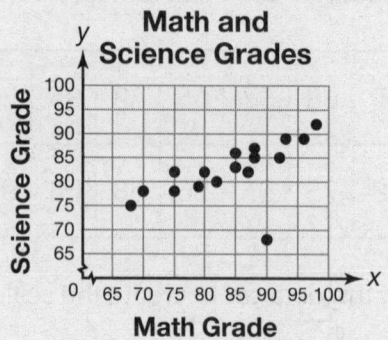

Strategy   Describe the variables shown. Identify the association, and explain what it tells about the variables. Make a conjecture about any outliers.

Step 1   Describe the variables.

Each point on the scatter plot shows the math and science grade for an individual student.

Step 2   Determine if the association is linear or nonlinear.

The points on the graph are not randomly scattered. They generally move from left to right along a line. So, the association is linear.

Step 3   Identify attributes of the slope of the linear association.

The data move upward from left to right. So, the association is positive.

Step 4   Explain outliers.

There is one student who is an exception. He or she has a high grade in math, but did not score high in science.

Solution   The math and science scatter plot shows data with a positive linear association. The plot shows that students who score high in math also score high in science, except for one outlier.

A straight line that shows the linear relationship between points of a scatter plot is called a line of best fit. A **line of best fit** may pass through all the data points, some of the points, or none of the points. When drawing a line of best fit, try drawing the line as close as possible to all points with an equal number of data points above and below the line, while ignoring outliers. You can also use a graphing calculator or computer spreadsheet program to construct lines of best fit.

The line of best fit can help you determine the strength of an association. If the data are closely grouped around the line of best fit, the association is considered to be strong. If the data are loosely scattered around the line of best fit, the association is considered to be weak.

Example 5

This scatter plot shows students' time spent per week on video games compared to their grade point average. Sketch a line of best fit on this scatter plot. How strong is the association between the variables?

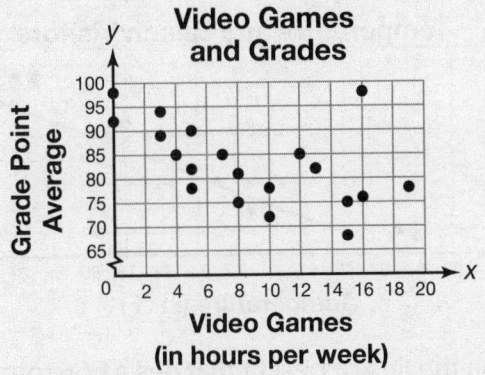

Strategy   Use a ruler to divide the points equally on both sides of the line of best fit.

Step 1   Use a ruler to draw a line that closely follows the linear pattern of the data, ignoring the outlier.

> The line may not go through any of the data points, but about half the points should be above the line and about half should be below the line. The line does not need to connect the first and last points.

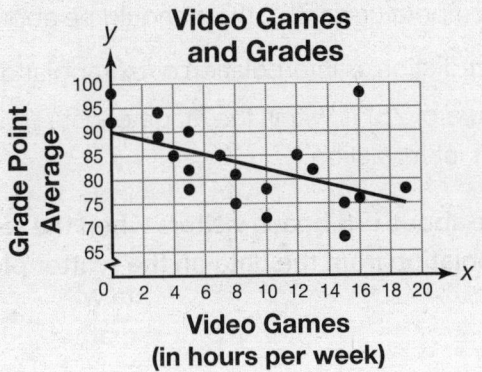

Step 2   Assess the strength of the association.

> Look at how close the points are to the line of best fit. The data points are not very close to the line of best fit. So, the association is weak.

Solution   **The association is a weak, negative, linear association. For this data set, students who spend more time on games generally receive lower grades.**

When a scatter plot shows a strong association, you can use a line of best fit to make predictions. If your prediction is in between points you are given, you **interpolate**. If your prediction is outside the range of the data you are given, you **extrapolate**. Usually, interpolating data is more accurate than extrapolating data. Also, the further out from the data you estimate, the less accurate your prediction is likely to be.

Example 6

Use this scatter plot to predict the number of beach visitors when the temperature is 75°F. Describe your prediction as interpolation or extrapolation.

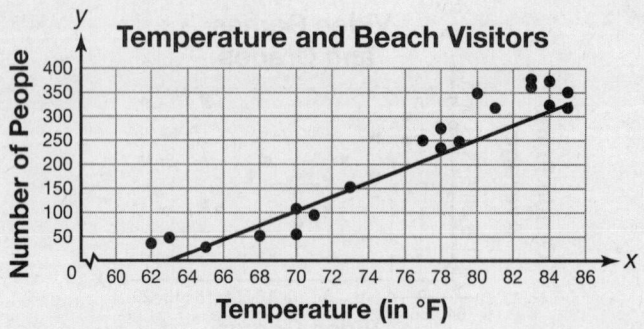

Strategy Find the point on the line of best fit that has a horizontal coordinate of 75.

Step 1 Find 75°F on the horizontal axis.

The axis is numbered by 2s, so the point for 75 degrees is halfway between 74 and 76.

Step 2 Find the point on the line of best fit with a horizontal coordinate of 75.

Find the vertical coordinate associated with 75 degrees. The point on the line of best fit is approximately (75, 175).

Step 3 Use the point on the line of best fit to make a prediction.

When the temperature is 75°, there should be about 175 beach visitors.

Step 4 Describe your prediction as interpolation or extrapolation.

A temperature of 75° is within the range of data given on the scatter plot. The prediction is interpolation.

Solution There should be about 175 beach visitors when the temperature is 75°. This is based on interpolation from the data on the scatter plot.

Use this scatter plot to predict the number of library visitors when the temperature is 90°F. Describe your prediction as interpolation or extrapolation. Give a reason why this prediction might be too low.

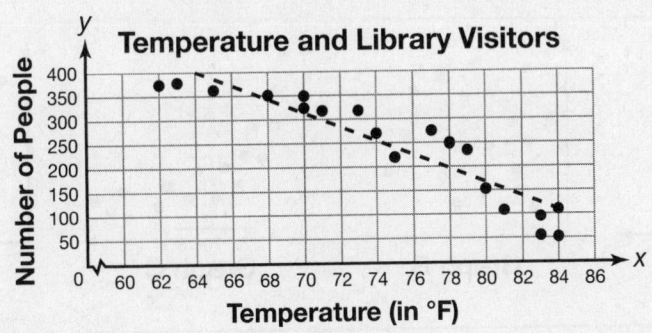

Describe the association. It is _____.

To estimate the number of visitors for 90 degrees, use _____ because 90 degrees is _____ the range of the data.

Extending the line of best fit shows that _____ will visit the library when it is 90°F.

This prediction might be too low because, when it gets really hot,

_____.

Extending the line of best fit to _____ degrees results in a prediction of _____ people. This uses _____ because 90 degrees is _____ the range of the given data. A prediction of _____ people might be too _____ because when it gets really hot, _____.

1 **Part A**

Describe the association shown on each scatter plot.

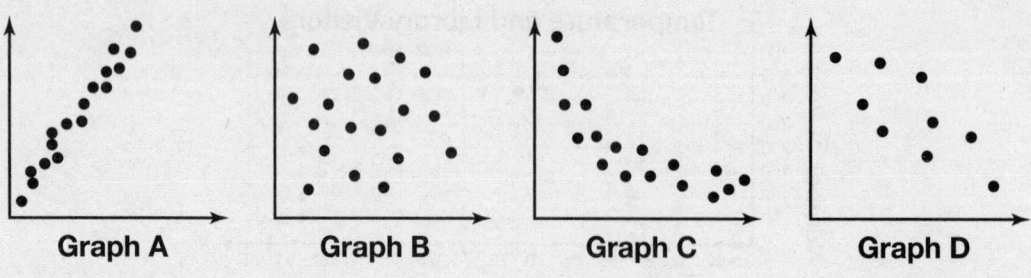

Graph A   **Graph B**   **Graph C**   **Graph D**

Part B

Which plot most likely shows the relationship between shoe sizes and math grades? Give a reason for your answer.

Part C

Which plot most likely shows the relationship between shoe size and height? Give a reason for your answer.

2 **Part A**

Use the bivariate data in these tables to construct a scatter plot on the grid provided.

x	8.8	4.6	9.2	8.3	0.8	1.5	9.5	2.3
y	11.4	8.5	12.2	11.6	13.1	11.6	11.8	11.3

x	2.8	5.8	4.1	1.2	6.2	6.8	3.1	7.8
y	10.5	9.3	9.6	12.4	9.5	10.2	9.3	10.6

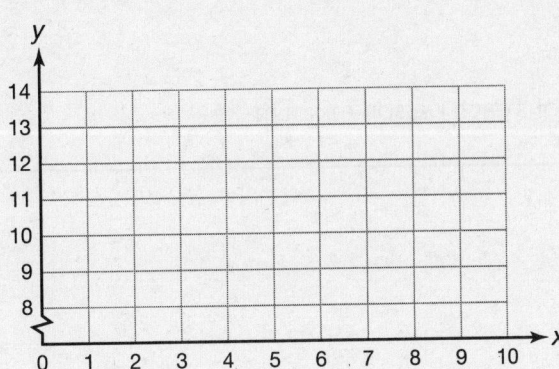

Part B

Describe the association between the variables.

3 Sheba and Maribel collected data on the number of hikers on days of different temperatures. They each made a scatter plot of their own data.

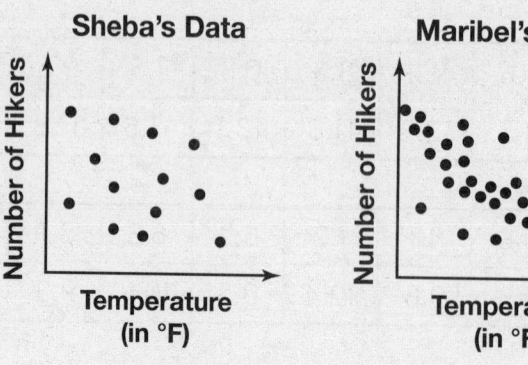

Part A

Compare the associations each person might make.

Part B

Why might insufficient data cause a scientist to reach a wrong conclusion?

4 The data show hours per week spent on sports compared to homework for a group of high school students.

Sports	15	8	8	18	15	0	3	4	5	5
Homework	5	11	9	4	6	8	9	10	3	10

Sports	10	16	7	16	0	3	10	12	5	13
Homework	8	7	11	5	10	8	9	7	11	7

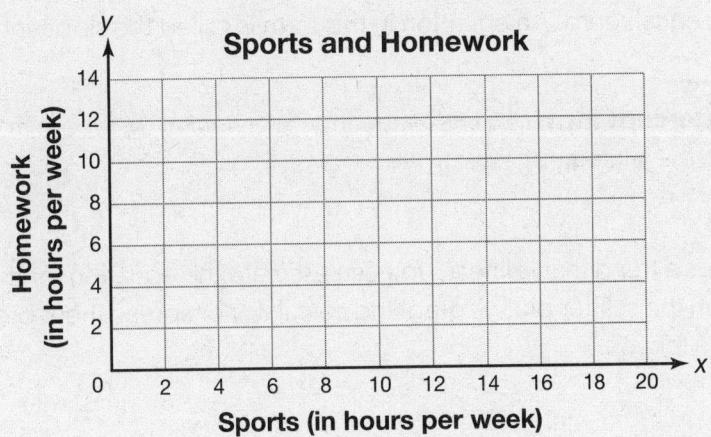

Part A

Use the data to construct a scatter plot.

Part B

Sketch a line of best fit.

Part C

Interpret the data shown on the scatter plot. Describe the association patterns. Is there an outlier? Are the data points close to the line of best fit?

Solving Problems Using Scatter Plots

1 GETTING THE IDEA

You can find an equation for a straight line using the slope and the y-intercept. The **slope** of a line is the ratio of the change in y-coordinates as compared to the change in x-coordinates. The **y-intercept** is the value of y when x equals zero. An equation in this form is called the slope-intercept form.

> The **slope-intercept form** of a linear equation is $y = mx + b$, where m is the slope and b is the y-intercept.

When a **scatter plot** has a trend that is linear, you can estimate the equation for the **line of best fit** using ordered pairs from the scatter plot. A graphing calculator or spreadsheet program will calculate a more precise equation for you.

Example 1

Estimate a line of best fit equation, and use it to estimate the number of downloads for a song with a 4-star review.

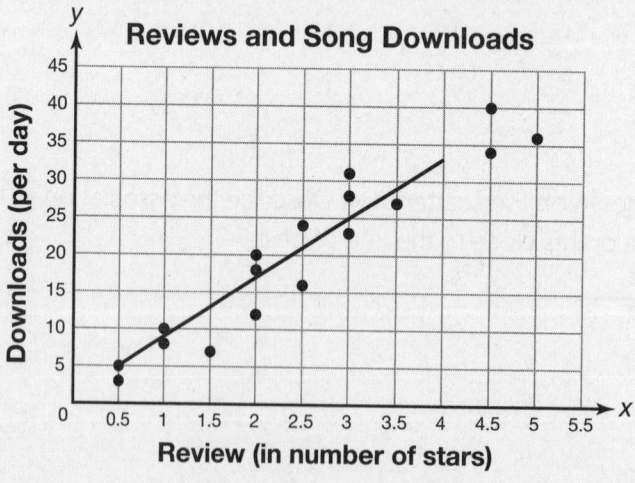

Strategy   Extend the line to find the y-intercept. Choose two points on the line to compute the slope.

Step 1 Find the *y*-intercept.

Extend the line of best fit until it meets the vertical line for 0 stars. The line approximately goes through (0, 0). So, the *y*-intercept is 0. Use $b = 0$ in the equation $y = mx + b$.

Step 2 Find the slope.

The line goes through (0.5, 5) and (2.5, 21). Use these points to estimate the slope.

$$m = \frac{21 - 5}{2.5 - 0.5}$$

$$m = \frac{16}{2}$$

$$m = 8$$

Step 3 Use the values of *b* and *m* to write the equation.

Use $b = 0$ and $m = 8$.

$$y = mx + b$$

$$y = 8x$$

Step 4 Use the equation to estimate the number of downloads when the number of stars, *x*, equals 4.

Substitute 4 for *x*, then solve for *y*.

$$y = 8x$$

$$y = 8(4)$$

$$y = 32$$

Solution An equation of $y = 8x$ estimates 32 downloads for a song with a 4-star review.

When you are estimating the equation of a line of best fit for a scatter plot, choose two points that appear to be on the line. These often are not the first and last points on the graph, or the two end points of the line.

Example 2

The line of best fit on this graph goes through (30, 3.0) and (52, 2.0). Use these points to write an equation. Then estimate the number of years an employee has been with the company if the worker was absent for 65 days.

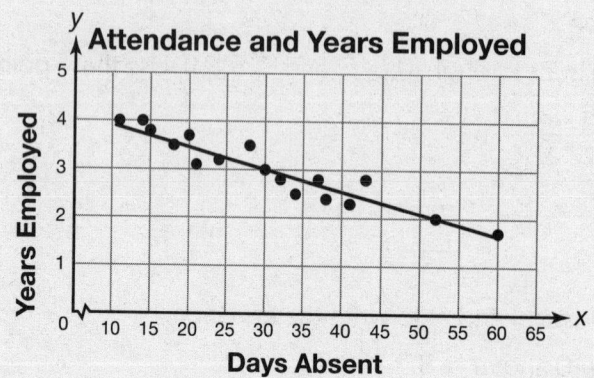

Strategy   **Find the slope. Then use the slope and one given point to solve for the y-intercept.**

Step 1   Find the slope using the given points.

$$m = \frac{2.0 - 3.0}{52 - 30}$$

$$m = \frac{-1}{22}$$

$$m \approx -0.05$$

Step 2   Find the y-intercept using (30, 3.0) and the slope.

$$y = mx + b$$

$$3 = -0.05(30) + b$$

$$b = 3 + 0.05(30)$$

$$b = 4.5$$

Step 3   Use the values of b and m to write the equation.

Use $b = 4.5$ and $m = -0.05$.

$$y = mx + b$$

$$y = -0.05x + 4.5$$

Step 4   Use the equation to estimate the number of years of employment for a worker who is absent for 65 days.

Substitute 65 for x, then solve for y.

$$y = -0.05x + 4.5$$

$$y = -0.05(65) + 4.5$$

$$y = -3.25 + 4.5$$

$$y = 1.25$$

Solution   Based on the equation $y = -0.05x + 4.5$, a worker who is absent 65 days would have been employed for about 1.25 years.

Example 3

Construct a scatter plot for these data, and sketch a line of best fit. Find an equation for the line. Use it to estimate how many hours per week someone who is 35 years old uses the Internet.

Internet Use and Age

Internet Use (in hours per week)	10	11	0	2	14	8	13	4
Age (in years)	27	26	34	42	25	30	25	41

Internet Use (in hours per week)	9	0	5	20	8	16	5	18
Age (in years)	28	45	40	18	22	21	40	20

Strategy Graph the scatter plot, draw a line of best fit, and find the equation. Then make an estimate.

Step 1 Graph the scatter plot.

Look at the ranges of the data to choose the scales for the scatter plot. Write the labels. Then plot the points.

Step 2 Draw the line of best fit.

Ignore the two outliers. Sketch a line of best fit. About half the points should be above the line and half below the line.

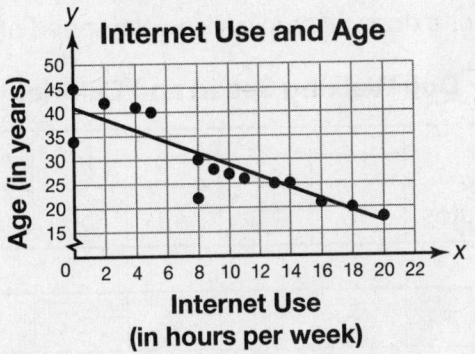

Step 3 Choose two points on the line.

Points at (13, 25) and (16, 21) are approximately on the line.

Step 4 Find the slope.

$$m = \frac{21 - 25}{16 - 13} = -\frac{4}{3}$$

$$m \approx -1.3$$

Step 5 Find the *y*-intercept using (13, 25) and the slope.

$$y = mx + b$$
$$25 = -1.3(13) + b$$
$$b = 25 + 1.3(13)$$
$$b = 41.9$$

Step 6 Use the values of *b* and *m* to write the equation.

Use $b = 41.9$ and $m = -1.3$.

$$y = mx + b$$
$$y = -1.3x + 41.9$$

Step 7 Use the equation to estimate how many hours per week someone who is 35 years old uses the Internet.

Substitute 35 for *y*, then solve for *x*.

$$y = -1.3x + 41.9$$
$$35 = -1.3x + 41.9$$
$$1.3x = 41.9 - 35$$
$$1.3x = 6.9$$
$$x \approx 5.3$$

Solution An equation of $y = -1.3x + 41.9$ estimates that someone who is 35 years old uses the Internet 5.3 hours per week.

Example 4

Construct a scatter plot for these data, and sketch a line of best fit. Find an equation for the line. Use it to estimate the number of calories a dog will burn walking at a speed of 6 miles per hour.

Dog Walking Speed and Calories

Speed (in miles per hour)	3.5	4	1.5	1.5	2	2.5	3	4.5
Calories Burned in 30 Minutes	90	110	45	50	60	75	85	125

Speed (in miles per hour)	3	1	2	5	7	5.5	2	6.4
Calories Burned in 30 Minutes	80	40	55	135	170	140	65	155

Strategy Graph the scatter plot, sketch a line of best fit, and find the equation. Then make an estimate.

Step 1   Graph the scatter plot.

Look at the ranges of the data to choose the scales for the scatter plot. Write the labels, then plot the points.

Step 2   Draw the line of best fit.

Sketch a line of best fit through the center of the data.

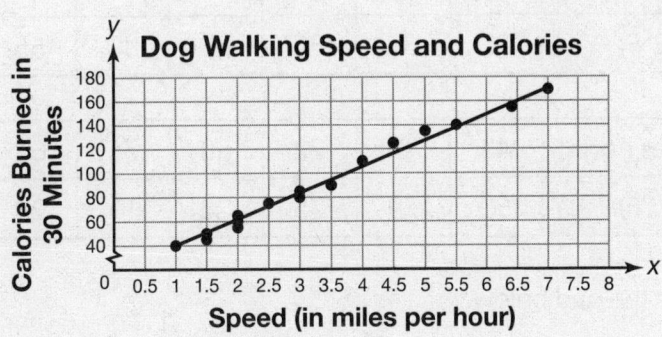

Step 3   Choose two points on the line of best fit.

Points at (2, 60) and (5.5, 140) are on the line.

Step 4   Find the slope.

$$m = \frac{140 - 60}{5.5 - 2}$$

$$m = \frac{80}{3.5}$$

$$m \approx 23$$

Step 5   Find the y-intercept using (2, 60) and the slope.

$$y = mx + b$$

$$60 = 23(2) + b$$

$$b = 60 - 23(2)$$

$$b = 14$$

Step 6   Use the values of b and m to write the equation.

Use $b = 14$ and $m = 23$.

$$y = mx + b$$

$$y = 23x + 14$$

Step 7   Use the equation to estimate the number of calories burned for a dog walking at a speed of 6 miles per hour.

Substitute 6 for x, then solve for y.

$$y = 23(6) + 14$$

$$y = 138 + 14$$

$$y = 152$$

Solution   An equation of $y = 23x + 14$ gives an estimate that a dog will burn 152 calories walking at a speed of 6 miles per hour.

Construct a scatter plot for these data, and sketch a line of best fit. Find an equation for the line. Use it to estimate the temperature for a location at 25° north.

Latitude and Temperature

Latitude (degrees north)	48	50	0	12	16	36	41	52
Temperature (in °F)	32	38	86	80	80	55	54	36

Latitude (degrees north)	43	9	22	58	75	62	32	70
Temperature (in °F)	50	79	75	28	10	23	64	18

Graph the scatter plot on the grid below.
Draw a line of best fit.

Estimate the *y*-intercept from the graph.

It is about _____.

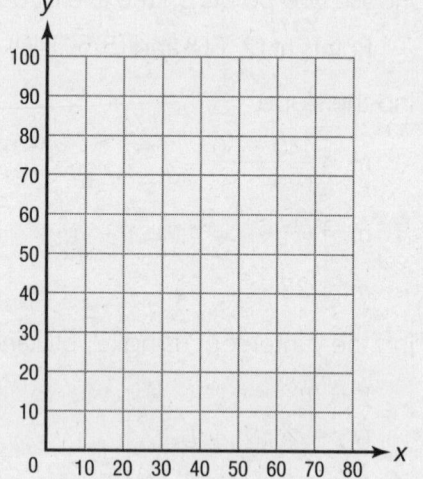

Choose two points to use to find the slope.

Points on the line are good choices.

Use (12, _____) and (50, _____).

Find the slope.

$$m = \frac{\boxed{} - \boxed{}}{\boxed{} - \boxed{}} = \frac{\boxed{}}{\boxed{}}$$

$m \approx$ _____

Use the *y*-intercept and the slope to write the equation.

$y =$ _____

Substitute _____ for *x*, and solve for *y*.

$y =$ _____ $x +$ _____

$y =$ _____ (_____) + _____

$y =$ _____ + _____

$y =$ _____

An equation of _____ gives an estimated temperature of _____ °F for a latitude of 25 degrees north.

1 Four students wrote equations for the line of best fit on the scatter plot shown below. Did the student write the correct equation for the line of best fit? Select Yes or No.

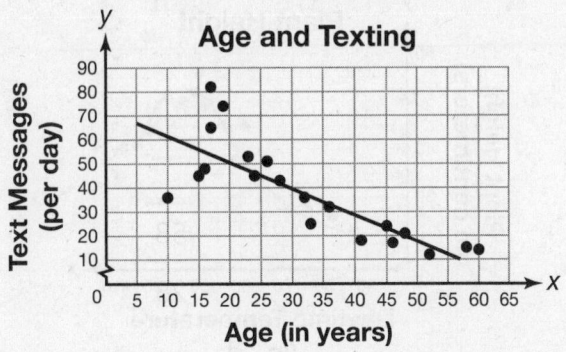

A. Kim's equation: $y = -x + 63$ ◯ Yes ◯ No

B. Eleanor's equation: $y = -x + 73$ ◯ Yes ◯ No

C. Jamie's equation: $y = x + 73$ ◯ Yes ◯ No

D. Arturo's equation: $y = x + 63$ ◯ Yes ◯ No

2 The data on the scatter plot show the number of siblings each person has.

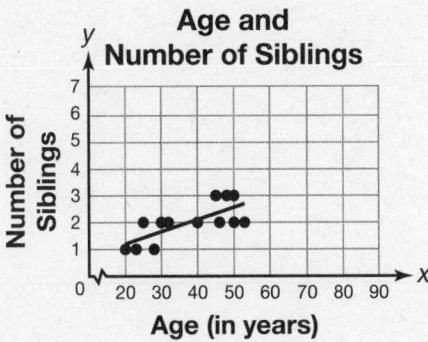

Part A

Find an equation for the line of best fit. Use the points (20, 1.2) and (53, 2.6).

Slope of line: _____

Equation of line: _____

Part B

Based on these data, how many siblings does a 35-year-old person have? Explain why only whole number answers make sense in the context of this problem.

_____

Use this scatter plot for questions 3 and 4.

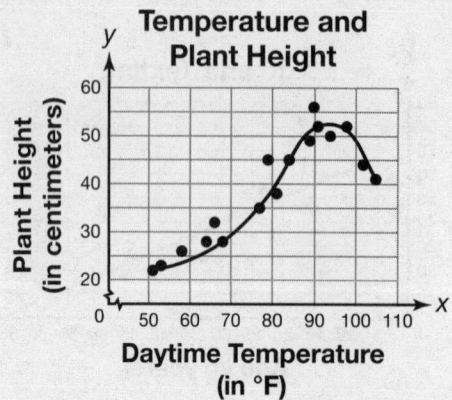

Temperature and Plant Height

y — Plant Height (in centimeters)

x — Daytime Temperature (in °F)

3 The scatter plot shows the data from an experiment. The scientist was looking for a relationship between daytime temperatures and plant heights.

Part A

Explain the experimental data summarized by this scatter plot, and describe the relationship shown by the data and the graph.

Part B

Estimate the slope of the graph up to 90°F using the ordered pairs (50, 20) and (90, 50) and interpret the meaning of the slope in the context of the problem. Use items from the box to complete the statements.

Estimate for slope: ⬜/⬜

For every _____°F that the temperature _____,

the plant height _____ by _____ centimeters.

| 3 |
| 4 |
| increases |
| decreases |

4 A scientist decides it will be easier to use two straight lines to approximate the data.

Part A

Why might it be an advantage to use two straight lines rather than one curved graph?

Part B

Write the equations of the two lines using these points.

First equation from (50, 20) to (90, 50): _____

Second equation from (90, 50) to (105, 40): _____

Part C

Use your equations to estimate plant height at these temperatures.

Height at 75°F: _____

Height at 110°F: _____

8.SP.4

Understanding Two-Way Frequency Tables

1 GETTING THE IDEA

Maria and David are using surveys to collect data about their classmates. Compare these two completed surveys.

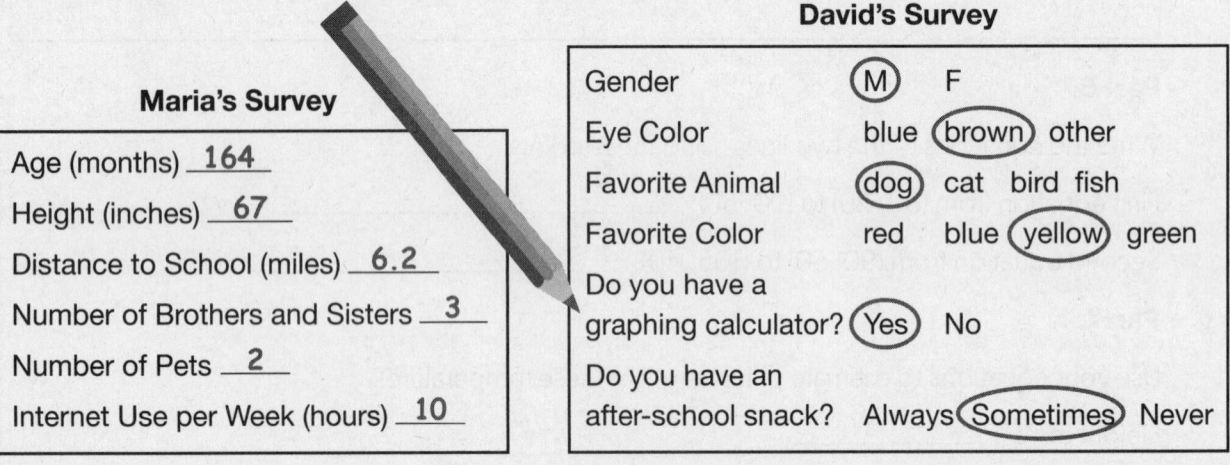

Maria's Survey

Age (months) __164__
Height (inches) __67__
Distance to School (miles) __6.2__
Number of Brothers and Sisters __3__
Number of Pets __2__
Internet Use per Week (hours) __10__

David's Survey

Gender	Ⓜ F
Eye Color	blue ⟨brown⟩ other
Favorite Animal	⟨dog⟩ cat bird fish
Favorite Color	red blue ⟨yellow⟩ green
Do you have a graphing calculator?	⟨Yes⟩ No
Do you have an after-school snack?	Always ⟨Sometimes⟩ Never

The variables on Maria's survey are **numerical variables**, also called quantitative variables. A numerical variable is data that are measured as a series of numbers. The variable says how much or how many. Examples of measurement variables are height, weight, distance, speed, and population.

The variables on David's survey are **categorical variables**. Any variable that is not numerical is categorical. These take on a value that is one of several possible categories. Sometimes, the categories are words—for example, the colors red, blue, yellow, and green. The categories can also be intervals of numbers such as age groups of 1–5, 6–10, and 11–20.

Example 1

Tell whether each of these variables is numerical or categorical.

    age in years   favorite kind of movie

    volume in cubic feet   type of weekend exercise

Strategy   Determine if the variables are numbers or words.

  Step 1   Find the numerical variables.

          Age and volume are numerical. They can be measured and described with numbers.

Step 2 List the remaining variables.

Favorite movie and type of exercise are not numerical, so they are categorical.

Solution Age in years and volume in cubic feet are numerical variables. Favorite kind of movie and type of weekend exercise are categorical variables.

Bivariate data involve two variables. When there are two categorical variables, data can be organized in a two-way table. A **two-way frequency table** shows the frequency, or count, of each category. In Example 2, the variables are Grade Range and Favorite Sports.

You can find the relative frequency of a specific event using data in a two-way table. **Relative frequency** is the ratio of the number of times an event occurs to the total number of events. For example, suppose you want to know about the favorite sport of students in elementary school. The relative frequency of elementary school students who chose baseball as their favorite sport can be described as the ratio of 27:57, or $\frac{27}{57}$. Twenty-seven elementary students chose baseball as their favorite sport out of the 57 elementary students who were surveyed.

Favorite Sports

	Elementary	Middle School	High School	Total
Baseball	27	22	18	67
Basketball	19	8	23	50
Football	11	24	48	83
Total	57	54	89	200

Example 2

Use the Favorite Sports table above to find the relative frequencies of the sport receiving the most votes by each grade range. Is there a relationship?

Strategy Write and compare the ratios as percents.

Step 1 Find the sport receiving the most votes in each grade range.

Most elementary students chose baseball. Most middle and high school students chose football.

Step 2 Write the frequency ratios.

Elementary students: $\frac{27}{57}$ baseball

Middle school students: $\frac{24}{54}$ football

High school students: $\frac{48}{89}$ football

Step 3   Write each frequency ratio as a percent rounded to the nearest whole percent.

Elementary students: $27 \div 57 \approx 0.473 \approx 47\%$ baseball

Middle school students: $24 \div 54 \approx 0.444 \approx 44\%$ football

High school students: $48 \div 89 \approx 0.539 \approx 54\%$ football

Step 4   Look for something the data have in common.

Less than 50% of elementary and middle school students chose a single sport as their favorite. On the other hand, over 50% of high school students chose football as their favorite sport. You can say that *most* high school students surveyed prefer football.

Solution   In the survey, about 47% of elementary students chose baseball, 44% of middle school students chose football, and 54% of high school students chose football. Most high school students prefer football over baseball or basketball. This is not true for elementary or middle school students.

Example 3

Some eighth grade students were asked what they did when they got home from school. The results are shown in the two-way table below. The school principal wants students to be more active after school. Of the students surveyed, what percent could be more active after school?

	Play Sports	Play Video Games	Do Homework
Females	45	12	36
Males	32	37	24

Strategy   Find the relative percent of all students who are not active after school.

Step 1   Find the number of students who are not active after school.

Students who play video games or do homework are not active.

$12 + 36 + 37 + 24 = 109$

Step 2   Find the total number of students.

Add the number of students who are active to the total from Step 1 to find the total number of students.

$109 + 45 + 32 = 186$

Step 3   Find the percent of students who could be more active after school.

$\frac{\text{nonactive students}}{\text{total students}} = \frac{109}{186} \approx 0.586 \approx 59\%$

Solution   Based on the survey, 59% of all eighth grade students could be more active after school.

Example 4

Carl asked the students in his school what activity they like to do in gym class. The results are shown in the table below. Construct a two-way frequency table to display the data. Carl wants to recommend that gym class is separated by gender and that students participate in different activities based on gender. Will these data support his proposal?

	Females	Males
Basketball	ⅢⅢ ⅢⅢ ⅢⅢ ⅢⅢ III	ⅢⅢ ⅢⅢ ⅢⅢ ⅢⅢ ⅢⅢ ⅢⅢ
Volleyball	ⅢⅢ ⅢⅢ ⅢⅢ ⅢⅢ ⅢⅢ ⅢⅢ II	ⅢⅢ ⅢⅢ ⅢⅢ ⅢⅢ ⅢⅢ I
Softball	ⅢⅢ ⅢⅢ ⅢⅢ I	ⅢⅢ ⅢⅢ II
Track	ⅢⅢ ⅢⅢ ⅢⅢ III	ⅢⅢ ⅢⅢ ⅢⅢ ⅢⅢ I

Strategy Construct a two-way frequency table. Compare the percents for each activity.

Step 1 Construct a two-way frequency table.

Since Carl wants to compare the results by gender, find the total number of females and males who were surveyed.

	Females	Males
Basketball	23	30
Volleyball	32	26
Softball	16	12
Track	18	21
Totals	89	89

Step 2 Find the percent of females who chose each activity. Do the same for males. Round to the nearest whole percent.

	Females	Males
Basketball	26%	34%
Volleyball	36%	29%
Softball	18%	13%
Track	20%	24%
Totals	100%	100%

| | Step 3 | Compare the percents for each activity by gender. |

Step 3   Compare the percents for each activity by gender.

More females chose volleyball than any other activity, but 36% does not represent the majority. More males prefer basketball than any other activity, but 34% also is not the majority. About the same percent of both males and females enjoy softball and track.

Solution   Carl cannot use these data to support his proposal because there is no significant difference in the results.

Example 5

In a group of 180 students, 110 are in the drama club, 80 are in the computer club, and 15 are in both clubs. Make a two-way relative frequency table, and look for a possible association between the variables.

Strategy   Construct a two-way frequency table. Compare the percents for each activity.

Step 1   Describe the variables.

The variables are membership in the computer club and membership in the drama club.

Step 2   Create the table. Fill in what you know.

	Computer Club Member	Not in the Computer Club	Total
Drama Club Member	15		110
Not in the Drama Club			
Total	80		180

Step 3   Subtract to find the missing values.

	Computer Club Member	Not in the Computer Club	Total
Drama Club Member	15	110 − 15	110
Not in the Drama Club	80 − 15		180 − 110
Total	80	180 − 80	180

	Computer Club Member	Not in the Computer Club	Total
Drama Club Member	15	95	110
Not in the Drama Club	65	5	70
Total	80	100	180

Step 4 Find the relative frequencies for the table. Divide every entry by 180. Round to the nearest tenth of a percent.

	Computer Club Member	Not in the Computer Club	Total
Drama Club Member	8.3%	52.8%	61.1%
Not in the Drama Club	36.1%	2.8%	38.9%
Total	44.4%	55.6%	100%

Step 5 Look for patterns in the percents.

Almost 90% of the people are in one of the two clubs. Only about 3% are not in one of the clubs.

Solution A student who is in the drama club is probably not in the computer club. A computer club member is not very likely to also be in the drama club. But 90% of students are in one of the clubs.

Gwen surveyed 100 students evenly split by gender. Use these data to make a two-way table. Find both the relative frequencies based on gender. Summarize the patterns you find in the data.

	Females	Males
Wears Glasses	ЖHt	ЖHt IIII
Wears Contact Lenses	ЖHt IIII	ЖHt III

Construct a two-way table.

	Glasses	Contacts	No Vision Correction Needed	Total
Females				
Males				

Find the relative frequencies based on gender. Divide by _____.

	Glasses	Contacts	No Vision Correction Needed	Total
Females				
Males				

A greater percent of _____ have corrected vision.

The same percent of males wears _____ as females wear _____.

1 Decide if each of these is a numerical variable or a categorical variable. Write the variable in the correct box.

favorite kind of movie	exercise in hours per week	area in square miles

U.S. region of residence (NE, SE, S, MW, W)	exercise (under 10 hours, 10 hours or more)	temperature in °F

Numerical Variables	Categorical Variables

2 Use numbers from the box to complete the two-way frequency table.

Should Dogs Be Allowed on the Public Beaches?

	Children	Adults	Total
Yes		53	
No	9		
Total	40		160

31
67
76
84
120

3 A survey asked 100 people what kind of exercise they did last weekend. This Venn diagram shows the results.

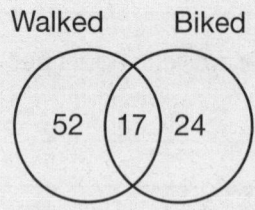

Walked   Biked

52 (17) 24

100 People Surveyed

Part A

Complete this two-way frequency table for the data.

	Walked	Didn't Walk	Total
Biked			
Didn't Bike			
Total			

Part B

Complete this two-way table showing the relative frequencies for the columns.

	Walked	Didn't Walk	Total
Biked			
Didn't Bike			
Total	100%	100%	100%

Part C

Did most people exercise? Did most people perform both types of exercise? Explain.

4 The table shows the votes in the last mayoral election and whether people voted for or against having concerts in the town park.

Votes in the Election for Mayor

	Kwon	Cogorno	Liebowitz	Total
Yes	318	578	217	
No	472	165	423	
Total				

Part A

Complete the table.

Part B

Who won the election for mayor? _____

Was having concerts in the park approved? _____

Part C

Did the people who voted for the winning candidate also vote for having concerts in the park? Explain your answer.

5 In this survey of 150 people, $\frac{4}{5}$ of the people who responded were adults. The survey found that 21 of the teenagers think it is safe to text while walking, but 87 of the adults don't think it is safe.

Part A

Make a table for the data.

Is It Safe to Text while Walking?

	Teenagers	Adults	Total
Yes			
No			
Total			

Part B

Use percents to complete this summary of the survey results. Explain how you found your percents.

The survey found that _____% of the teenagers think it is safe to text and walk, but _____% of the adults don't think it is safe.

6 This relative frequency table shows the results of a survey. People were asked about how many hours of homework high school students should have per night. The relative frequencies are based on the age groups.

How many hours of homework per night?

	0–1	2–3	More than 3	Total
Students	40.6%	47.7%	11.7%	100%
Teachers	30.5%	57.1%	12.4%	100%
Parents	57.8%	28.9%	13.3%	100%
Total	40.1%	47.8%	12.1%	100%

Select a question that **cannot** be answered from the table. Circle all that apply.

A. How many people were included in the survey?

B. What fractional part of the survey group were students?

C. Which number of hours is preferred by more than half of the teachers?

D. Should the survey have included a greater proportion of parents?

E. Which number of hours was chosen by the fewest number of people in all three groups?

F. How do the parents and teachers differ in their beliefs about the amount of homework?

7 This table shows the sizes and colors of shirts in an inventory of T-shirts.

T-Shirt Inventory

	Red	Blue	Yellow	Green	Total
Medium	150	100	200	150	
Large	50	200	50	100	
Total					

Part A

Complete the table.

Part B

Make a two-way table showing relative frequencies based on T-shirt sizes.

T-Shirt Inventory

	Red	Blue	Yellow	Green	Total
Medium					100%
Large					100%
Total					100%

Part C

Sketch two circle graphs comparing the color distributions by size.

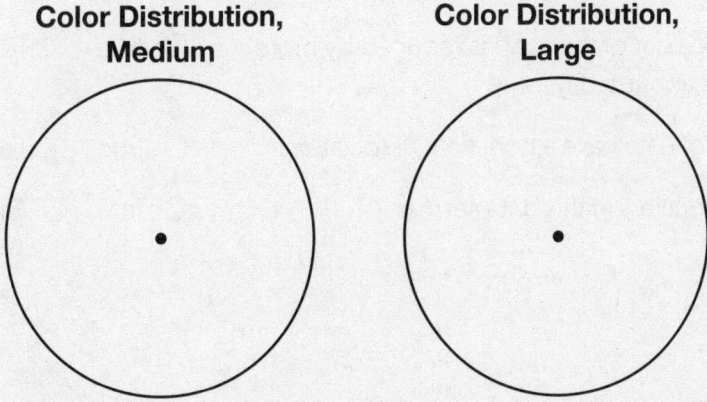

Color Distribution, Medium   **Color Distribution, Large**

1 Use the scatter plot below. Select True or False for each statement.

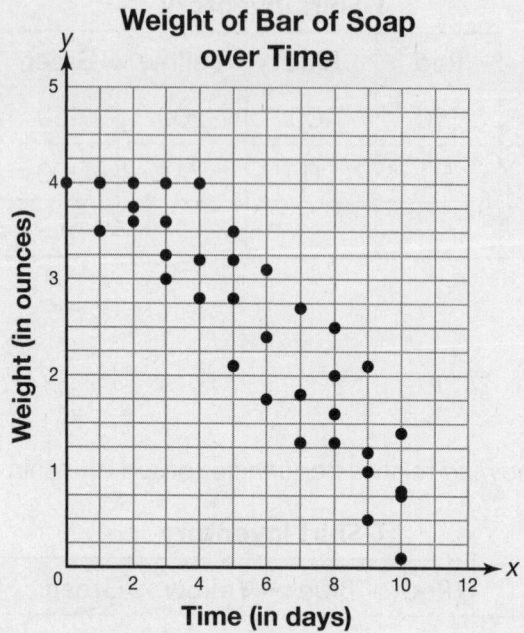

Weight of Bar of Soap over Time

A. Because the data cluster closely around a line, the data have a strong association. ○ True ○ False

B. A trend line that accurately fits the data will have a positive slope. ○ True ○ False

C. The initial weight of one bar of the soap is about 4 ounces. ○ True ○ False

D. The weight of a bar of the soap is reduced by more than half after about 5 days. ○ True ○ False

E. The two sets of data have a nonlinear association. ○ True ○ False

F. There are no outliers in this data set. ○ True ○ False

2 Consider each situation described below. Indicate with an "X" whether it can be described using numerical data or categorical data.

Situation	Numerical Data	Categorical Data
Number of items in Roman's backpack		
Types of apps on Mia's tablet computer		
Hair color of students in Mrs. Pruitt's math class		
Students' favorite subjects in school		
Number of triangles in a geometry book		
Types of events at a track and field meet		

3 The relationship between the temperature T, in degrees Fahrenheit, outside an airplane and the altitude a, in meters, of the airplane can be modeled by the equation $T = -0.01a + 68.3$. Interpret the meaning of the slope and the y-intercept in the context of the situation. Use items from the box to complete each statement.

For every _____ meter(s) the altitude

_____, the temperature outside

the plane _____ by _____°F.

The temperature outside the airplane, when

its altitude is 0 meters, is _____°F.

0.01
1
68.3
increases
decreases

4 Use the data below to answer the questions that follow.

Outdoor Temperature and Amount of Ice Cream Sold

Temperature (in °F)	55	82	73	97	42	61	74	78	91	89	67	58
Ice Cream Sales (in dollars)	38	118	97	123	21	76	92	95	122	112	72	39

Part A

Make a scatter plot of the data.

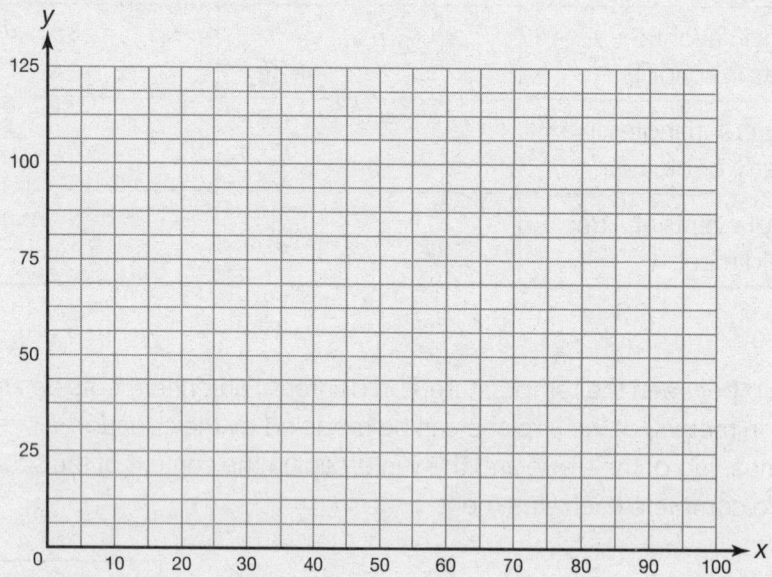

Part B

Sketch the line of best fit for the data. Write an equation of the line of best fit. Show your work.

Part C

What do the slope and *y*-intercept mean in terms of the given situation?

5 The Venn diagram shows the area(s) of interest of the students in a food sciences program. Use data from the Venn diagram to complete the two-way frequency table.

**Student Interest
in Food Sciences Program**

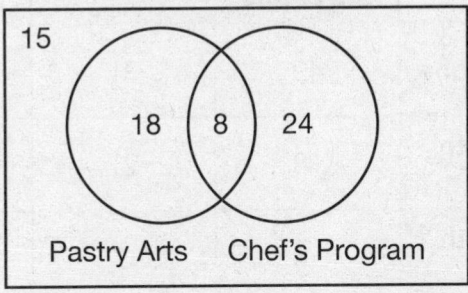

15

| 18 | 8 | 24 |

Pastry Arts   Chef's Program

Food Sciences Program

	Interest in Pastry Arts	No Interest in Pastry Arts	Total
Interest in Chef's Program			
No Interest in Chef's Program			
Total			

6 The two-way table shows several extracurricular activities that some students from Nichols Middle School participate in. Which is greater: the percentage of boys in the Drama Club or the percentage of girls in the Drama Club? Explain your reasoning.

	Boys	Girls
Science Club	12	19
Drama Club	16	18
Debate Team	15	15

7 Use the data in the table to answer the questions that follow.

Amount of Time Students Exercise per Week

	Less Than 3.5 Hours	3.5 Hours	More Than 3.5 Hours
Exercise Alone	49	31	27
Exercise with a Partner	8	21	23
Exercise with a Group	4	17	28

Part A

Find the relative frequencies by row.

Amount of Time Students Exercise per Week

	Less Than 3.5 Hours	3.5 Hours	More Than 3.5 Hours	Total
Exercise Alone				
Exercise with a Partner				
Exercise with a Group				

Part B

Is there evidence to suggest that those who exercise with a group tend to spend more time exercising each week than those who exercise alone? Explain your reasoning.

Cell Phones

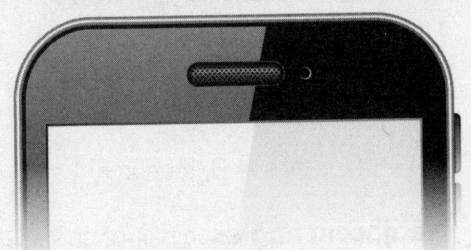

Doug and Lisa have conducted surveys. They want to know if the age of a cell phone user is related to phone loss or breakage. Doug started with an informal random survey of 20 people.

Doug's Data: How Many Cell Phones Have You Lost or Broken in the Last 5 Years?

Age (in years)	30	36	20	36	41	47	25	48	52	54
Number of Phones	3	0	5	1	2	0	5	1	0	1

Age (in years)	28	28	16	23	32	24	24	19	24	68
Number of Phones	2	4	4	3	2	2	4	3	2	0

Part A Construct a scatter plot for Doug's data. Draw the line of best fit and find its equation. Describe the association, and interpret the slope of the line of best fit in the context of this problem.

Part B Lisa took a larger survey, asking a slightly different question. Lisa organized her data in a two-way frequency table. Complete her table.

Lisa's Data: Have You Lost or Broken a Cell Phone in the Last 5 Years?

Age Group	0 to 20	21 to 30	31 to 40	41 to 50	over 50	Total
Yes	52	52	67	13	26	
No						
Total	66	102	130	30	72	

Part C Describe the size of Lisa's sample and the distribution by age group. Interpret her overall results and any patterns of association.

Part D Make a new two-way table for Lisa's data. Show the relative frequencies as percents relative to the age groups. Round the percents to the nearest tenth.

Age Group	0 to 20	21 to 30	31 to 40	41 to 50	over 50	Total
Yes						
No						
Total						

Part E Compare the data in the two tables. How could the first table be considered misleading? Explain your reasoning.

Part F Compare Doug and Lisa's results. Could the age of a cell phone user be related to cell phone loss or breakage? Use the data to support your conclusion.

GLOSSARY

addition property of equality if $a = b$, then $a + c = b + c$ (Lesson 9)

If $x = 3$, then $x + 4 = 3 + 4$

adjacent angles a pair of angles that share a common vertex and ray (Lesson 23)

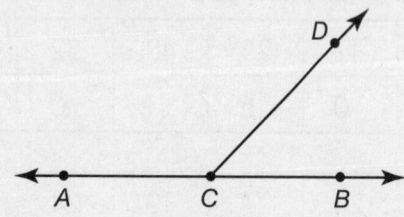

∠ACD is adjacent to ∠DCB

alternate exterior angles a pair of angles on opposite sides of a transversal outside the two parallel lines (Lesson 22)

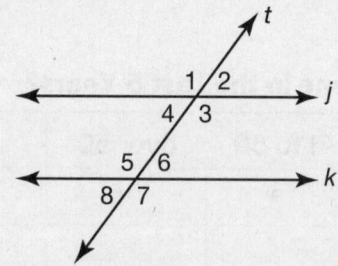

∠1 and ∠7 are alternate exterior angles.

∠2 and ∠8 are also alternate exterior angles.

alternate interior angles a pair of angles on opposite sides of a transversal inside the two parallel lines (Lesson 22)

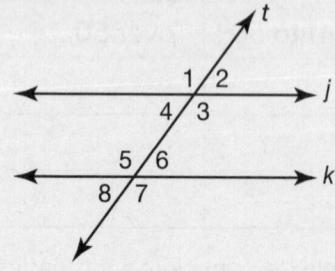

∠4 and ∠6 are alternate interior angles.

∠3 and ∠5 are also alternate interior angles.

angle-angle similarity theorem when two pairs of corresponding angles in a triangle are congruent, the triangles are similar (Lesson 23)

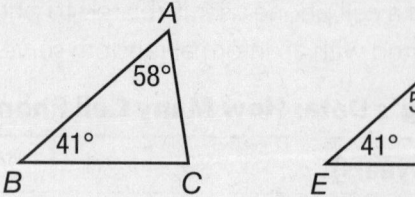

△ABC is similar to △DEF.

base (number) a number that is multiplied by itself a certain number of times (Lesson 3)

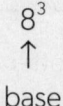

bivariate data data for two variables (Lessons 27, 29)

Temperature	50°	60°	70°	80°	90°	100°
Number of Cups of Lemonade Sold	0	1	2	8	22	25

categorical variable a variable that is not numerical (Lesson 29)

favorite color(blue, green, pink)

clockwise turning in the same direction as a clock's hands (Lesson 19)

cluster a set of closely grouped data (Lesson 27)

A = {74, 74, 75, 76, 76, 76}

coefficient a numerical factor in a multiplication expression (Lesson 5)

$$2 \times 10^5$$
↑
coefficient

coincident lines two or more lines that have the same slope and *y*-intercept (Lesson 10)

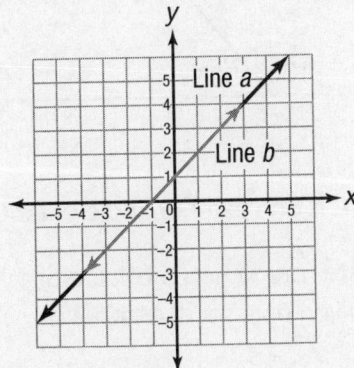

complementary angles a pair of angles whose measures have a sum of 90° (Lesson 23)

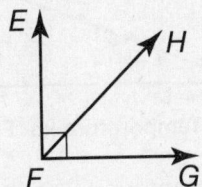

∠*EFH* and ∠*HFG* are complementary.

congruent a pair of geometric figures having the same size and shape (Lessons 17, 18, 19, 21)

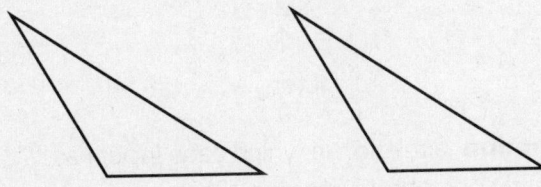

converse the reverse of an if-then statement (Lesson 24)

Statement: If it is cloudy, then it will rain.

Converse: If it rains, then it is cloudy.

corresponding angles the angles that lie on the same side of the transversal and on the same side of parallel lines (Lesson 22)

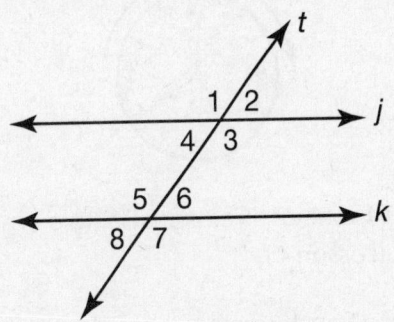

∠1 and ∠5 are corresponding angles.

∠2 and ∠6 are corresponding angles.

∠3 and ∠7 are corresponding angles.

∠4 and ∠8 are corresponding angles.

corresponding angles (in similar figures) a pair of angles that are in the same position and are congruent (Lesson 23)

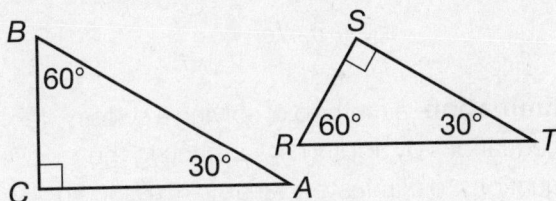

∠*A* and ∠*T* are corresponding angles.

corresponding sides (in similar figures) a pair of sides that are in the same position and are proportional (Lesson 23)

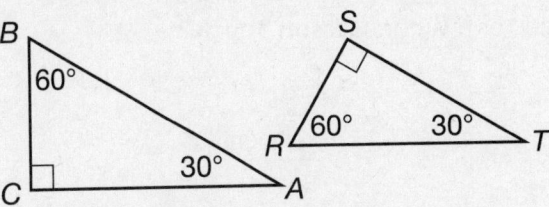

$\overline{AB}$ and $\overline{TR}$ are corresponding sides.

counterclockwise moving in the opposite direction as the hands on a clock (Lesson 19)

cube root one of three equal factors of a number (Lesson 4)

dilation a transformation that enlarges or shrinks a figure (Lesson 20)

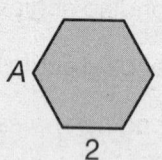 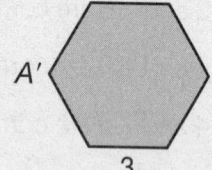

division property of equality if $a = b$ and $c \neq 0$, then $\frac{a}{c} = \frac{b}{c}$ (Lesson 9)

$$\text{If } x = 8, \text{ then } \frac{x}{2} = \frac{8}{2}$$

elimination a method of solving a system of equations by adding or subtracting the equations to eliminate a variable (Lesson 11)

$$3x + 2y = 6 \;\rightarrow\; 3x + 2y = 6$$
$$3x + 4y = 12 \;\rightarrow\; \underline{-(3x + 4y = 12)}$$
$$-2y = -6$$

exponent tells how many times the base is used as a factor (Lesson 3)

$$8^3$$
↑
exponent

exterior angle an angle formed by the side of a triangle and the extension of one of its sides (Lesson 23)

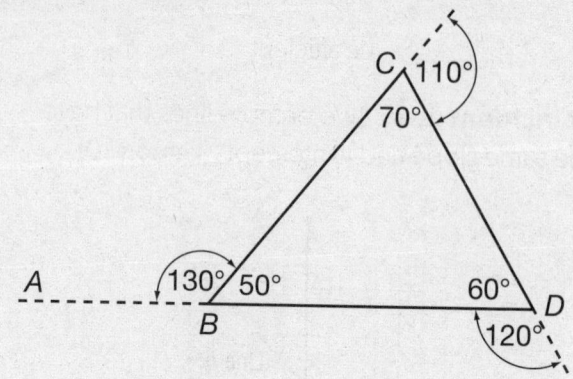

$\angle ABC$ is one exterior angle of $\triangle BCD$.

extrapolate predicting the value of a variable outside a given data set (Lesson 27)

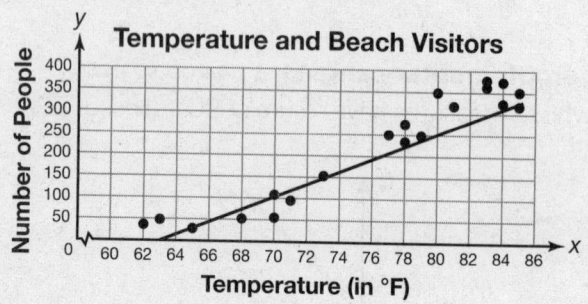

When the temperature is 86°, there should be about 400 beach visitors.

factor a number multiplied by another number to find a product (Lesson 3)

$$3 \times 2 = 6$$
↑ ↑
factor

function a relation in which each input has exactly one output (Lesson 12)

function: {(1, 2), (2, 7), (3, 2), (4, 8)}

not a function: {(1, 2), (1, 3), (1, 4), (1, 5)}

hypotenuse the side of a right triangle opposite the right angle (Lessons 24, 25)

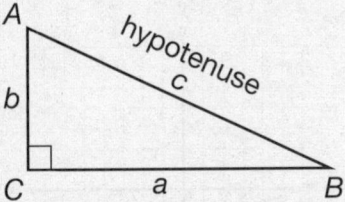

image the figure that is formed from a pre-image after a transformation (Lessons 17, 18, 19, 20)

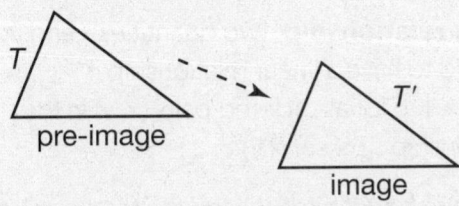

△T' is the image.

initial value the *y*-value of a function when *x* = 0 (Lesson 15)

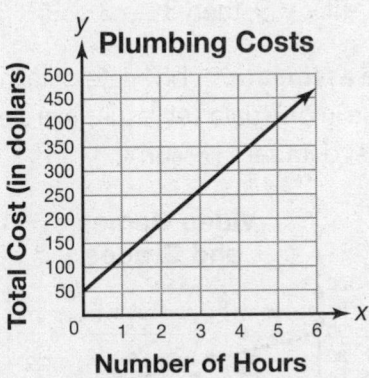

The initial value of the graph is 50.

inputs the *x*-coordinates in a relation (Lesson 12)

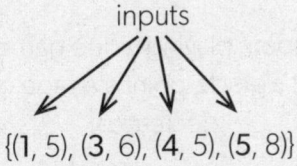

inputs

{(1, 5), (3, 6), (4, 5), (5, 8)}

interior angle an angle inside a polygon formed by the sides of the polygon (Lesson 23)

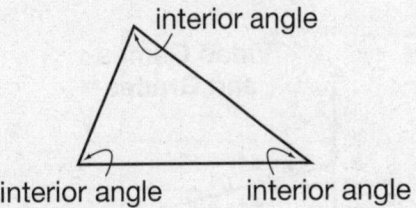

interpolate predicting the value of a variable between two given points (Lesson 27)

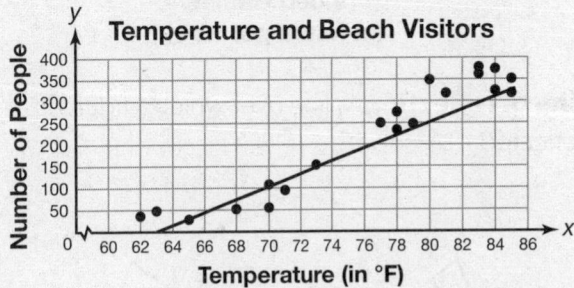

When the temperature is 76°, there should be about 200 beach visitors.

irrational number any real number that cannot be expressed in the form $\frac{a}{b}$ (Lessons 1, 2)

π and $\sqrt{5}$ are irrational numbers.

leg one of the two sides of a right triangle that form the right angle (Lessons 24, 25)

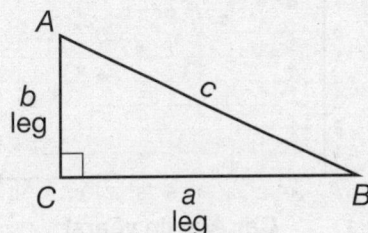

line of best fit a line that shows the general direction of a group of points on a graph (Lessons 27, 28)

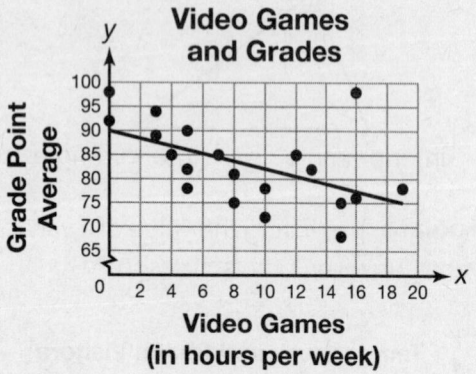

Video Games and Grades

line of reflection a line over which a figure is reflected (Lesson 18)

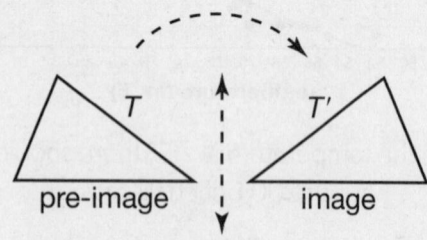

pre-image   image

linear association data that clusters along a line (Lesson 27)

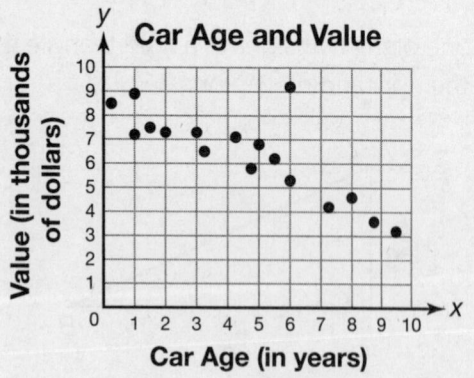

Car Age and Value

linear equation an equation that describes points that form a line (Lessons 8, 9)

$y = 2x + 1$ is a linear equation.

linear function a function whose graph is a straight line (Lessons 14, 16)

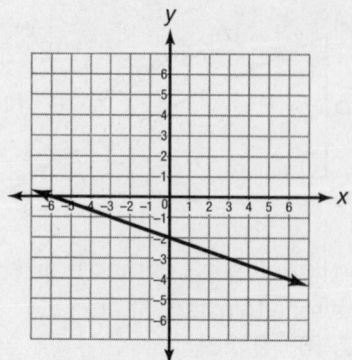

linear relationship two quantities x and y are said to have a linear relationship if $y = mx + b$ for all ordered pairs (x, y) in the relationship (Lesson 15)

The number of birds (b) and the total number of wings (w) have a linear relationship $w = 2b$.

multiplication property of equality if $a = b$, then $ac = bc$ (Lesson 9)

If $x = 9$, then $3x = 3 \times 9$.

negative association bivariate data in which an increase in one data set results in a decrease in the other data set (Lesson 27)

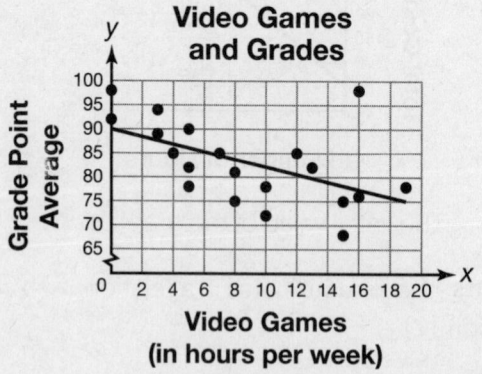

Video Games and Grades

As the time spent playing video games increases, a student's grade-point average generally decreases.

negative exponent property for any nonzero number x and positive integer a, $x^{-a} = \frac{1}{x^a}$ (Lesson 3)

$$3^{-2} = \frac{1}{3^2} = \frac{1}{9}$$

nonlinear association a set of data that do not cluster around a line (Lesson 27)

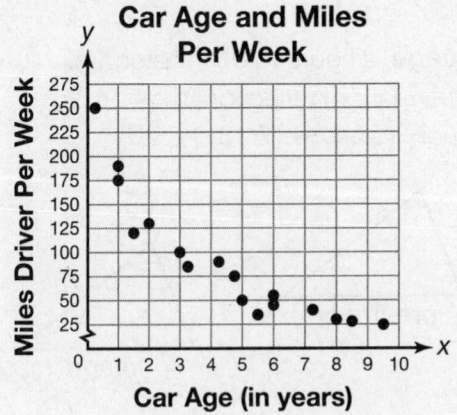

The data do not have a linear association.

nonlinear function a function whose graph does not form a straight line (Lessons 14, 16)

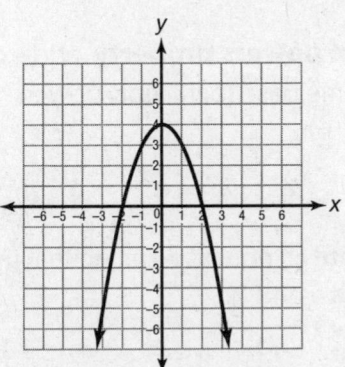

non-linear function

numerical variable a variable that describes a numerically measured value (Lesson 29)

origin the point where the x-axis and y-axis of a coordinate plane intersect; the point (0, 0) (Lesson 7)

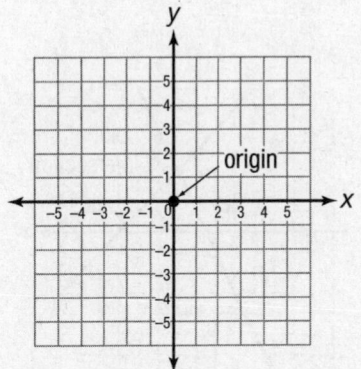

outlier a data point with a value significantly greater or less than most other values in the data set (Lesson 27)

$$\{1, 2, 3, 6, 7, 7, 8, 105\}$$

105 is an outlier.

outputs the y-coordinates in a relation (Lesson 12)

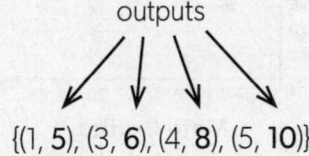

parallel lines two or more lines that never intersect; on the coordinate plane; lines that have the same slope (Lessons 10, 22)

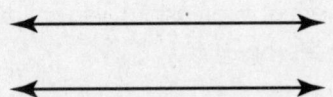

perfect cube a number that has a rational number as its cube root (Lesson 4)

8, 27, and 64 are perfect cubes

perfect square a number that has a rational number as its square root (Lesson 4)

4, 9, 16, and 25 are perfect squares

point(s) of intersection the solution of a system of equations; the point or points where two or more equations cross on the coordinate plane (Lesson 10)

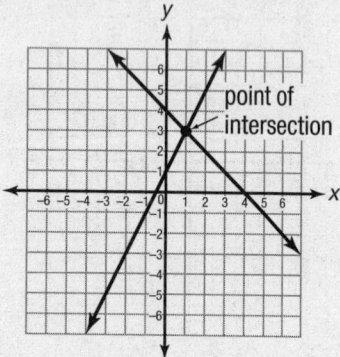

point of intersection

positive association bivariate data in which an increase in one data set results in an increase in the other data set (Lesson 27)

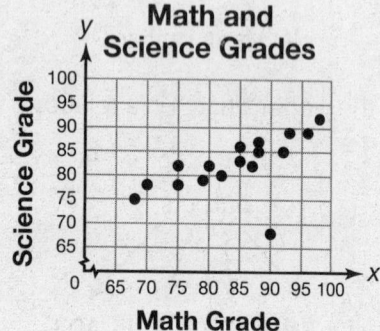

As math grades increase, science grades also generally increase.

power the number that a base is raised to in an exponential expression; also called an exponent (Lesson 3)

power of a power property multiply exponents to raise a power to a power (Lesson 3)

$$(7^3)^2 = 7^{3 \times 2} = 7^6$$

power of a product property find the power of each factor to find the power of a product (Lesson 3)

$$(3 \times 2)^4 = 3^4 \times 2^4$$

power of a quotient property find the power of the numerator and the denominator to find a power of a quotient (Lesson 3)

$$\left(\frac{2}{3}\right)^3 = \frac{2^3}{3^3}$$

power of 10 a number in the form 10^n, where n is an integer (Lesson 5)

$$10^5$$

pre-image a figure to be transformed with a translation, reflection, rotation, or dilation (Lessons 17, 18, 19, 20)

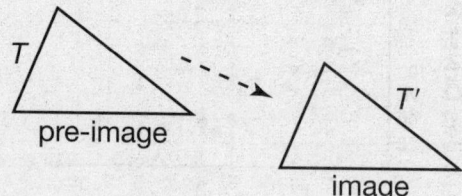

T

pre-image

T'

image

$\triangle T$ is the pre-image.

principal square root a nonnegative square root (Lesson 4)

$$\sqrt{1} = 1 \qquad \sqrt{9} = 3 \qquad \sqrt{49} = 7 \qquad \sqrt{x^2} = x$$

product of powers property add exponents with the same base to multiply powers (Lessons 3, 6)

$$4^2 \times 4^3 = 4^{2+3} = 4^5$$

proportion an equation stating that two ratios are equal (Lesson 7)

$$\frac{2}{3} = \frac{4}{6}$$

proportional relationship a term used to describe a pair of equivalent ratios (Lesson 7)

The ratios $\frac{2}{3}$ and $\frac{4}{6}$ have a proportional relationship.

Pythagorean theorem the sum of the squares of the lengths of the two legs of a right triangle equals the square of the length of the hypotenuse (Lessons 24, 25)

$$a^2 + b^2 = c^2$$

quotient of powers property subtract exponents with the same base to divide powers (Lessons 3, 6)

$$\frac{5^5}{5^2} = 5^{5-2} = 5^3$$

radius a line segment that can be drawn from any point on a circle to the center of the circle (Lesson 26)

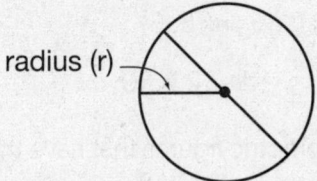

radius (r)

rate of change a comparison of two quantities that are changing (Lessons 7, 13, 15)

If 50 miles are traveled every 1 hour, the rate of change is $\frac{50 \text{ miles}}{1 \text{ hour}}$, or 50 miles per hour.

rational number a number that can be expressed as a ratio $\frac{a}{b}$, where a and b are integers and $b \neq 0$ (Lesson 1)

$$\frac{1}{2}, \frac{5}{9}, \frac{3}{7}$$

reflection mirror image of a figure (Lesson 18)

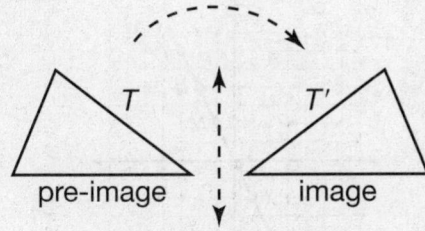

T T'

pre-image   image

$\triangle T$ is reflected over the vertical line.

relation a set of ordered pairs (Lesson 12)

$$\{(1, 2), (3, 9), (5, 8), (14, 10)\}$$

relative frequency a ratio of the number of times a specific event occurs to the total number of events (Lesson 29)

	Blue Eyes	Brown Eyes
Girls	7	19
Boys	8	21

The relative frequency of a girl having blue eyes is $\frac{7}{26}$, or about 27%.

remote interior angles the interior angles in a triangle that do not share a side with an exterior angle (Lesson 23)

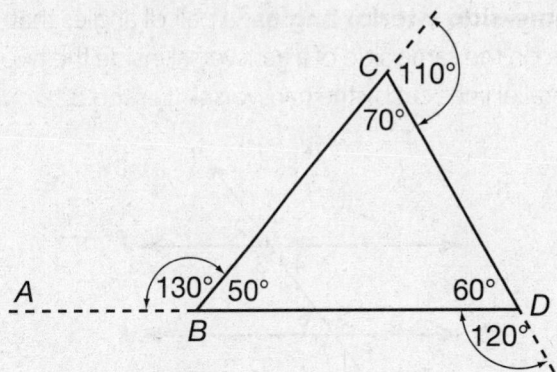

$\angle C$ and $\angle D$ are remote interior angles to exterior angle $\angle ABC$.

repeating decimal a decimal with a repeating pattern of digits (Lesson 1)

$$4.2323232323\ldots = 4.\overline{23}$$

rigid motion a movement of a figure in a plane such that its size and shape do not change (Lesson 21)

right triangle a triangle with one right angle (Lesson 24, 25)

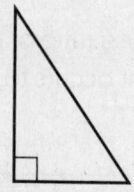

rotation a turn around a point (Lesson 19)

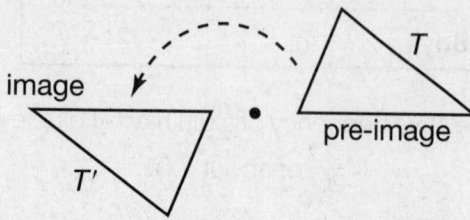

Triangle *T* is rotated counterclockwise around a point.

same-side interior angles a pair of angles that are on the same side of a transversal inside the two parallel lines cut by the transversal (Lesson 22)

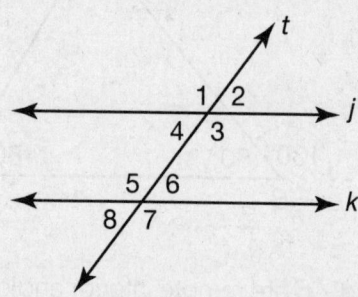

∠4 and ∠5 are same-side interior angles.

∠3 and ∠6 are same-side interior angles.

scale factor the ratio of the length of one side of an image to the corresponding length of a pre-image (Lesson 20)

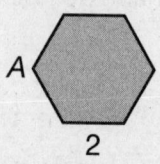 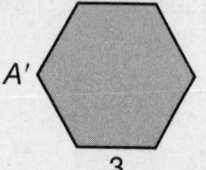

The scale factor of *A'* to *A* is $\frac{3}{2}$ or 1.5.

scatter plot a graph that shows the relationship between two variables in a data set (Lessons 27, 28)

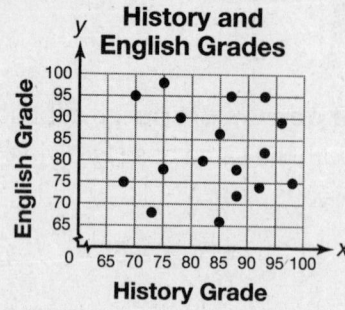

scientific notation a multiplication expression in which the first factor is greater than or equal to 1 but less than 10 and the second factor is a power of 10 (Lessons 5, 6)

$$7.2 \times 10^3$$

similar geometric figures that have the same shape but not necessarily the same size (Lessons 8, 20, 21, 23)

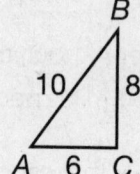 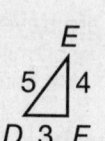

Triangle *DEF* is similar to triangle *ABC*.

slope a ratio that describes the change in *y*-coordinates as compared to the change in *x*-coordinates (Lessons 7, 8, 13, 14, 28)

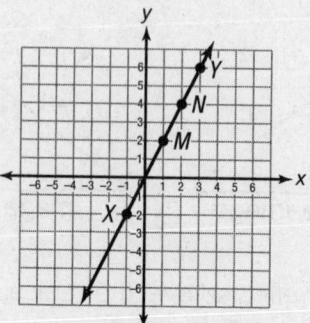

The slope of $\overleftrightarrow{MN}$ is $\frac{2}{1}$ or 2.

slope-intercept form of a line $y = mx + b$, where m is the slope of the line and b is the y-intercept (Lessons 8, 13, 15, 28)

$y = \frac{1}{3}x + 2$ is in slope-intercept form.

The slope of the line is $\frac{1}{3}$.

The y-intercept is 2.

solution a number that, when substituted for the variable in an equation, makes the equation true (Lesson 9)

When $x + 3 = 5$, the solution is $x = 2$.

square root one of the two equal factors of a number (Lesson 4)

substitution a method of solving a system of equations by substituting the value of a variable in one equation into the other (Lesson 11)

$x = 2y - 6 \quad \rightarrow \quad 2(2y - 6) + y = 5$

$2x + y = 5$

subtraction property of equality if $a = b$, then $a - c = b - c$ (Lesson 9)

If $x = 9$, then $x - 3 = 9 - 3$.

supplementary angles a pair of angles whose measures have a sum of 180° (Lessons 22, 23)

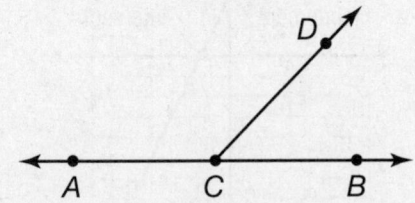

$\angle ACD$ and $\angle DCB$ are supplementary.

system of linear equations a set of two or more linear equations that have the same variables (Lessons 10, 11)

$3x + 2y = 5$ and $y = 3x - 2$

terminating decimal a decimal that has a finite number of digits (Lesson 1)

3.1672

transformation the result of a change made to an object; a transformation may be a translation, a rotation, a reflection, or a dilation (Lessons 17, 20)

translation a transformation of a figure that moves the figure without changing its orientation (Lesson 17)

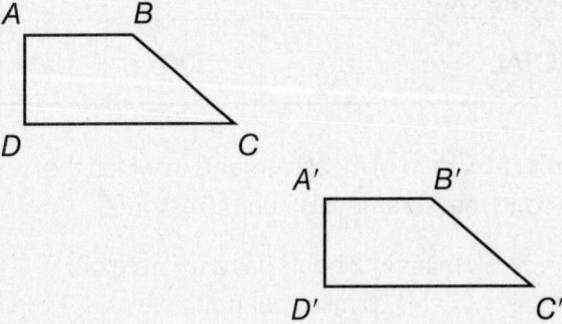

transversal a line that intersects two or more lines (Lesson 22)

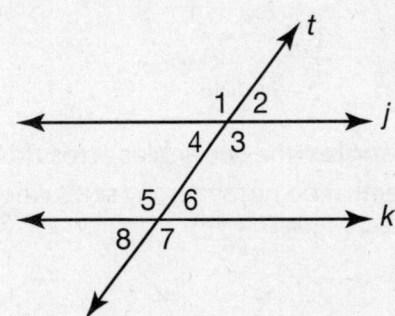

Line t is a transversal.

two-way frequency table a table that shows bivariate data; the rows show one variable and the columns show a different variable (Lesson 29)

	Computer Club Member	Not in the Computer Club	TOTAL
Drama Club Member	15	95	110
Not in the Drama Club	65	5	70
TOTAL	80	100	180

unit rate ratio of measurements in which the second measurement is 1 unit (Lesson 7)

50 miles in 2 hours has a unit rate of 25 miles per hour

variable a symbol or letter that represents one or more numbers (Lesson 9)

$$x + 4 = 9$$
↑
variable

vertical angles the two angles across from each other that do not share any sides when two lines intersect (Lesson 22)

∠1 and ∠3 are vertical angles.

∠2 and ∠4 are vertical angles.

vertical line test if a vertical line can be drawn so that it passes through more than one point on a graph, the relation is not a function (Lesson 12)

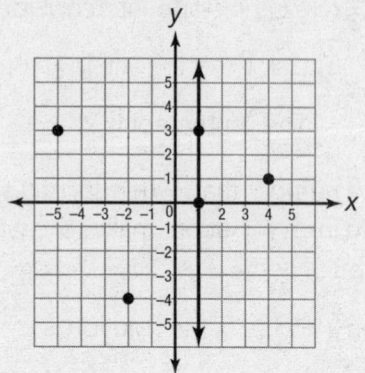

The relation is not a function.

volume the measure of the amount of space a solid figure occupies (Lesson 26)

x-intercept the point where a line crosses the x-axis; the value of a function when $y = 0$ (Lesson 13)

y-intercept the point where a line crosses the y-axis; the value of a function when $x = 0$ (Lessons 8, 13, 14, 15, 28)

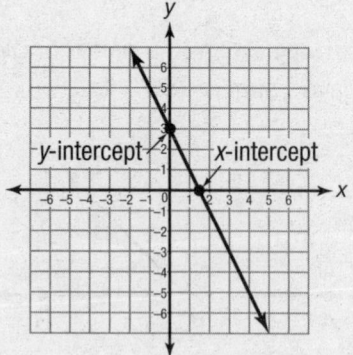

zero exponent property any nonzero number raised to the power of 0 is 1 (Lesson 3)

$$52^0 = 1$$

MATH TOOL

Number Lines

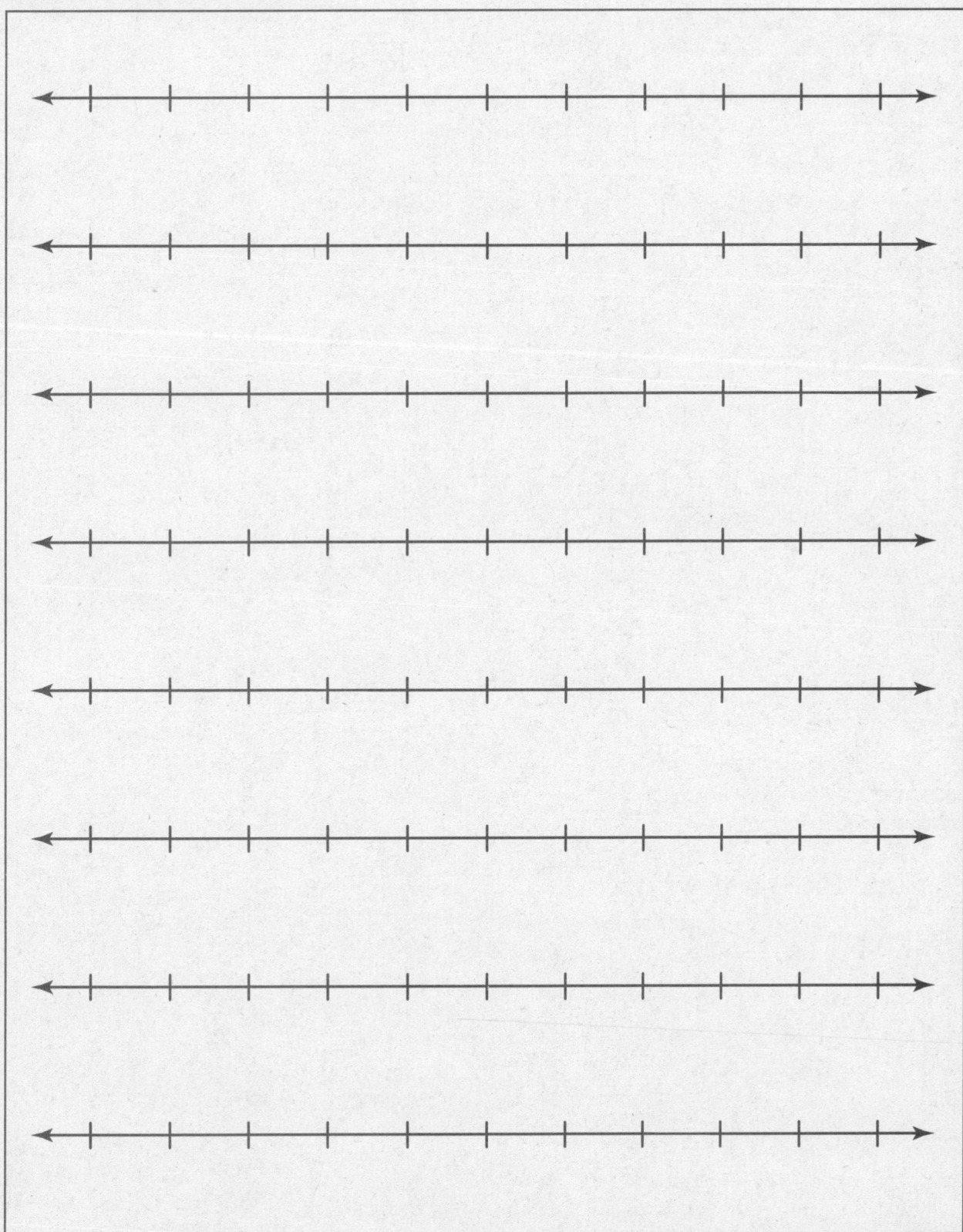

Properties

Addition Properties
Associative Property of Addition $(a + b) + c = a + (b + c)$
Commutative Property of Addition $a + b = b + a$
Additive Identity Property of 0 $a + 0 = a$
Sum of Additive Inverses $a + (-a) = 0$

Multiplication Properties
Associative Property of Multiplication $(a \times b) \times c = a \times (b \times c)$
Commutative Property of Multiplication $a \times b = b \times a$
Multiplicative Identity Property of 1 $a \times 1 = a$
Product of Multiplicative Inverses $a \times \frac{1}{a} = 1$

Addition and Multiplication
Distributive Property of Multiplication over Addition $a \times (b + c) = (a \times b) + (a \times c)$
Distributive Property of Multiplication over Subtraction $a \times (b - c) = (a \times b) - (a \times c)$

Properties of Equality	
Addition Property of Equality If $a = b$, then $a + c = b + c$.	Multiplication Property of Equality If $a = b$, then $a \times c = b \times c$.
Subtraction Property of Equality If $a = b$, then $a - c = b - c$.	Division Property of Equality If $a = b$ and $c \neq 0$, then $a \div c = b \div c$.

Grid Paper

Numbered Coordinate Plane

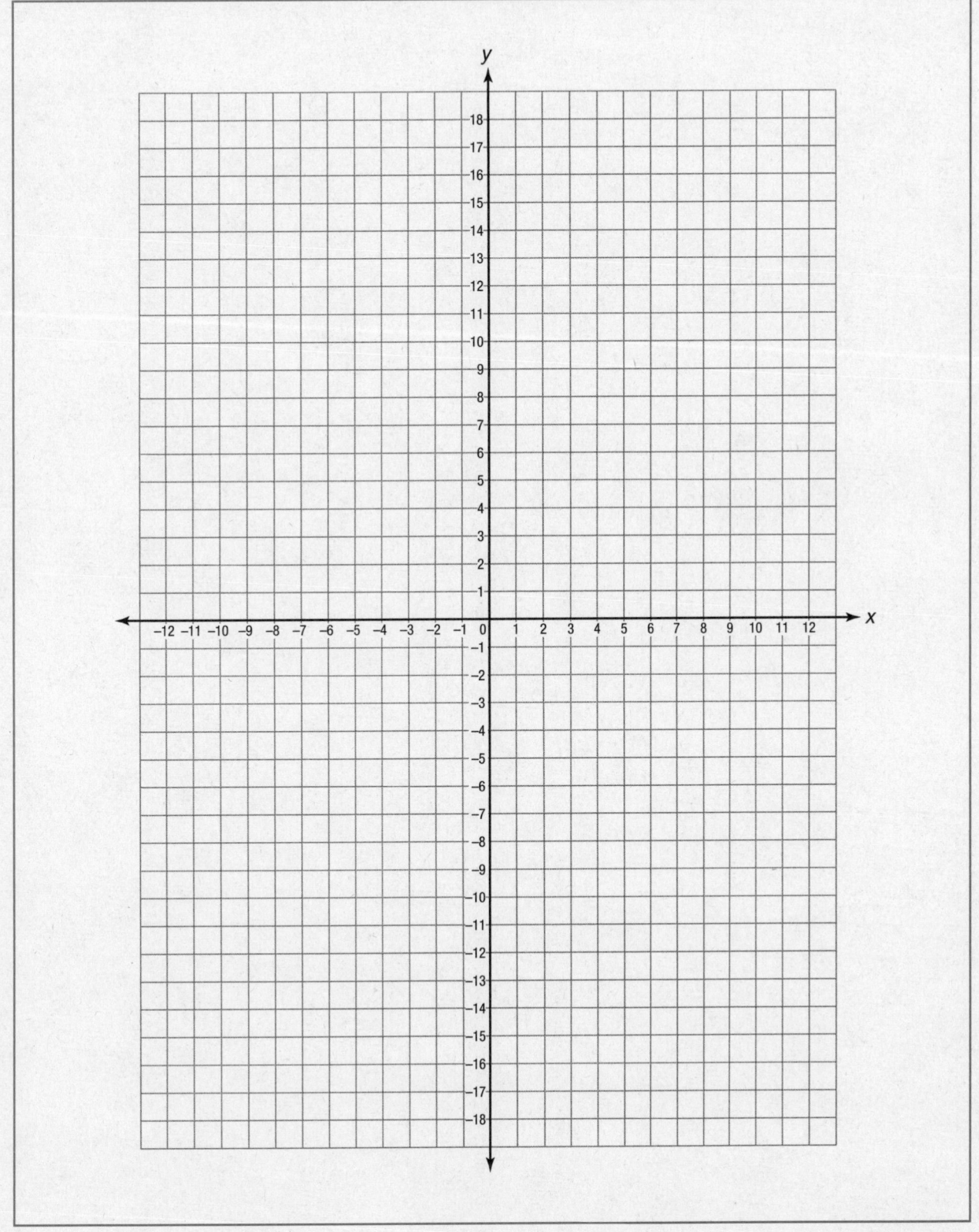

Solving Equations

Steps	Work
1. Simplify each side.	
2. Isolate the variable.	
3. Use the addition or subtraction property of equality.	
4. Use the multiplication or division property of equality.	
5. Substitute to check your work.	

Steps	Work
1. Simplify each side.	
2. Isolate the variable.	
3. Use the addition or subtraction property of equality.	
4. Use the multiplication or division property of equality.	
5. Substitute to check your work.	

Coordinate Planes

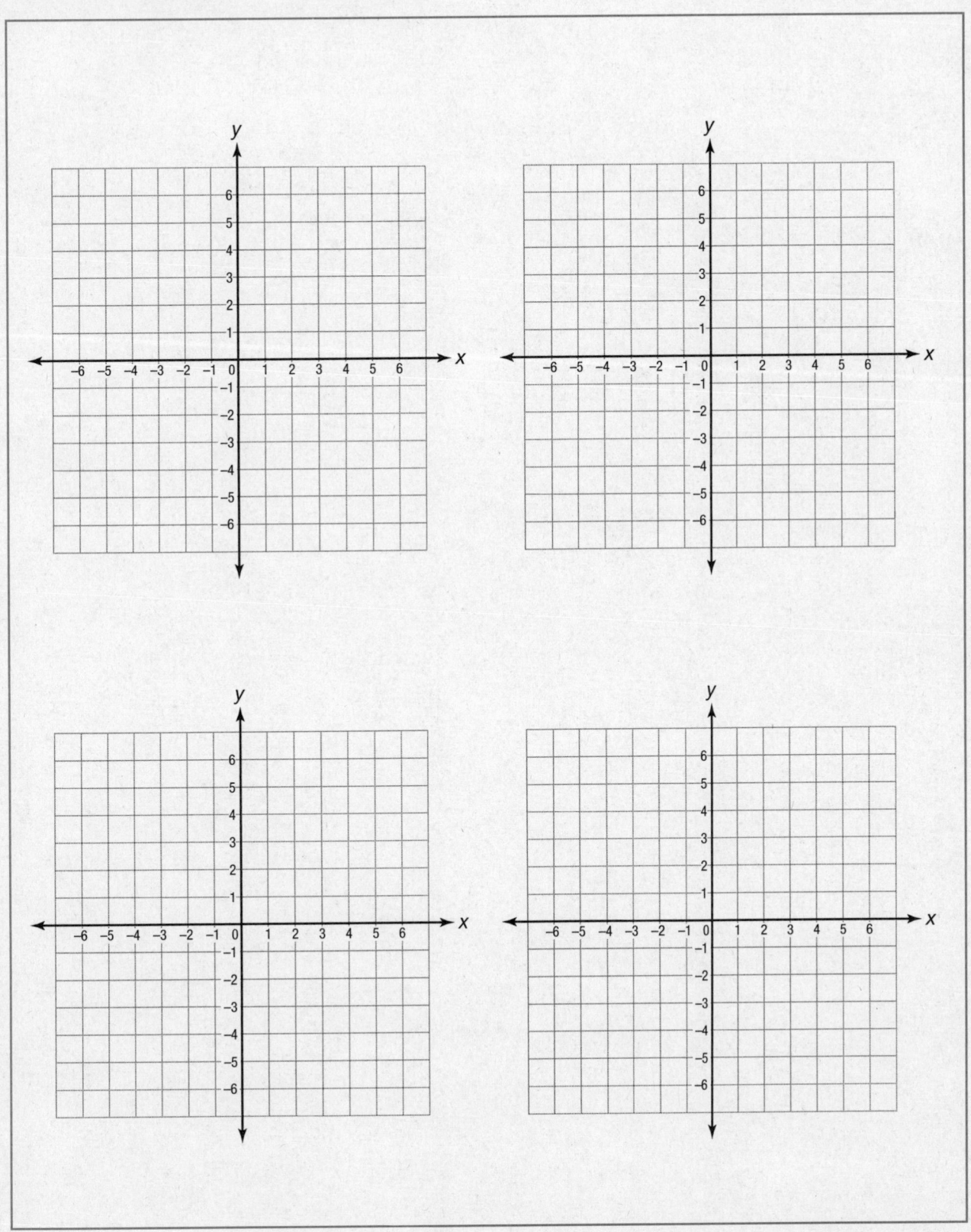

Input-Output Machines

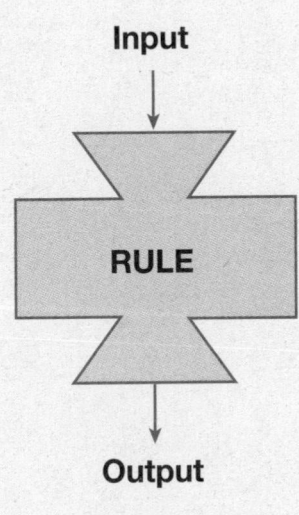

Input	Output

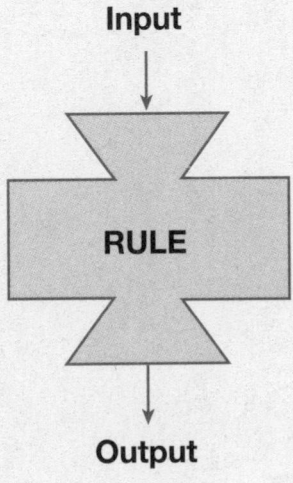

Input	Output

10 by 10 Grids

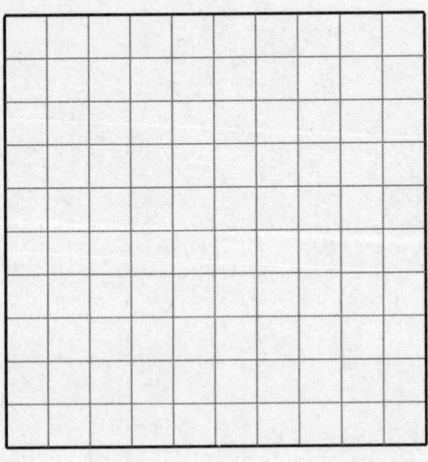

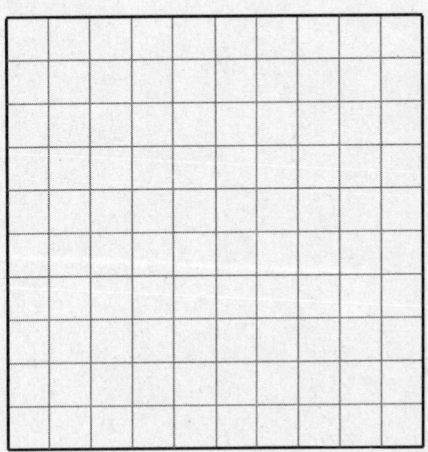

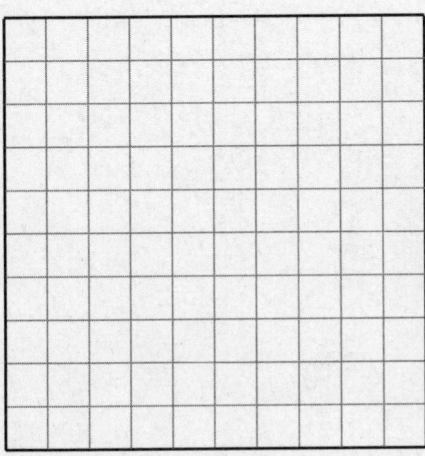

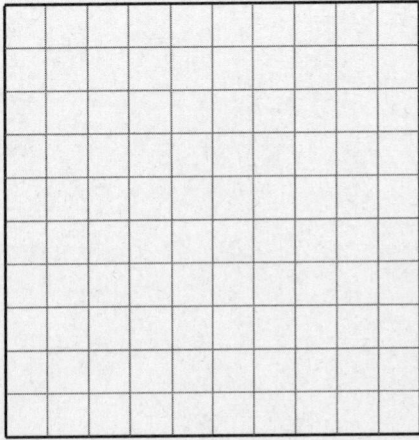

Coordinate Grids

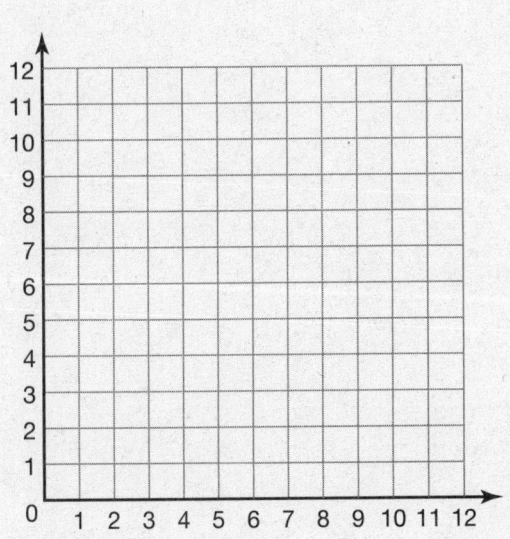

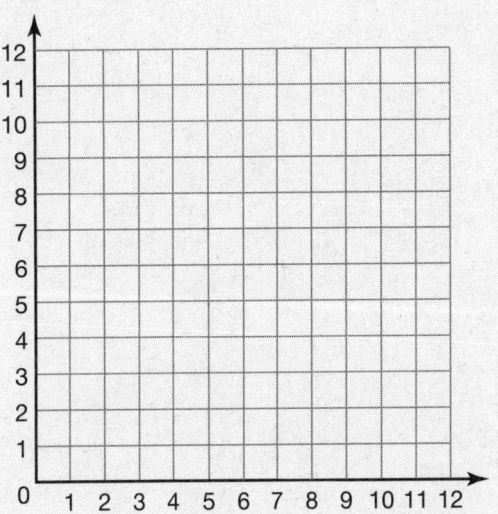

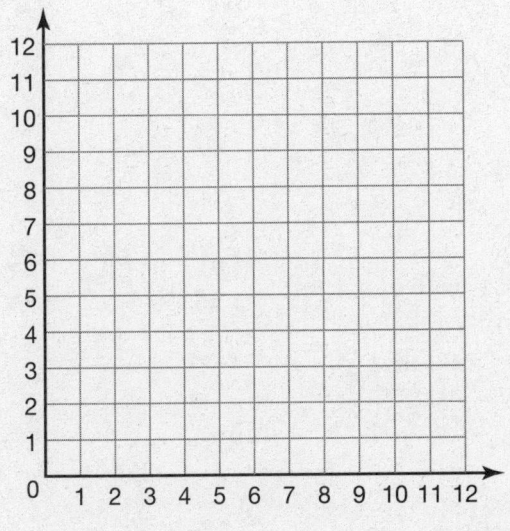

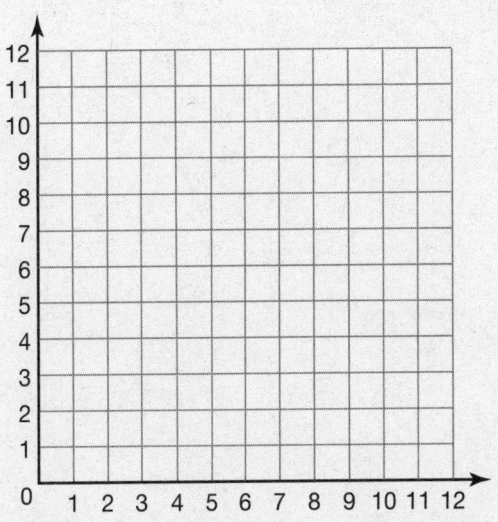

Centimeter Grid Paper

Protractor

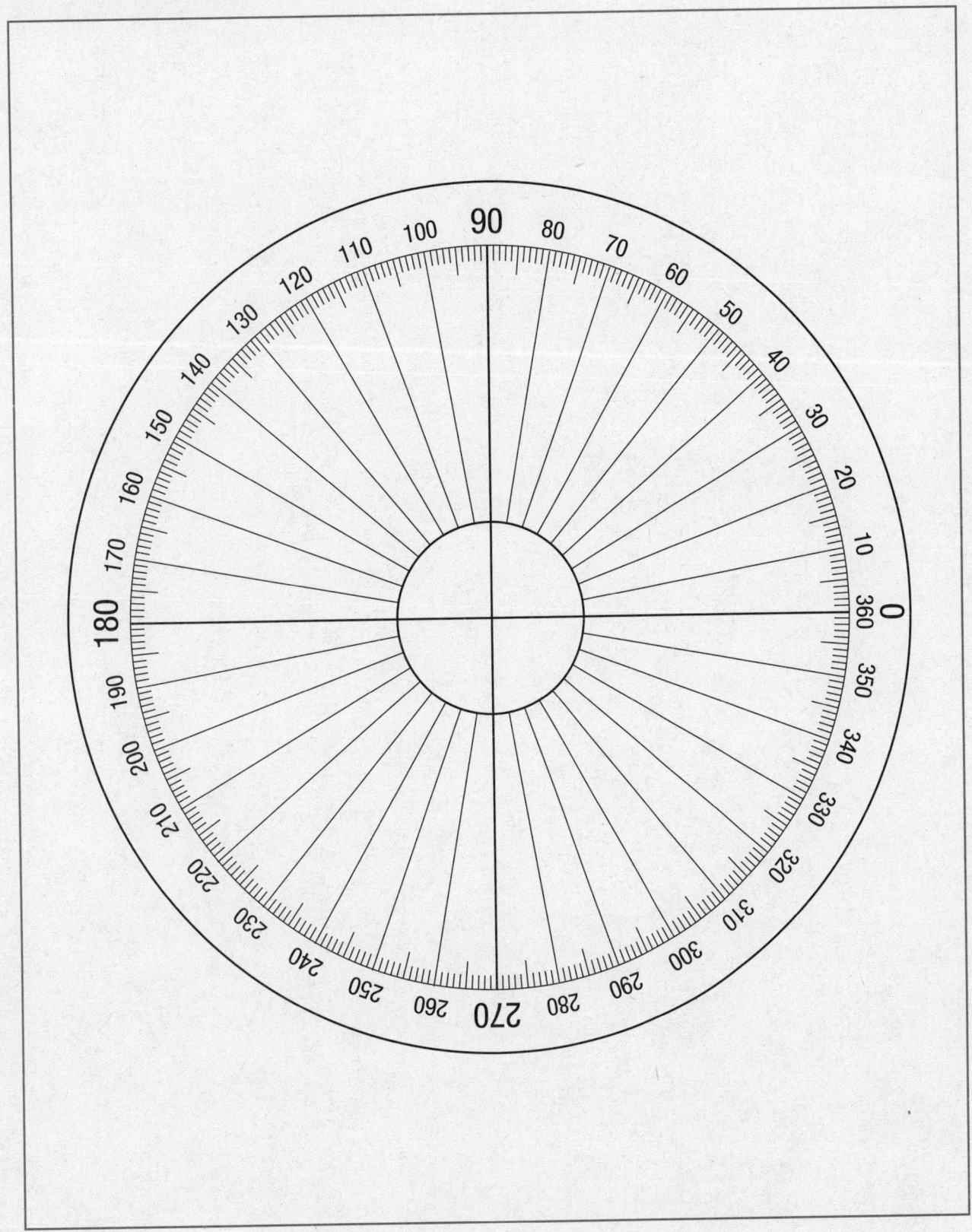

Pythagorean Theorem Proof

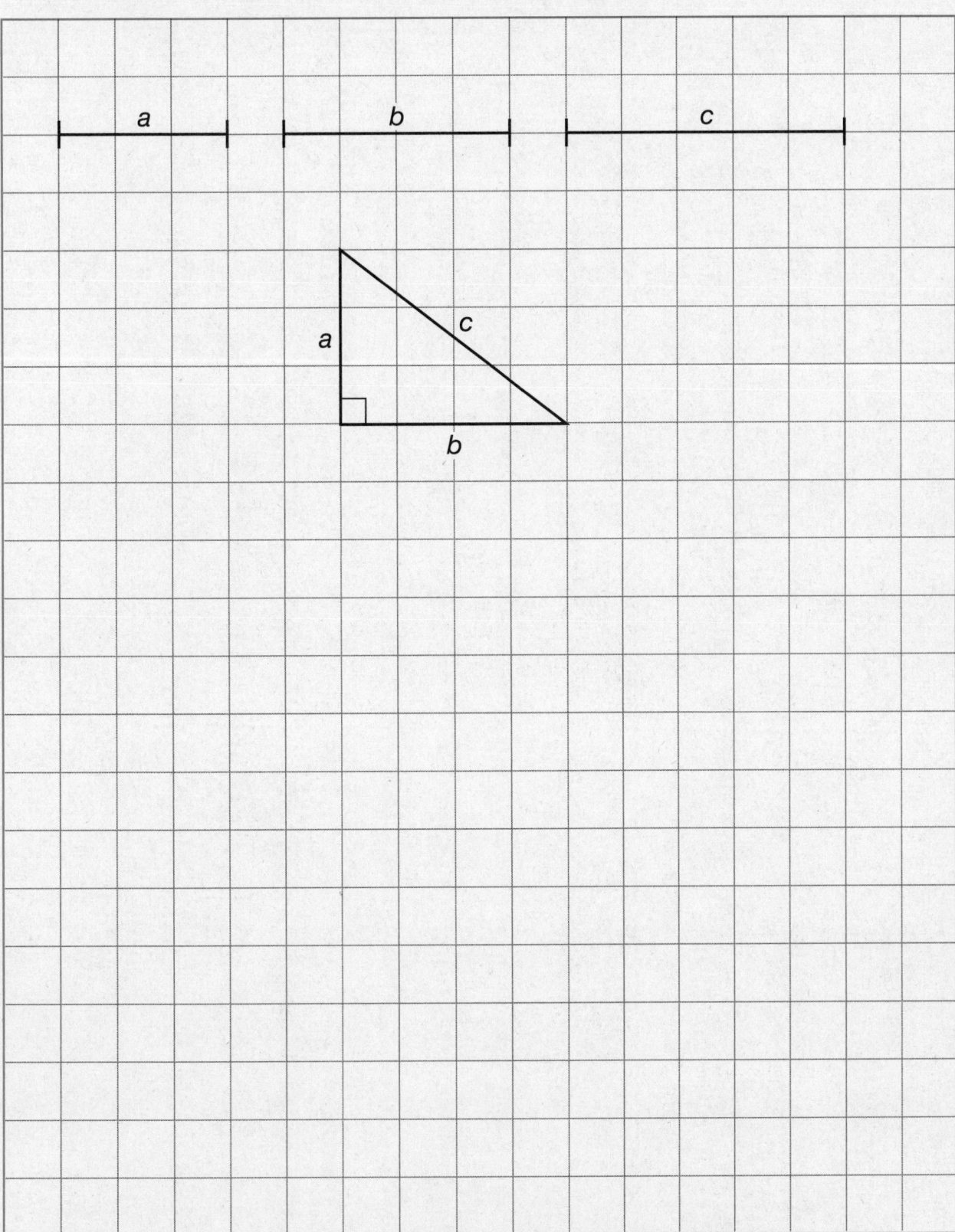